MANAGING THE CONTINUUM OF CARE

Edited by

Connie J. Evashwick, ScD
CEA-Consulting & Evaluation Associates
Los Angeles, California

Lawrence J. Weiss, PhD
Mount Zion Hospital and Medical Center
San Francisco, California

AN ASPEN PUBLICATION®
Aspen Publishers, Inc.
1987
Rockville, Maryland
Royal Tunbridge Wells

Library of Congress Cataloging-in-Publication Data

Managing the continuum of care.

"An Aspen publication."
Includes bibliographies and index.
1. Continuum of care—Management. I. Evashwick,
Connie. II. Weiss, Lawrence J. [DNLM: 1. Health
Services for the Aged—United States. 2. Long Term Care
—in old age. WT 30 M246]
RA644.5.M35   1987   362.1'6   87-1205
ISBN: 0-87189-640-0

Editorial Services: Marsha Davies

Library of Congress Catalog Card Number: 87-1205
ISBN: 0-87189-640-0

Printed in the United States of America

1 2 3 4 5

Table of Contents

Contributors

Jeffrey A. Alexander, PhD
Department of Health Services
  Administration
School of Community and Allied Health
University of Alabama
Birmingham, Alabama

Laurence G. Branch, PhD
Health Services Section
School of Public Health
Boston University
Boston, Massachusetts

Patricia Bucalo, Esq.
Weissburg and Aronson, Inc.
San Francisco, California

Russell C. Coile, Jr.
The Health Forecasting Group
Alameda, California

Dean M. Crowder
San Diego, California

Robert S. DiPrete
Peat, Marwick, Mitchell and Co./Compass
  Consulting Group
Portland. Oregon

Ernst & Whinney
Cleveland, Ohio

Connie J. Evashwick, ScD
CEA—Consulting & Evaluation Associates
Los Angeles, California

Peter N. Grant, Esq.
Weissburg and Aronson, Inc.
San Francisco, California

Marcella J. Griggs, RN, MS
College of Nursing and Health Services
Radford University
Radford, Virginia

Jay N. Hartz, Esq.
Weissburg and Aronson, Inc.
Los Angeles, California

William R. Hazzard, MD
Department of Medicine
Wake Forest University
Winston Salem, North Carolina

Koreen Kelleher, Esq.
Weissburg and Aronson, Inc.
San Francisco, California

Mary C. Kreger, MPH
San Francisco Institute on Aging
Mount Zion Hospital and Medical Center
San Francisco, California

William C. McMorran, MDiv
Los Angeles, California

Carol O'Shaughnessy, MA
Education and Public Welfare Division
Congressional Research Service
The Library of Congress
Washington, D.C.

Richard Price, MA
Education and Public Welfare Division
Congressional Research Service
The Library of Congress
Washington, D.C.

W. June Simmons, MSW, LCSW
Senior Care Network
Huntington Memorial Hospital
Pasadena, California

Arthur A. Sponseller
Hospital Council of Southern California
Los Angeles, California

Thomas E. Terrill, PhD
Peat, Marwick, Mitchell and Company
Short Hills, New Jersey

Paul Torrens, MD
Department of Health Services
School of Public Health
University of California
Los Angeles, California

Donna G. Vaughan
Department of Health Services
  Administration
School of Community and Allied Health
University of Alabama
Birmingham, Alabama

Bruce C. Vladeck, PhD
United Hospital Fund
New York, New York

Lawrence J. Weiss, PhD
Mount Zion Care Account
San Francisco Institute on Aging
Mount Zion Hospital and Medical Center
San Francisco, California

Preface

Continuum of care, vertically integrated system, diversification, campus of comprehensive care, multi-health care system, managed care programs, community-based long term care. . . . These are the buzz words of the 1980s health care industry, and they portend the evolving products of the 1990s.

In response to intense environmental upheavals, organizations are expanding, diversifying, and restructuring at a rapid rate. Configurations of services are coming together under a variety of organizational, legal, and financial arrangements. The underlying assumptions are that providing a broader array of services will enable an organization to be more effective and more efficient in providing care, will result in greater market share, and will produce higher financial return. Yet the management techniques required to operate multiple services as *systems of care* have not been developed at a commensurate rate.

Experience indicates that without integrating structure and management systems, an aggregation of individual services does not constitute a continuum of care—nor produce the expected results. The purpose of this book is to examine the issues involved in creating and managing a comprehensive, integrated continuum of care in the health field. This is not a theoretical text: It is a description of practical problems encountered by administrators, planners, and clinicians.

There are very few extant models of continuums of care, and there is no universally accepted definition. In numerous instances, organizations that have many of the pieces of a continuum of care operate with the same degree of fragmentation as the set of individual service organizations prior to aggregation. Multicomponent, comprehensive organizations are emerging. However, their evolution has not reached the stage where the components are smoothly or automatically integrated to achieve the efficiencies of operation that characterize a system. The management techniques essential to the operation of an effective, efficient continuum of care are being developed and tested by each organization to solve its own problems. The field is not yet at the point where generic management mechanisms of a continuum have been well defined, let alone modeled to be available for easy application and adaptation.

This book presents the issues faced by managers—administrators and clinicians—in operating a continuum of care. The authors strive to differentiate the management of a continuum from the basic management of separate health care or social service organizations. The purpose of the book is to articulate the issues—not to provide answers. The development of continuums is still too nascent and the evolving organizations are too different to put forward any isolated techniques as uniform resolutions to management problems.

A continuum of care requires great breadth of expertise. Many of the concepts and their implementation require cross-disciplinary knowledge, and new concepts and management techniques are emerging daily. This book is not for the expert. The tax section, for example, is not written for the accountant. Rather it is an overview for those who suddenly find themselves enmeshed in challenges and responsibilities that are new, immensely complicated, and involve topics and issues with which they have little experience. This book is intended for the director of nursing who must suddenly understand the tax principles of joint ventures in order to be able to deliver high-technology therapy in the home or for the director of management information systems who is called upon to extend the hospital's data base to accommodate case management.

While many of the concepts, examples, and lessons apply to or come from the public sector, the emphasis is on the private sector. The government or public sector has its own sets of organizational principles and financing considerations, and it would have been necessary to expand the text considerably to deal with it adequately. We have chosen to acknowledge that public sector continuum of care management issues are equally important but to refrain from covering them. Exploring the public sector experience is recommended to those in the private sector who intend to pursue development of a continuum.

The book does not go into detail about existing systems, private or public. First of all, few comprehensive model continuum systems exist, especially in the private sector. Second, for programs that do exhibit select characteristics of the continuum, there is a wealth of readily available anecdotal material. Third, each continuum is unique—tailored to its own community and organizational environment. Finally, the purpose of this book is to articulate concepts and general lessons.

We believe that continuums of care, vertically integrated systems, diversified yet comprehensive organizations, managed care programs will be—by whatever name—the predominant health care organizations of the future. Forward-thinking managers will thus find it essential to address the basic structures, operating systems, and human relations techniques inherent in management of such complex organizations.

AN OVERVIEW

Although this is not intended to be a theoretical text, the basic tenets of the book are drawn from the field of organizational behavior. The fundamental assumption underlying the theory is that organizations exist in order to accomplish goals. The three basic components of organizations are tasks, structures, and people. In addition, each organization exists in an environment that may be stable or changing and that may have a greater or lesser impact on day-to-day operations.

Research and literature on organizational behavior have, more or less, been consistent with this succinct concept of organizations. Extant organizational literature and current thinking can be classified into three kinds of approaches: structural (which relates to structure and task delineation), human relations (which deals with the human aspects of organizations), and corporate cultural (which emphasizes the intangible modus operandi that characterizes the interrelationships among goals, structure, people, and tasks). The examination here of the management issues of the continuum of care focuses on the structural and human relations aspects of organizations, with corporate culture touched upon as it relates to each of these.

This book is divided into four major sections. Part I presents the rationale for focusing on the continuum of care concept and gives an overview of its current context. In general, the environment is rapidly changing, highly unpredictable, and has dramatic impact on day-to-day, as well as long-term, operation. In Chapter 1, Bruce Vladeck describes the current state of conceptualizing the continuum of care. In Chapter 2, futurist Russell Coile outlines the environmental trends that are forcing health care and social service agencies to diversify, expand, consolidate, and collaborate: cost containment among hospitals, changes in reimbursement systems, limits on access to capital, increased market competition, changing consumer expectations, and a population growing older. Chapter 3 presents our definition of a continuum of care, outlining both the service components and the integrating mechanisms essential to achieve efficient operation. This provides the framework for the chapters that follow.

Chapter 4, by Connie Evashwick and Laurence Branch, characterizes the population segments and consumer trends that will produce heightened demand for organizations that provide a full spectrum of health and social support services. There will be more older people with chronic illnesses and more people with functional disabilities who need support services on an ongoing basis. Other mentioned trends in health care include continued rapid discharge from acute inpatient care, consumer preferences for one-stop shopping, and expectations that health care providers will arrange for all services, not just acute short-term care.

In Chapter 5, Jeffrey Alexander and Donna Vaughan trace the rapid emergence of multi-health care systems, the expansion of hospital activities into diverse fields, and the proliferation of corporate reorganization. They discuss changes in corporate structure and management responsibilities that are accompanying changes in service orientation and expansion.

Organization and structure is the theme of Part II. This section, derived from the structural school of organization theory, presents an extensive assessment of the structural issues of managing the continuum. Chapter 6, delineates the goals and objectives of creating a continuum of care. Health care organizations are responding to complex, changing environments, and thus they may have very different reasons for creating a continuum of care. Specific objectives may be complementary—or contradictory.

In Chapter 7, Thomas Terrill and Connie Evashwick present issues of structure and organization. Hospitals, which have traditionally used a matrix approach to organization, are adding layers and undergoing corporate restructuring, as well as forming affiliations with organizations that are not accustomed to matrix management. What are the appropriate lines of authority, accountability, and responsibility? Who supervises clinical staff? Who controls the budget? How should affiliations and associations with other community providers be arranged? This chapter raises the basic questions that must be considered in designing a management structure to operate a continuum of care.

As organizations implement new structures, the applicable laws and regulations become a complex web. Peter Grant and Koreen Kelleher consider legal and regulatory issues of restructuring in Chapter 8. They juxtapose the conceptual ideal with the realities of regulatory constraints. Appendix 8-A further explicates the legal and financial details of restructuring to create a continuum of care.

Joint ventures offer one means of achieving expansion into a continuum of care. Chapter 9 reports on a nationwide survey of joint ventures conducted by the accounting, tax, and consulting firm of Ernst & Whinney.

Arthur Sponseller outlines key personnel issues in Chapter 10. At first glance, it seems sensible to assume that staff will follow patients as they travel throughout the continuum of services, and that staff of an expanded organization will share similar personnel policies and compensation. In reality, a series of legal, administrative, financial, and staff preference issues make staffing a continuum of care highly complex.

William McMorran discusses marketing in Chapter 11. He emphasizes the need to define the product of a continuum of care. He also examines internal and external marketing, pricing, analysis of the consumer market, assessment of market competition, and the development of a marketing plan that incorporates all of the above issues.

Part III focuses on key integrating mechanisms that must accompany structural changes. Carol O'Shaughnessy and Richard Price provide an overview in Chapter 12 of financing trends that affect continuums of care: the growth of health maintenance organizations (HMOs), Medicare HMOs, and social/health maintenance organizations (S/HMOs), long-term care insurance, capitated payment systems, and tightened and limited reimbursement from federal and state governments. Capitated and prospective payment systems—the forces driving development and molding operation of a continuum of services—are reviewed by Robert DiPrete in Chapter 13.

Designing and implementing the management information systems appropriate for a continuum of care are highly complicated tasks. The need for integrated clinical and financial data, as well as the ability to track patients through use of one service to another over time, is addressed by Mary Kreger and Lawrence Weiss in Chapter 14. Chapter 15 describes care management, which is the clinicians' technique for assuring that care is appropriate, comprehensive, and continuous over time.

Part IV focuses on the human dimension of organizations. Corporate culture, the third focus of organizational behavior research, is dealt with in discussions of employee motivation and morale, leadership, and marketing. The chapters in Part IV, each written by professionals from different disciplines, assess the continuum of care from the perspective of the providers of patient care. In Chapter 16, Paul Torrens describes the real and the ideal continuum of care from the perspective of the client and family. In Chapter 17, Jay Hartz and Patricia Bucalo summarize the basic legal and ethical issues that require understanding and attention by both providers and clients.

Geriatrics has made a major contribution to the concept and realization of the continuum of care. In Chapter 18, William Hazzard, summarizes the evolution and future of medical geriatrics and the impact that it is likely to have on the physician's role in continuums of care. He suggests the actions that physicians must initiate if they are to be integrally involved in shaping the future health care delivery system. Marcella Griggs presents the nurse's view of the continuum of care in Chapter 19.

June Simmons, in Chapter 20, reflects on the challenging and controversial role of the social worker. In Chapter 21, Dean Crowder tells of the vision and leadership required of the chief executive officer to move an organization from being insular to expansive, from being a single-service to a continuum of care perspective.

The concluding chapter recaps the major themes of the book. The editors consider from their perspective the necessity of preparing for the future by moving to create a continuum of care. They summarize the challenges that remain in order to develop prototypes and models that will confirm that, correctly organized and managed, a continuum of care does indeed result in higher quality, more effective, more efficient, more responsive patient care.

Acknowledgments

We are grateful to the 23 authors who contributed the various chapters of this book. As any of us working in the field are all too well aware, health care is a swirl of activity. If instability, change, and uncertainty characterize the environment, it inevitably affects the lives of the people who work in it. Living in an unpredictable, shifting world is difficult for all of us, even when change means growth, excitement, opportunity, stimulation, and challenge. The authors' lives reflect the pressure that most health care and social service professionals are facing. In the brief period during which this book was compiled, one got married, two had their first baby, three started their own business, no fewer than eight changed jobs, six moved to new states, and most traveled hundreds of miles to consult with colleagues. And these are only a few of the pressures we knew about.

We would like to thank these authors—and the colleagues who assisted them—for their dedication despite other demands. We believe that their interest is indicative of the power of the continuum of care approach. We are all struggling with some aspect of it: nurses are learning the tax constraints of joint ventures, administrators are learning about case management, and so on. The amount to understand is great. Yet, because much is new, there are few guidelines. Not much has been written; there are not many experts to call upon. The breadth of the field complicates our need to learn, for our resources tend to be discipline or service specific.

Once immersed in it, a continuum of care is captivating. It makes such good sense—from management, clinical, and human perspectives. This, we believe, is why our authors took time out of busy schedules and hectic lives to reflect on their experience with continuums of care. Once engrossed in the management and clinical benefits, they have become committed to the continuum approach. They also appreciate the nascent state of the field, and how far we must progress to realize its potential. That they are willing to share their experience is evidence of their commitment and of the reward they believe that continuum care offers clients and colleagues.

It is always a challenge to write about something new. It is infinitely easier to pull a previously written article out of the drawer or refer to the works of a dozen others. As we exchanged chapters and reworked drafts, we also saw thoughts evolve and crystallize. Always there was the juxtaposition of where we want to be ideally and the reality of what is feasible. We all expect that our service delivery systems, our understanding, and our writings about them will evolve and grow refined over time. We appreciate the willingness of the contributing authors to work with us in breaking new ground—and to take the chances inherent in discussing a concept that remains to be fully realized.

In addition to the contributing authors, we would like to acknowledge the American Society on Aging, which sponsored the 1985 conference that led to this publication. This book was in part supported by a grant from the Robert Wood Johnson Foundation Program for Hospital Initiatives in Long-Term Care (Grant #9975).

Many thanks are owed to our many friends, colleagues, clients, and students, who heard about our work both in proposal and in process and who offered comments, suggestions, and, most of all, encouragement to continue. Special thanks to Edward J.J. Olson for his detailed review and to colleagues at the Mount Zion Care Account (Debbah Godin, Susan Orkin, Kassie Raab, and Gayle Stewart). Bill Evashwick deserves thanks and praise for his invaluable assistance in writing and editing.

The continuum of care is, at this stage, largely elusive, but nonetheless intriguing. Its implementation, based on the experiences described herein, is complicated and challenging. Yet those with a vision of the future believe that this ideal must be articulated and translated into practice. We hope that this work, despite its many shortcomings, will contribute to the advancement of the field. We hope it will assist those trying to create a continuum of care to solve day-to-day problems and simultaneously enhance the quality of care for those clients whom the continuum serves.

Part I

Background and Definition

The health care field is changing dramatically and rapidly. Organizations are expanding, diversifying, and creating continuums of care. But what is a continuum of care? What are the forces prompting its development? Why are health care organizations moving in this direction rather than another? This part presents an introduction to the concept of a continuum of care and the context in which it has developed. It elucidates the current and future environment of the health care field that provides the rationale for the portending organizational changes and it explores the operational meaning of the rather vague concept of the ideal continuum of care.

Chapter 1

The Continuum of Care: Principles and Metaphors

Bruce C. Vladeck, PhD

Introducing a book on the continuum of care is a daunting task. The subject is complicated, with each of many aspects meriting detailed consideration—which is why this book was prepared in the first place. Yet the reader is entitled, at the outset, to something other than an anticipatory rehash of what is to follow. There should be at least some intimation of what the subject is, in the large as well as the small.

What is needed is a conceptual framework—some way or set of ways of thinking about the issues posed throughout this volume that can lend them some coherence and provide a rationale for dealing with them. The subject at hand must be placed in an appropriate context, and, in a world where many issues and many books cry out for attention, its importance must be established.

In that regard, being given responsibility for preparation of this introduction is as fortunate as it is daunting, since it entails both the obligation and the opportunity to consider some very basic issues. What I propose to do here is to explore the concept of the continuum of care in terms of a set of very broad metaphors—of images—that embody beliefs, expectations, and assumptions about long-term care of the frail elderly in ways that have a powerful influence on how we think about the continuum of care, how we define the agenda of issues that need to be addressed, and how we arrange our organizations and our policies.

Speaking in terms of metaphors and images is not, admittedly, an entirely conventional approach in a volume prepared for health care professionals and program designers. But, in this instance, it is absolutely essential. Most of us walk around with implicit models of the continuum of care in our heads. Those models, however implicit, serve to filter information, to precondition perceptions, to act as a road map to reality—which is helpful only as long as the map is at least reasonably accurate. My major contention here is that our dominant metaphors for the continuum of care are misleading and potentially destructive; yet until we recognize what those models are and how they may mislead us, we will have great difficulty in going beyond them.

If the contents of this book are to be usefully understood and, more importantly, applied, they must necessarily be within the framework of constructive and appropriate metaphors. The best ideas and recommendations in the world will provide little benefit if they are utilized in an inadequate or inappropriate context. Conversely, a more appropriate set of conceptual principles, grounded in the right kinds of metaphors, constitute in themselves a large part of what is needed to develop effective and successful continuums of care.

This chapter proceeds by first defining and exploring what I take to be the three dominant contemporary metaphors for the continuum of care, and then by explaining why they are inadequate or misleading or downright damaging. I will then suggest two alternative metaphors that better capture the key elements of an effective continuum of care. Exploration of the second set of metaphors leads, in turn, to an inductive definition of four guiding principles for construction and management of effective caring systems for the frail and chronically ill.

THE CONTINUUM OF CARE IS NOT A LADDER

The most prevalent metaphor of the continuum of care is that of a ladder. Indeed, the choice of the term *continuum* may embody a predisposition towards an image of that kind. However, we are probably stuck, at least for the time being, with *continuum*. The ladder is what we must stop standing under, lest bad luck befall us.

In the metaphor of the ladder, the image is of the intensive care unit in a general hospital on top, with the general medical-surgical bed one or two steps below. All the way at the bottom, back on terra firma, is unsupported community living. Patients enter the system, in this model, at the top, presumably as the result of an acute episode of illness or injury. The task of the caring system is to assist the patient in descending step-by-step down the ladder as far as attainable function will permit.

If one doubts the power of this metaphor as an implicit guide in much of the conventional thinking about long-term care, it is only necessary to ponder for a moment some of the language that is generally used. The clearest case is the *step-down* unit or service. But we also talk of *vertical integration*, of *higher* and *lower levels of care*, and of *subacute* care.

Not only language reveals the power of this metaphor. It provides the basis for the logic of Medicare coverage of skilled nursing facility and home health care benefits; it's hard to explain or define the logic of those policies in any other way. Similarly, the regulatory distinctions between "skilled" and "intermediate care" nursing homes are based on the image of separate and distinct rungs on a ladder. One suspects this is also true of what might be called the naive version of the argument that home health care should be cheaper than institutional care. While neither logic nor empirical evidence provides any basis for expecting it to be less expensive to deliver a given set of services in the home than in an institution, it is hard to escape the notion that home care is somehow "lower level" care and should thus have a lower cost.

The image of a ladder of care is widely shared not only among health professionals, but also among policymakers and much of the general public as well. Clients and their families often seem to expect caregivers to be able to figure out at just what level of care they belong, and they perceive one of the caregiver's jobs as matching their needs with the right level of service. Similarly, health planners at state, community, and institutional levels have often devoted an extraordinary amount of energy to extremely elaborate calculations of the likely need or demand for highly specific levels of service. Their job, as it is often perceived, is to identify and help fill the missing rungs on the ladder.

The principal flaw of this metaphor is that it is fundamentally an acute care model. It has evolved from the notion of *progressive patient care* developed by hospital and nursing administrators at the University of Michigan in the 1950s. Otherwise healthy people experience an acute disease, the hospital provides a set of interventions for them, and the patients get gradually better, requiring fewer resources at each subsequent stage in the recuperative process. The episode begins at the top of the ladder with the onset of illness and ends at the bottom with complete recovery.

Most long-term care, of course, has nothing to do with such simple, unidirectional processes. Long-term care clients typically have multiple interactive problems, are continually at risk for setbacks and exacerbations, and are extremely vulnerable to nonbiological environmental forces. While entry into the long-term care system is often precipitated by events similar to those that trigger acute care, exit from the need for long-term care, as opposed to exit from the acute care system, hardly ever occurs except by death.

This is not to say that efforts to create a continuum of care based on the ladder model would not constitute an improvement in many communities, where the pre-existing nonsystems of care might more accurately be depicted using the metaphor of a swamp. Clients slide slowly and circuitously through the morass, rarely ending up where they want. When catastrophic events occur, clients fall into a hole, and are either pulled out—by crisis interventions—or else drown. But whereas a ladder may be a good way to get out of a swamp, it is still an inadequate design for a community long-term care system.

THE CONTINUUM OF CARE IS NOT A SET OF CONCENTRIC CIRCLES

Gradually replacing the ladder as the dominant metaphor for the continuum of care, at least in the hospital community, is the notion of a set of concentric circles. As expressed most eloquently, perhaps, by Jeff Goldsmith, this model has the inpatient hospital at the center, with the intensive care unit at its core. The proximate surrounding ring includes nursing home and rehabilitation facilities, as well as hospital-based ambulatory services and technologically intensive home care. Further out are primarily residential facilities, supportive in-home services, and office-based physicians. One purpose of the outer circles is to feed a proportion of their clients to the hospital at the center while shielding it from patients it can't serve effectively. The more important role of the outer circles is to fend off the concentric circles belonging to other hospitals in the competition for an increasingly scarce supply of patients.

This rather Dantean vision does provide not only for a two-way flow of patients between core and outer ring, but also for horizontal movement within circles. Of course, the metaphor of concentric circles is merely a rendering of the one-dimensional ladder into two dimensions, but that is hardly its major shortcoming. The model is literally hospital-centered, and it is generally unspecific and largely indifferent about the contents of the outer circles. It continues to focus on moving clients among levels of acuity or intensity as if they were a kind of raw material flowing through an elaborate set of pipelines—indeed, *patient flows* is an invariably recurring phrase in discussions of this model. Perhaps the most basic flaw is that the function of the outer rings, according to this model, is to feed and support the core, in terms both of patients and revenues. But if community-based, long-term care systems work well, they contribute to a shrinking of the core, maintaining a larger and larger proportion of clients in the outer circles and causing a growing share of total resources to be consumed at home.

A variant on the concentric circle model puts the system into motion, like a giant spaceship in a Star Wars movie. Each set of circles collides with the other sets in conflict for control of the perimeters, seeking aggrandizement by knocking the competition further into the interstellar void. That may indeed be a useful strategic model, one that captures much of what is now occurring in many communities. But it's not very helpful as a template for service configuration.

THE CONTINUUM OF CARE IS NOT A MATRIX

As health planners and policy analysts get ever more sophisticated, their metaphors move from two dimensions to three. In place of both ladders and concentric circles, they now increasingly talk and think in terms of three-dimensional matrixes. The axes are payment source, service mix, and site. Taken together, these axes define a number of cells or boxes—the number limited only by the imagination or energy of the analyst. The job of program developers or community planners is to enumerate and fill in the missing boxes. If there is no Medicaid-reimbursable social day care in the community, it must be developed; home care services must be reorganized to provide for the non-Medicare client; and so forth.

Similarly, the task of service coordinator, discharge planner, or case manager in this model is to perform an assessment of each client seeking to enter the system in order to determine in precisely which box the client belongs. If the appropriate box does not exist, then the client presumably bounces randomly until he or she ends up in a wrong box, with consequent excessive expense and inappropriate service. Woe be to the planner whose list of needed services— derived from attending conferences or reading books—is insufficiently exhaustive; woe be to the service coordinator whose knowledge of available community services is incomplete. Personal computers with good software would presumably permit the optimization of client placements within the matrix.

The primary fallacy in this model is that it is service- and profession-based, not client-based. It is not designed using empirical inferences about the needs of the frail and chronically ill in the community, but rather based on some abstract notion of what a system of care should look like. There are communities in which very disabled, very frail, functionally dependent people with limited financial resources receive excellent, comprehensive long-term care despite the absence of 90 percent of the boxes one would expect in any self-respecting matrix. Conversely, some communities and institutions have sought to install a full-blown continuum of care by establishing elaborate service matrixes, only to react with frustration and surprise when many of the carefully defined boxes remain half-empty and clients remain unsatisfied and underserved.

Defining systems of care around the needs and preconceptions of professionals has certain advantages in terms of theoretical coherence and intellectual neatness, but in developing really good systems of long-term care, neatness doesn't count, at least not for very much. What counts is fitting the system in certain ways to the needs.

What's wrong with all these metaphors, no matter the number of dimensions, is that they're based on notions of the service system, not on the characteristics of clients. In long-term care, those clients are usually quite frail, easily subject to confusion, afflicted with multiple problems that interact in all sorts of subtle ways, and quite unstable. On the other hand, they are also, by definition, adult human beings who have coped with life and the world successfully enough for a long enough time to have gotten to the point of needing long-term services. It's not easy to develop systems that are adequately flexible, responsive, and supportive for such people while also, at the same time, both comprehensive and cost-effective. But oversimple metaphors won't help.

USER FRIENDLINESS

I propose two alternative metaphors, neither of which is perfect or even close to it, but both of which capture some of the essential attributes of an effective continuum of care better than the current metaphors. The first might be described as an idealized sort of user-friendly computer system. Such a system contains an infinite number of potential menu combinations that can be employed to meet the particular needs or concerns, perhaps even whims, of each individual user, and these menu combinations can be instantaneously rearranged whenever those needs, concerns, or whims change. The system has a large number of preprogrammed routines that it will perform automatically, such as quarterly reassessments or prescription profiling and monitoring, but any of those routines can be readily readjusted in order to accommodate particular needs or circumstances of the user. It is hard-wired to embody a range of scientific knowledge and professional shortcuts, but at the same time is constantly capable of learning new things and performing old tasks in new ways as necessary. Most importantly, it is user driven; the system's array of competences and resources exist to be mixed and matched in a user-specific process.

Elaborating upon this metaphor, this system needs four things in order to function effectively. First is a coherent and reliable source of power; in the real world of long-term care services, this would be a reliable and predictable stream of financing. Second is a memory that contains and maintains an adequate set of information about clients; the memory is available, without additional effort or expense, to all service providers and it gives the same message to each. This is comparable to a sophisticated management information system that integrates clinical, financial, and service use data and incorporates comparable information from several service sites. Third is a basic "systems architecture," i.e., a structure for making decisions, setting priorities, and identifying problems. This could be thought of as a combination of product line organization and case management. Finally, there are the pre-installed, standard routines, which might be equated to relatively standardized service packages routinely provided by various professionals.

ROOT AND BRANCH

If the metaphor of the user-friendly computer is too technocratic, too cold, or too abstract, a radically different but still useful metaphor is that of a root system. The tree or plant supported by that system is the client. The function of the root system is to reach out in whatever directions are necessary to find resources and sustenance to support the client. As the environment changes or the plant matures, new branches evolve from the mainstems, sometimes supplementing them, sometimes replacing them functionally. Over time, the system becomes more complex, more interdependent, and more fragile in its totality; it becomes harder and harder to continue to meet the client's needs, not least because new radicles keep colliding with older ones. But as long as an adequate supply of resources, whatever their origin, flows back to the mainstem, the system continues to work.

The root system is in many ways the least complex, and certainly the least sophisticated, of all these metaphors, but it has one great advantage. It reminds us that there is no good justification for the entire system other than the benefit to the individual client; the system exists to support the client, not for any other reason.

So much for metaphors. Inadequate or inappropriate metaphors can be misleading or even counterproductive in thinking about systems of long-term care. Better metaphors, were we able to discover them, might be able to teach us more about how we should proceed from here in developing our real world programs.

BUILDING A CONTINUUM OF CARE

Building a flexible, interactive, nurturant, client-centered continuum of care system is not an easy task. Worse, there is no readily available blueprint or set of basic designs. Metaphors are necessarily and inherently imprecise, evocative rather than specific, suggestive rather than prescriptive. The ideal long-term care system in any community depends critically and almost entirely on the particular characteristics of that community: the needs and resources of its clients, the configuration of existing services, the agendas of existing service providers, and the peculiarities of local culture and tradition. A few basic principles can, however, be enumerated.

First, integration of financing is essential, de facto if not de jure. The clients are whole human beings, and providing them with integrated services necessitates some integration of payment sources. Where those sources won't integrate themselves, some one else has to do it—at the level of the individual case, the individual provider agency, or the broader community. Ad hoc integration of the kind most people now have to rely on can produce perfectly satisfactory service configurations, at the cost of considerable effort on the part of whoever is doing the integrating. It is almost certainly less cost-effective, however, than truly integrated financing of the sort at least theoretically possible under social HMO arrangements, some 2176 waiver programs, or organizational mechanisms such as Oregon's integrated long-term care funding programs. Cost-saving trade-offs are hard to effect when the payers won't trade.

Second, common records or shared data systems, while they smack of dull, bureaucratic routines, are also essential. What is required, after all, is not just a set of shared procedures or forms, but the creation and maintenance of a communications system and a common language among all of those involved in providing care to the client. Without such a system and such a language, the client is at considerable risk of being pushed or pulled in one direction by the right hand and the opposite direction by the left, which will result in going around in circles (to add another geometric metaphor to those discussed above).

Third, in each particular case someone has to be in charge. The boundary between the client's needs and preferences, on the one hand, and the service system, on the other, must be straddled and managed. Increasingly, the occupant of that role is termed a *case manager*, although precise definitions of case management are subject to considerable controversy, as is the even less consequential question of which profession is best suited to provide case managers. Again, situations and circumstances vary, and who case managers should be and precisely what they should do probably depend on specific circumstances. More importantly, there should be increased sensitivity to the potential of empowering clients or, more frequently, their family members to be de facto case managers.

Finally, what always sounds like boilerplate but is unavoidable because it is so basic and so true, the provision of effective, comprehensive, integrated, ongoing services requires effective multidisciplinary teamwork, and it is simply essential to develop the necessary mechanisms to ensure that such teamwork occurs. Common records systems help in that process, as does effective case management, but there must also be an underlying personal and professional commitment on the part of nurses, social workers, therapists, administrators, nonprofessionals, and, not least, physicians, along with educational and organizational processes that reinforce that commitment and provide an arena in which it can be carried out.

All of these four elements—integrated financing, integrated recordkeeping, case management to integrate services, and interdisciplinary teamwork—are interrelated, and all are essential. But these are just the starting point, the elements of the foundation on which the system must be constructed. How to construct it is the subject of the rest of this volume.

Chapter 2

Overview: Environmental Forces and Trends

Russell C. Coile, Jr.

These are changing times. The health care industry is in transition from a regulated to a free-market economy. Change—continuous but sometimes with jolting shifts in every aspect of health care—will be common for the next 10–15 years. Not until the turn of the twenty-first century will the industry be restabilized.[1]

What will the future bring? The trendlines of change point in all directions. New patterns are forming, but which will dominate?

While the future may be near, it is far from clear. For some health care providers, the years ahead are threatening. Doomsday forecasts suggest hundreds of hospitals could be swept into bankruptcy by payer pressure and vicious market competition.[2] Social service agencies are being squeezed not only by decreasing public monies but by the entry of their former colleagues, health services providers, into their lines of business.

For other health care services and settings, the future will bring opportunity—creation of new products, new markets, and redefinition of the basic focus of the health care industry as *health*, not illness. The future of these services will only be limited by the imagination of their administrators. The starting point for managing the future is awareness of the driving forces that will transform the industry in the next 5–15 years.

HEALTH CARE IN TRANSITION

For now, health care is very much in transition. Old patterns are eroding rapidly and new forces are beginning to make a noticeable impact.[3] The experience of other recently deregulated and more competitive industries—airlines, banking, brokerage, communications—is instructive.[4] In every case, the industry was underprepared for the magnitude and speed of the transition. Managers of top companies like United Airlines, Continental Illinois Bank, and American Telephone & Telegraph underestimated how quickly and powerfully their market

Table 2-1 Role of Major Factors

Major Buyers	Trigger Factors	Cost-Containment Strategies
Government	Medicare cost rise Federal deficits Social security bankruptcy	Shift to prospective payment Freeze physician fees Reduce Medicaid funds
Business	1981–83 recession Health expenses rise 15–30%/year	Use of HMOs/PPOs Form employer health coalitions Reinstall employee front-end deductibles and co-insurance
Insurance	Hospital costs rise 15–30%/year No effective controls over hospital and M.D. use	Develop HMO and PPO contracts Concentrate on administrative services to employers Require second opinions
Consumers	Increasing out-of-pocket costs Rising co-insurance Malpractice	Enroll in HMOs Engage in fitness/wellness programs Form consumer advocacy coalitions
Integrated Health Plans	Fee-for-service system not cost-competitive Rising HMO enrollment Physician surplus creates labor pool	Form national HMOs/PPOs Create new alliances between providers and insurance companies Mainstream M.D.s join HMOs/PPOs

would shift. The companies and entrepreneurs who saw opportunities in the transition and moved swiftly to capitalize upon them—like Security Pacific Bank, Compaq computer, and MCI communications—have become some of America's most successful and highest-growth corporations.

The dramatic change in America's health care industry has multiple causes, summarized in Table 2-1.

For the long term, these changes signal a profound shift in consumption patterns that will reshape the health care industry over the next 5–15 years.

MACROTRENDS IN HEALTH CARE FOR 1990

The health care industry is in the midst of a fundamental restructuring of supply and demand, moving rapidly away from a predictable pattern of cost-based payment to the rough-and-tumble of a competitive market. Ten macro-trends for 1990 are summarized as follows:

1. Expanding Boundaries and Growth

The health industry continues to grow.[5] The health component of the gross national product (GNP) is rising still: In 1985, health comprised more than 12 percent of the GNP, up from 10.5 percent in 1984. Consumer spending accounts for more than two-thirds of the GNP, and health continues to be a high priority. The health market—the entire range of health care services—goes well beyond the "medical care" marketbasket tallied by the Department of Labor as a component of the Consumer Price Index. Real health and health-related spending could be 15 percent of national expenditures by 1990 and 20 percent in the year 2000. At present spending rates, the national tab for health will easily reach $1 trillion in the early 1990s.

2. Recession in Inpatient Services

On the product life cycle curve, the hospital industry is mature and beginning to decline (see Figure 2-1). Like any producer whose product has reached the mature phase, a hospital is faced with three strategic choices:[6]

1. *Sell* while the product still has potential market value.
2. *Hold* operating costs down and defer capital investment while taking maximum profit out, then pursue strategies (1) or (3).
3. *Innovate* to break through the life cycle curve by creating new markets for the existing product or recycling through product extension, enhancement, or renewal.

3. Diversification

With increasing pressure on traditional lines of business, a number of health care organizations are setting diversification goals to achieve 25–40 percent of revenues from noninpatient sources by 1990. These goals may be overambitious. Even companies whose hallmark is innovation, like 3M and General Electric, do well to gain 20–25 percent of revenues from new (one to five years old)

Figure 2-1 Product Life Cycle

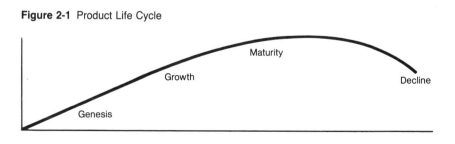

product lines. The experience of the private sector is clear: Diversify only into related businesses and capitalize on the organization's existing strengths.[7]

Alternatively, health care organizations may develop new business alliances with other firms whose strengths facilitate market entry into the desired new field.[8] Joint ventures with medical staff fall in this category of business development. Acquisition as a market entry strategy is gaining momentum, and not just among the investor-owned health care firms. Acquisition of physician office practices is one of the hottest recent market trends. To develop new products and business ventures, health care organizations are increasing their research and development (R&D) investment. Companies like Hospital Corporation of America, Sisters of Mercy, and American Medical International's Presbyterian/ St. Luke's Medical Center have established R&D units to foster innovations.

4. Integrated Health Plans

The distinction between health care providers and payers is disappearing rapidly. Tomorrow's very large health care companies will be integrated health plans (IHPs) that combine insurance, financing, and service delivery in a broad range of care services. The health industry is entering a period of rapid change and experimentation. Capitation and prepayment for a comprehensive continuum of benefits and services will come to dominate the industry. Health maintenance organizations (HMOs) are entering a new growth phase, with a quickening pace of consumer and Medicare acceptance. Annual enrollment gains are expected to be 15–25 percent, giving them a 25–30 percent market share by 1990—and it could be higher.[9] HMOs are one type of IHP, but preferred provider organizations will also contend for market share, as will the OCAs—other creative arrangements—the new experimental organizational forms that are now taking shape. Large hospital companies are acquiring insurance companies or developing joint ventures with the carriers. There will probably be a turnabout strategy, as major insurance companies buy hospital chains, or merge with them. Many investor-owned health care companies are candidates for this scenario.

5. Technopush

The pace and importance of technological development are increasing. The technological capital investment in "knowledge workers" like health care professionals is less than $5,000 per employee, compared with $25,000 in the manufacturing sector.[10] The health care continuum might be thought of as the factory of the future. All efforts will be made to speed up the "through-put" on a case management approach, reducing inpatient length of stay and increasing efficient use of all resources in the continuum of care. Computer-aided diagnosis and computer-assisted medicine will move beyond the prototype phase into early market entry before 1990. The new software of medicine will link hospital, physician, and payer, providing a common data base via computer local area network. Genetically engineered diagnostics and therapeutics are just coming to market. Laser and microsurgery have enormous potential. Linking new imaging technologies with robotic surgery will become widely available by 1990. Technology-rich hospitals can differentiate themselves from competitors and charge premium prices.

6. New Managers

As the baby boom generation begin to move into their 40s during the second half of the 1980s, the glut of middle managers becomes more apparent. Health care will follow the lead of insurance, retail, communications, and manufacturing companies by downsizing middle management ranks and "flattening" the organization, removing redundant tiers in corporate offices and operational units. An estimated 15–25 percent of today's middle managers may be affected. Many of those displaced by management cuts will move out into other services and settings in health care, raising the level of professional management expertise in areas such as group practice and social service agency management. Reduction of the middle ranks may actually increase administrative opportunities for front-line supervisors, as part of the "worksite democracy" movement to decentralize authority and extend it to the operating units. Women are rising rapidly in health care management.[11] Incoming students in health administration programs are more likely to be women. Carol McCarthy's selection in 1985 to head the American Hospital Association heralds the arrival of the woman health care executive.

The physician administrator common in earlier decades is likely to return. A growing number of hospitals are hiring physicians as the president or chief executive officer. Medical directors will take on increasing levels of administrative responsibility and line authority, with titles such as Vice President for Patient Care Services.

7. Market Warfare

As the traditional base business of the health care industry—inpatient care—shrinks, competition for market share will become intense. In the past ten years, a number of other industries have experienced sharply rising competition and economic destabilization, often prompted by deregulation. Hospitals and health care organizations can learn how to beat the life cycle curve from the ABCs—the airlines, banking, and communications industries. Competition and deregulation shook these groups to the core. If their history is any guide to the future of the health care industry, these strategic responses can be predicted:

- increased marketing
- price competition
- new competitors
- niche seeking
- diversification
- consolidation

Take the airlines industry, for example. Price competition is rampant, and fare wars have become a permanent facet of the market. People Express, Muse Air, Regency Air, and other new competitors overcame barriers to entry and created new niches in the marketplace. Consumer choice increased substantially, in price, service, and amenities. Air miles and passengers are up, but not without side effects. Low airlines margins cut service to many small communities. Not all carriers will survive. Braniff perished, while Continental, Pan Am, Eastern, and Frontier have been driven to the financial wall. Airline mergers are epidemic. Industry consolidation is predicted to reduce the major carriers ($1 billion annual revenues) from twelve to eight, or even six, by 1990. In the same marketplace, American, and TWA are thriving. Hospitals, HMOs, home health agencies, and other health care providers can expect their future to follow much the same pattern.

8. Merchandizing

In the fiercely competitive watch industry, the Japanese watchmaker Casio calculates it has a three-month lead from the time it introduces a new product before competitors copy it. Merchandizing is making health care buyers more fashion conscious, and health care product life cycles are shortening. Thanks to advertising, the American consumer believes there are epidemics of disorders such as stress, anorexia, bulimia, and sexual dysfunction. Even baldness is being treated as a health problem. Advertising and promotional expenditures are projected to double in the next two to three years.[12] The continuum of health care is a merchandizing smorgasbord. A range of related health care services are being bundled for major purchasers such as employers and preferred provider organizations. From the private sector, the health care industry is importing concepts such as product line management and customer relations. Pricing will become a primary merchandizing weapon. Already, popular products such as cataract surgery are being discounted heavily. HMO price wars are rampant, and the tactic of discounting will spread. The national battle for brand-name leadership is taking shape now. Humana has put its corporate brand on all products, and other investor-owned companies are following suit, as are, although more tentatively, nonprofit ''supergroups'' like Voluntary Hospitals of America.

9. Global Market

With its surplus of physician supply and hospital management capacity, American health care firms will develop new markets overseas. A preferred target will be the countries of the Triad—the U.S., Europe, and Japan—comprising 600 million customers with similar values, attitudes, and consumption patterns.[13] Beverly Enterprises, for example, has already been to Japan to examine the potential of managing the Japanese version of the nursing home. In the Triad, as well as in lesser and newly industrialized countries, the continuum of American-style health care is the standard that is aspired to. Overseas expansion will follow the global strategies of industries like electronics, automotives, and computers. Joint ventures, consortia, and innovative arrangements will create market entry points for American health care products and will expand opportunities for foreign investment in American companies. The potential influx of foreign capital into the American health system could be significant. Direct foreign investment in American companies and assets has swelled from $30.6 billion in 1978 to $174 billion in late 1985.

10. Spirit of Enterprise

If Peter Drucker is right, health care will be galvanized by innovation and entrepreneurship in the next decade.[14] Corporate restructuring among hospitals has created new vehicles like B.E.D.S. (Business Enterprise Development Services of Santa Monica Hospital Medical Center) to pursue diversified business development. Use of financial incentives for health care managers is low, but rising. Only 2.6 percent of health care managers have incentive programs, while more than 50 percent of senior managers in private industry receive an average of one-third of their compensation from pay-for-performance.[15] Health care organizations like Good Samaritan Hospital of San Jose and Minnesota's Health Central system are experimenting with "intrapreneurship" initiatives to foster employee entrepreneurship. A recent study by Illinois-based Witt Associates of hospital chief executive officers revealed a new executive type, the "sociopreneur," who can maintain the social values of an organization while pursuing complicated, risky business ventures.[16] These farsighted managers are changing the shape of the health care marketplace from a protected enclave to an innovative, competitive business arena.

As these trends gain momentum, they will reshape the face of the American health care industry. All are evident today, but the new patterns are not fully established. The question each health care organization must ask is: If this is the shape of the future, how do we participate?

LOOKING FORWARD

The health care industry today can be divided into three groups. The first group—perhaps 50 percent of today's health care organizations—are well-positioned, have a sound market strategy, and are pursuing their future with vigor. A second group—estimated at 25 percent of health care organizations—are searching for a strategic path and will probably find it. The final 25 percent of health care organizations are just awakening to market realities. This latter group could be in real peril. Size, location, and case mix are not the critical factors. It will be the quality of farsighted leadership that will determine success or failure.

Health care will be like the computer industry. Just as today's $1,500 micro-computer has the computing power of a $250,000 room-sized mainframe computer of two decades ago, so technologies like lasers, magnetic resonance imaging, and new medical software will become cheaper and more widely available, allowing even a 50-bed hospital to be a "medical center." Technology in health care will be more affordable, accessible, efficient, and capable than ever imagined, and the continuum of care will become an affordable reality for the mass of health care consumers.

STRATEGIC IMPLICATIONS: INNOVATION, COMPETITION, AND INTEGRATION

There is no secret path to future success. In health care, as in other industries, the high performance organizations will be masters of the strategic triangle: innovation, competition, and integration (see Figure 2-2).

Innovation

Innovation provides the "attacker's advantage." That is the message of a new management best seller by Richard Foster of McKinsey and Company.[17] From

---

Figure 2-2 The Strategic Triangle

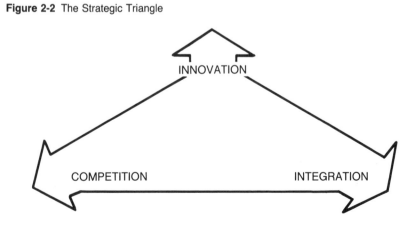

his studies of American industry, Foster has learned that businesses that are on the cutting edge of their industry achieve above-average returns. Sustaining high-level performance depends upon how successfully these companies can maintain their innovative stance. If they coast, more innovative competitors will take away their markets and their margins.

When a breakthrough technology is introduced, the market share of defending producers can erode as quickly as one share-point per month. Take the case of computer tomography (CT). Introduced barely ten years ago, CT has already evolved through three generations of technological innovation. The next innovation—enhanced imaging speed from 10 seconds to 50 milliseconds per scan—gives cine CT the potential to make a dynamic image of the heart in real time, heartbeat by heartbeat.

Time has already taken its toll. EMI, the British company that introduced CT, could not sustain its advantage and exited the imaging market after five years. Hospitals that brought the first million-dollar brain scanners are now writing them off as obsolete. CT is moving out of the hospital into free-standing diagnostic imaging centers, often owned by entrepreneurs. What's next? CT is about to be replaced by magnetic resonance imaging, a superior technology with both imaging and biochemical analysis capacities. As the CT experience graphically illustrates, innovation is a continuing necessity in a dynamic marketplace.

Competition

Competition now provides the central dynamic for the health care industry. Competition is taking place at four levels:

1. among major buyers of health care—government, employers, insurance companies—who foment price wars of competitive bidding
2. among integrated health plans (IHPs)—the health maintenance organizations, preferred provider organizations, and health insurance plans that also are direct care providers—competing to entice the 85 percent of Americans who use fee-for-service medicine into the IHPs' capitated plans
3. among hospitals and physicians, who are battling for the fastest-growing marketplace in health care—ambulatory services
4. among health, mental health, and social service providers, each of which is expanding and encroaching upon the historical turf of the others

Competition in health care is still in its adolescence. Many providers still know very little about their competitors, but they are learning. Intelligence about competitors will become a critical piece of every strategic decision. Marketing is more than a management hula hoop or amusement. It is a central preoccupation of all levels of health care management, affecting every provider and every management decision. Health is the archetypal intangible product—a product that does not exist except in the mind of the customer.[18] The ultimate market test is customer satisfaction. The shift from being a product to being a market-driven industry will affect every service and setting on the health care continuum.

The future of the health care industry will be shaped in the marketplace. Seeking and purchasing health care is still a complex decision, but no longer doctor dominated. Today, consumers make 30–70 percent of the decisions to purchase health care services, for serious as well as routine health needs.[19] In this new market-driven environment, every health care program, product, and service must meet the test of the market: Does it sell with the ultimate customer— the patient?

Integration

Integration is the management key to future success. The many and varied health care services offered under a wide range of sponsorship are converging. Old boundaries are breaking down. As fee-for-service medicine declines and more consumers are covered by IHPs, case management will integrate the clinical and financial decisions of health care. In a managed care environment, the distinctions between a physician's office and hospital practice are rapidly disappearing. So are the differences between health insurance, financing, and service delivery. Often, they are coordinated or combined by a single entity—an HMO, PPO, or services broker.

The continuum of health care is becoming a marketplace reality. Both consumers and providers accept the concept, and the market shift is gaining speed. More comprehensive health care benefit plans are being offered in the marketplace, and more integrated provider organizations are making coordinated services and settings available. As one-third to one-half of all Americans become enrolled in capitated health plans in the next 5–10 years, this powerful trend will reshape health care for the twenty-first century.

CONCLUSION

Who prospers next? As health care organizations look to the future they may take heart from the experience of stock brokerage. A decade ago, on May 1, 1975, brokerage was deregulated. Forecasters predicted widespread calamity: more than 20–25 percent of the 500 Wall Street firms would fail and the surviving brokerage houses would cater only to the big institutional buyers, abandoning individual investors. The reality was quite different—Wall Street flourished! Competition unleashed innovation. Options and no-load funds and specialty funds of all sorts developed; consumer choices multiplied. Major buyers did get discounts averaging 30–40 percent of fees, but Charles Schwab gave individuals the same price break and was quickly followed by dozens of other discount brokers. On Wall Street, only 38 firms consolidated or disappeared. Today, more than 640 brokerage houses exist. Wall Street broke through the Dow-Jones 1000—and then broke through 2000.

There is a lesson for health care here.

NOTES

1. Russell Coile, *The New Hospital: Future Strategies for a Changing Industry* (Rockville, MD: Aspen Publishers, 1986).

2. Jeff Goldsmith, *Can Hospitals Survive?* (New York: Dow Jones Irwin, 1981).

3. Richard L. Johnson, "Old Memories and New Dreams: Economics for Non-profit Hospitals," *Health Matrix*, Spring 1985.

4. Joel Bleeke, "Deregulation: Riding the Rapids," *Business Horizons*, May-June 1983, pp. 15–24.

5. Anne B. Fisher, "Who Prospers Next in Health Care," *Fortune*, February 14, 1986.

6. Michael E. Porter, *Competitive Strategy* (New York: Free Press, 1980).

7. Donald K. Clifford and Richard E. Cavanagh, *Winning Performance: How America's High Growth Midsize Companies Succeed* (New York: Bantam, 1985).

8. Jonathan B. Levine and John A. Byrne, "Corporate Odd Couples," *Business Week*, July 21, 1986, pp. 100–105.

9. Arthur D. Little, Inc., *Health Care System in the Mid-1990's* (Cambridge, Mass.: Arthur D. Little, 1985).

10. Bro Uttal, "What's Detaining the Office of the Future?," *Fortune*, May 3, 1982.

11. Emily Friedman, "Room At the Top," *Healthcare Forum* 29, no. 1 (January-February 1986).

12. Kari E. Super, "Hospitals Will Demand Results After Big-Budget Advertising," *Modern Healthcare* 16, no. 8 (1986): 69–73.

13. Kenichi Ohmae, *Triad Power: The Coming Shape of Global Competition* (New York: Free Press, 1985).

14. Peter F. Drucker, *Innovation and Entrepreneurship* (New York: Harper & Row, 1985).

15. David Barkholz, "Hospitals Need Incentive Plans to Keep Executives," *Modern Healthcare* 16, no. 11 (1986): 51–52.

16. Richard Foster, *Innovation: The Attacker's Advantage* (New York: Basic Books, 1986).

17. Ibid.

18. Theodore Leavitt, *The Marketing Imagination* (New York: Free Press, 1983).

19. Joyce Jensen, "Those With Serious Health Problems Generally Seek Help Picking Providers," *Modern Healthcare* 16, no. 11 (1986): 50.

Chapter 3

Definition of the Continuum of Care

Connie J. Evashwick, ScD

For all of the rhetoric about the continuum of care, there is no universal definition. Few have articulated the meaning of the concept, and no consensus has yet evolved. The chapter presents a simplified conceptual framework for understanding the continuum of care. It describes the basic principle of the continuum and gives an overview of the issues presented in more detail in subsequent chapters of the book. Appendix 3-A gives examples of existing continuum of care programs.

A *continuum of care* can be defined as:

> an integrated, client-oriented system of care composed of both services and integrating mechanisms that guides and tracks clients over time through a comprehensive array of health, mental health, and social services spanning all levels of intensity of care.

THE CONCEPTUAL FRAMEWORK

The basic justification of a continuum of care is that it provides a cost-effective way to meet the full range of health, mental health, and social support needs a person might have over a period of a time, including periods of wellness and illness. The coordinating organization takes responsibility for coordinating and arranging access to all services for its clients and for maintaining contact with the clients so that services can be changed as the clients' needs change. An organization need not have all services under its direct control; rather, it may have a variety of formal and informal relationships with other providers in the community.

For many people, families and friends serve as the structure orchestrating a continuum of care. However, as the population requiring continuing care grows, and as the health care system comes under multiple and increasing pressures, it becomes evident that informal sources alone will not be able to meet the demand for coordinating care. More significantly, there is growing awareness that the fragmentation of the formal structure is inadequate and inappropriate for meeting the future needs of clients, providers, and payers of care. As the health care industry changes, this coordinating agency may be a health maintenance organization (HMO), an insurance company, or a direct provider of health care or social services.

It is assumed that compared to individual services, a continuum of care offers the following advantages:

1. Due to the complex, ongoing needs of many clients, comprehensive and integrated care is more beneficial (i.e., of higher quality) than fragmented care.
2. An organized system of care is more efficient and makes better use of scarce resources than fragmented, disorganized services.
3. An integrated set of services has both market and financial advantages that are not offered by individual services.

The goals of the continuum of care are described in more detail in Chapter 6. In brief, they are:

- to meet consumer demand
- to enhance quality
- to maintain and increase market share
- to increase financial viability

The continuum of care is composed of services and integrating mechanisms. There are over sixty distinct potential services and several fundamental integrating mechanisms. For heuristic purposes, the services are grouped into broad categories. Schematically, the seven basic categories of services of the continuum are presented in Figure 3-1. This figure also shows the four major types of integrating mechanisms that make the continuum operate as a system rather than as a collection of fragmented services.

To reiterate, the schematic is for heuristic purposes only. As so eloquently stated by Dr. Vladeck in Chapter 1, no visualization of the continuum captures its full essence. The order of the categories of services can vary, depending upon whether the critical dimension is length of patient or client contact, intensity of technology, status of client health, type of facility, or some other pertinent characteristic. Even the services within each category can be rearranged: Sometimes hospice is an inpatient service in a nursing home, sometimes it is a service provided in the patient's home. The benefit of a diagram of the conceptual framework of the continuum of care is in helping those managing and planning services to organize an efficient, client-oriented *system of care*.

Figure 3-1 Continuum of Care Services and Integrating Mechanisms

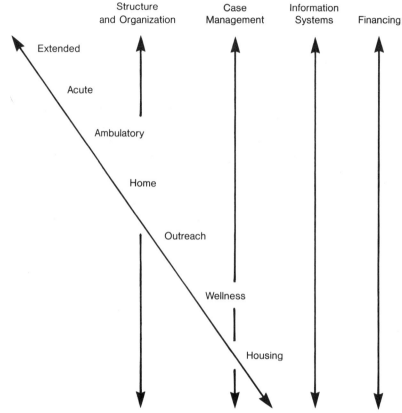

The seven categories and sixty-plus services of the continuum of care can be ordered on several dimensions; the order thus can vary. The integrating mechanisms are management systems that encompass and coordinate services of all categories.

THE CONTINUUM IN OPERATION

Because no schematic is adequate in presenting the multiple dimensions of the continuum of care, the construct used was chosen to be as simple a construct as possible. In practice, the complexities and interactions of the continuum become evident. For an individual client, the ideal continuum would operate as follows.

Metropolitan Health Systems (MHS) operates a continuum of care. Mrs. Jones, an 82-year-old woman, is admitted to the Metropolitan Hospital for a broken hip. For convalescence, Mrs. Jones goes to Metropolitan Nursing Home.

After two months, Mrs. Jones goes home and receives home nursing and physical therapy from Metropolitan Home Health. A walker, and later a cane, is provided by Metropolitan Durable Medical Equipment & Supplies. Meals on Wheels, a community agency, provides one hot and one cold meal per day for several weeks until Mrs. Jones is able to move about in her kitchen. Metropolitan Home Care, a private home care agency, sends a homemaker twice a week to help Mrs. Jones with personal care, bathing, light housekeeping, and grocery shopping.

A social worker contacts Mrs. Jones and her adult children to make sure that the latter understand her need for assistance with functional activities until she regains her independence and that they are able to provide it. Six months after the accident, an MHS case manager calls Mrs. Jones to inquire about her well-being and any need for additional services.

All of these services were arranged by MHS. Once Mrs. Jones was admitted to the MHS system, a single case manager was responsible for arranging and monitoring the delivery of each service. The case manager stayed in regular contact with Mrs. Jones, her family, and her physician during the six months of her recovery. A common patient record with all basic information was shared by all MHS services. A single patient identification number and an integrated financial billing system enable MHS to maintain a comprehensive record of all services received by Mrs. Jones, except those services provided by community agencies. All services were covered by the Medicare HMO that contracts with MHS, except Meals on Wheels, which was provided by a community agency at minimal cost, and Metropolitan Home Care, which was billed directly to Mrs. Jones based upon her prior authorization.

THE TARGET POPULATION

A guiding principle of the continuum of care is that it should be client-oriented: it should provide services according to the client's needs and wants, not according to the convenience of the provider or payer. The continuum of care should concentrate on those individuals who need ongoing, coordinated care. However, once the structures and mechanisms are in place, all other clients should benefit.

The primary target population of a continuum of care is persons who have long-term, complex problems requiring some type of formal service. Target groups would include the frail elderly, survivors of stroke and accidents, those with mental health problems, and infants and children with congenital abnormalities. The goal of a continuum and each of its services is to assist the client to maintain functional independence at the highest possible level.

Chapter 4 describes the numerous groups for whom a continuum of care is most appropriate. Many individuals and families would enjoy the attention and assistance provided by a well-organized continuum. However, the operation of a client-oriented continuum of care consumes a great amount of resources. To use these resources in the most cost-effective manner, the continuum must focus first on clients who have the complicated, chronic illnesses that warrant a highly developed management system.

THE SERVICES

In discussions of community-based systems of long-term care and types of assistance needed by seniors and those with chronic illnesses, more than 60 different services have been identified. This large a number is overwhelming when one considers planning or management issues. Thus, the wide range of possible services have been grouped into a few basic categories. Within each category are health, mental health, and social services—services potentially provided by professional clinicians, provider organizations, families, or the patients themselves.

A delineation of some of the many services under each category is presented in Exhibit 3-1. Detailed definitions are given in Appendix 3-B. The categories were developed partially through experience with provider agencies and partially through research.

The second basic principle of the continuum of care is that it should provide access to a comprehensive range of services spanning all levels of intensity of care. A corollary is that services should be changed as the client's needs change.

INTEGRATING MECHANISMS

The third principle of the continuum of care is that it should be more than a collection of services related to the same organization. Rather, the continuum is an "integrated system of care." The goals of a continuum of care, discussed in more detail in Chapter 6, include enhancing quality of patient care by providing coordination and continuity and improving the financial status of the organization by achieving economies of scale, efficiencies of operation, and increased market share.

The population groups described in Chapter 4 are composed of people who have multifaceted, multiple, and chronic problems best treated by a coordinated, continuing approach to care. One of the major complaints of those involved in providing long-term care to these client groups is that services are highly fragmented. This fragmentation among community service providers and within the same organization results in poor quality and high costs. The trend in the 1980s has been for organizations to create or acquire many services, but to allow each service to operate independently. A major thesis of this book is that the benefits of a continuum of care do not occur automatically with the addition or aggregation of many services. Rather, the integrating management structures are necessary

Exhibit 3-1 Continuum of Care Services by Category

Extended Inpatient
Skilled nursing care
Intermediate care
Psychiatric intermediate care
Swing beds
Nursing home follow-up
Respite care

Acute Inpatient
Medical/surgical
Psychiatric
Rehabilitation
Comprehensive geriatric assessment
Geriatric consultation service

Ambulatory
Physician care
Outpatient clinics
Geriatric assessment clinics
Day hospital
Adult day care
Mental health clinic
Satellite clinics
Psychosocial counseling
Alcohol and substance abuse

Home Care
Home health (Medicare)
Home health (private)
Hospice
High technology home therapy
Durable medical equipment (DME)
Home visitors
Home delivered meals
Homemaker and personal care

Outreach/Linkage
Screening/outreach
Information and referral
Telephone contact
Transportation
Emergency response system
Support groups

Wellness/Health Promotion
Educational programs
Wellness clinics
Recreational and social groups
Senior volunteers
Congregate meals
Meal discounts

Housing
Continuing care retirement communities
Senior housing
Congregate care facilities
Adult family homes

to realize the potential of a continuum to improve the quality and cost-effectiveness of patient care.

There are at least four basic integrating mechanisms:

- intra-organization and inter-entity planning and administration
- integrated management information systems
- case management or care coordination
- comprehensive financing

In subsequent chapters of this book, these are discussed in detail. The following is a brief introduction to each integrating management mechanism.

Intra-Organization and Inter-Entity Planning and Administration

Patient services are not likely to be coordinated unless the units that are providing the services are coordinated administratively, particularly when budgeting and financial issues arise. Administrative structures are necessary to (1) ensure channels of communication and cooperation, (2) establish clear lines of authority, accountability, and responsibility for patient care services, (3) negotiate budgets and financial tradeoffs, and (4) present a coherent, consistent message in interactions with external agencies and the community. Administrative mechanisms include committees that crosscut service areas, designation of a senior administrator to be responsible for decisions that affect several different departments, interdisciplinary team conferences for clinicians, assignment of clinical liaisons to service programs that have frequent patient referrals, multidepartment planning teams, and multidisciplinary, multidepartment task forces that focus on specific short-term issues. When a continuum is developed as a collaborative effort of several community agencies, these mechanisms for coordinating management become all the more important.

Integrated Management Information Systems

Many health and social service organizations still maintain separate clinical, financial, and utilization data systems; many, particularly social service agencies, are not computerized. Very few health care organizations have data systems set up to track patients as they move from one type of service, such as acute hospital care, to another, such as home care. Almost no community agencies are linked to other local providers through formal information systems, computerized or otherwise. Yet, financing of health care and social services is increasingly dependent upon prepaid and/or capitated systems encompassing a comprehensive service package. In order to implement quality assurance programs and utilization review programs, to assess efficiency of operation and economies of scale, and to track and aggregate patient experiences, comprehensive and integrated data systems and accompanying management report systems are essential.

Case Management or Care Coordination Programs

In instances where there are multiple service programs under the same organization, patient referral and tracking and continuity of care do not necessarily occur automatically. The more comprehensive and complex the service organization or the coalition of providers, the more essential it is to have a mechanism for client referral and tracking and a means of maintaining personal contact with clients as they move from one clinical provider to another. Continuity of care, with changes in types of care as the clients' needs change, requires ongoing contact with clients, even when they are well.

Case management, also referred to as service management, care coordination, and service coordination, is becoming understood and accepted in the health care field. The basic steps of case management include client identification, assessment, care planning, service arrangement, monitoring, and follow-up. When dealing with a continuum of care, the role of the case manager is to facilitate access by clients to the various services constituting the continuum. Some of the services might be owned and operated by the primary organization; some might be arranged through contracts or informal agreements. The authority of the case manager varies. In a brokerage model, the case manager facilitates access to services in a total control model and can also authorize payment for services.

Practicing in a continuum of care creates changes in the traditional roles of all health, mental health, and social services professionals. New roles and responsibilities arise—in relation to patients and families, to provider and payer institutions, and to other professionals. The human component is the single most important aspect of a continuum of care for the patient and practitioner. The challenges and opportunities provided by a continuum of care to families, administrators, and clinicians are described in more detail in Part IV.

Comprehensive and Capitated Financing

Because of third party payers' efforts to limit total expenditures for health care, capitated financing systems are proliferating. Capitated financing not only enhances the operation of a continuum of care, it also provides incentives to develop such a continuum. The clinical provider seeking to offer services tailored to a client's needs requires the flexibility to order the most appropriate service without being constrained by financial considerations. Capitated financing, when it covers a comprehensive range of services, can offer this flexibility.

Capitated financing also encourages organizations to operate more efficiently. In the absence of payer-required billing and reporting by a fee-for-service cost center, health care institutions do not have the incentive to maximize reimbursement by cost shifting among services. Under the present situation, many health care organizations are still able to operate multiple services as distinct entities, receiving capitation for basic inpatient care and cost reimbursement for other services. As capitated financing grows more common, the health care organization cognizant of reimbursement trends will want to position itself to maximize capitated payment across a wide range of services.

Capitated financing is accelerating the development of comprehensive health care delivery systems, i.e., continuums of care. In particular, the enrollment of Medicare beneficiaries in HMOs and CMPs (competitive medical plans) is causing many health care organizations, both provider-based and insurer-based, to offer a broader range of services at a competitive price in order to attract or retain Medicare clients. When such an offering is marketed, the provider and the insurer share (at least ideally) a common commitment to the efficient delivery of services. Success is more likely when internal incentives encourage the delivery of high-quality health care services in the most appropriate setting and when data processing systems are effective in tracking and reporting cost and utilization levels. The problems that have been encountered with HMOs' operations, as well as the successes, foster the further development of the streamlining, integrating mechanisms of the continuum.

Diversification, too, contributes to the trend toward comprehensive financing. As health care organizations offer a wider array of services, they want to be certain the payment will be forthcoming for all services. They also prefer to minimize the billing and collection effort. Thus, insurance that covers a wide array of services and arrangements that enable and entice consumers to pay for a package of services are growing in type and number.

A word on the financing of a continuum of care is in order. The financial justification for a continuum involves savings due to economies of scale, efficiencies of operation, increased market share, and revenue from new lines of business. Each of these may occur, and the success of each has been documented. The model continuums of care that exist (e.g., On Lok and the Mount Zion Hospital Medical Center, both in San Francisco, ACCESS in Rochester, New York, and Triage in Connecticut) have conducted research that shows that the clients of a continuum can be cared for at a cost less than that for other clients with similar needs. Nonetheless, to achieve the full potential financial advantages, a continuum must be organized and operated with financial objectives in mind and with the kind of ongoing data collection that will enable it to monitor financial performance and revise operations accordingly.

CASE EXAMPLE: GENERAL HOSPITAL

General Hospital was a large, aggressive, progressive, nonprofit community hospital in a highly competitive environment. After deciding to diversify to gain financial benefits and to focus on the elderly population in order to secure and increase market share, General Hospital moved quickly to develop a continuum of care. Within one year it did all of the following:

- started its own Medicare-certified home care program
- bought a nursing home located adjacent to the hospital campus
- entered into an agreement with a local company to provide high-technology home therapy
- expanded its rehabilitation hospital activities
- started a senior care program with outreach clinics
- offered discount dinners to seniors at off-hours in the cafeteria
- entered into negotiations with several HMOs for Medicare plans

When the senior administrators had time to catch their breath and assess the status of what they had created, they found the following:

- Over fifty percent of the referrals from each of the above services went outside the organization.
- Many of the staff of the hospital did not know that the nursing home or high-tech program had joined the system.
- Conflicting referral and acceptance criteria inhibited the internal referral of patients.
- Pre-existing staff loyalties to community agencies remained the primary dictator of referrals, regardless of the new services available within the system.
- Financial benefits were not being realized because each service believed that its goal was to maximize the financial status of its own cost center rather than the total organization. (Hence, neither home care nor the nursing home wanted heavy care long-stay patients, despite the savings to the hospital under diagnostic related group (DRG) reimbursement.)
- The management information system could not track patients using multiple services because each service used different computer systems and there were no common patient identification numbers.
- Referral codes available within the management information system were not used because no one had requested that patient dispositions be recorded in any more detail than *dead, home, elsewhere*—despite the fact that the codes were available.
- Morale of clinical and administrative staff was low because everyone was confused about priorities.

Once these issues were identified, the organization began to consider the management systems that would increase its overall ability to provide a coordinated, comprehensive array of services. Actions included forming a continuity of care committee composed of the administrators of all of the key services, delineating patient referral and acceptance criteria for each service, generating internal and external publicity measures to create awareness of the total range of services offered by the organization, expanding the budget process to enable negotiation between services and to foster cost center losses that in fact increased the financial return to the total organization, creating a single access center for clients that could direct families and patients to the appropriate service, revising existing management information, and educating staff to use detailed codes on disposition, status, and referral.

SUMMARY

The major theme of this book is that the clinical needs of clients and the financial and market environments require that the health care organization of the future be able to offer a comprehensive, efficient array of services. The availability of services, however, is not enough. Integrating mechanisms are required in order to manage the services as an efficient, cost-effective, client-oriented system of care.

Appendix 3-A

Examples of the Continuum of Care

Lawrence J. Weiss, PhD, and Mary C. Kreger, MPH

San Francisco Institute on Aging, Mount Zion Hospital and Medical Center

During the 1940s, Mount Zion Hospital and Medical Center started developing programs for the elderly. Services have continued to be developed, and today there are 17 geriatric services. They include the following:

- Acute Geriatric Assessment and Rehabilitation Unit
- Adult Day Health Care
- Alzheimer's Day Care
- Artworks
- Care Account (PPO)
- Consortium for Elder Abuse Prevention
- Educational Programs
- Geriatric Assessment Services
- Geriatric Patient and Family Services
- Geriatric Medical Clinic
- Home Care
- Information, Counseling, and Referral
- Lifeline
- Linkages
- L'Chaim Senior Center
- Multipurpose Senior Services Program
- Senior Health Screening and Referral

Mount Zion Hospital and Medical Center also offers traditional inpatient, outpatient, and skilled nursing facility services. The continuum of care within the San Francisco Institute on Aging is designed to maintain maximum functional independence for seniors with a wide range of needs. The variety of services available enables the services provided to be tailored to the specific needs of the individual. As a client's needs change, of course, so do the types of care provided. Client transition among services is facilitated by the services all being within one organization. Coordination and integration of services within the continuum occur through care management and interdisciplinary conferences. Coordination occurs not only among the formal services, but also among the informal services provided by family and friends. Clients are routinely re-evaluated to determine changes in functional capabilities.

On Lok Senior Health Services, San Francisco

On Lok was established in the 1970s to address the need for community health services of San Francisco's Chinese population. The nucleus of the On Lok service system is the day health center. All clients attend the day health center on a schedule designed to meet their needs. Admission, assessment, and case management of clients is performed by a multidisciplinary team. Additional services include social health maintenance (a less medically oriented day center), participant-volunteer activities, in-home services, and housing. Since 1979, On Lok has been a model project serving the dependent elderly who have been certified eligible for either skilled nursing or intermediate level institutional care on admission. All services required are provided and coordinated by On Lok; in this manner, On Lok maintains complete control over service provision. The purpose of the model project is to examine how this method of service provision is cost-effective.

Senior Care Action Network (SCAN), Long Beach, California

SCAN is a Social/Health Maintenance Organization (S/HMO) federal demonstration project. A S/HMO integrates the acute and chronic services necessary to provide care to the elderly. SCAN has five years of experience providing chronic care services for the elderly. It employs a brokerage model of service provision, contracting for all services except case management with existing providers. Case management is provided directly by SCAN. SCAN negotiated an ''at risk'' contract with a local hospital for inpatient, pharmacy, and skilled nursing facility services. The prepayment contract for physician services is with a 47-member group practice with a strong interest in geriatric care. The coordination of services among medical and chronic services, as well as intake into chronic services, is performed by the care coordinator (or case manager). This care coordinator then refers the client to the appropriate services within the SCAN network.

Mount Sinai Medical Center, Geriatrics Institute

Mount Sinai Medical Center is a major medical facility affiliated with the Medical College of Wisconsin-Milwaukee and the University of Wisconsin School of Medicine-Madison. In July 1983, the Geriatrics Institute began serving older adults after being developed through a research and demonstration project. The institute provides comprehensive health and social inpatient and outpatient services such as: Care Coordination Program, Geriatric Outpatient Clinic, The Geriatric Acute Care Unit, the Rehabilitation Day Hospital Program, the Alzheimer's Disease Day Care Program, four community-based wellness clinics, Inpatient and Outpatient Geropsychiatry, The Physicians' Outreach Consultation Service, and Geriatric Team Consultation Service.

The Geriatrics Institute's care coordination system is funded by the Robert Wood Johnson Foundation Program for Hospital Initiatives in Long-Term Care and, along with the data management system, provides the integrated components that link the institute's continuum of services.

Appendix 3-B

Continuum of Care Services Definitions

Extended Inpatient

Skilled Nursing Care

Provides medical and continuous nursing care services to patients who are not in the acute phase of illness and require primarily convalescent, rehabilitative, and/or restorative services.

Intermediate Care

Provides nursing, supervisory, and supportive services to patients who do not require the degree of care or treatment that a skilled nursing unit is designed to provide.

Psychiatric Intermediate Care

Provides medical care, nursing services, and intensive supervision to the chronically mentally ill, mentally disordered, or other mentally incompetent persons.

Swing Beds

Beds, usually in small or rural hospitals, that may be used flexibly to serve long-term care or acute patients.

Nursing Home Follow-Up

A program whereby geriatric specialists from the hospital or home health program follow patients during their stay in a nursing home. This is arranged with the administrator of the nursing home and legally may be done on a formal or informal basis.

Respite Care

Facilities and services that assist caregivers by providing short-term care for frail or disabled individuals to help meet family emergencies, planned absences (e.g., vacations or hospitalization), or to allow for family caregivers to shop or do errands.

Acute Inpatient

Medical/Surgical

Provides acute care to patients in medical and surgical units on the basis of physicians' orders and approved nursing care plans.

Psychiatric

Provides acute care to emotionally disturbed patients (including patients admitted for diagnosis and/or treatment of psychiatric problems or substance abuse) on the basis of physicians' orders.

Rehabilitation

Therapies include physical, occupational, and speech. Provides coordinated multidisciplinary physical restorative services to inpatients.

Comprehensive Geriatric Assessment

Also: Geriatric Evaluation Unit (GEU), Geriatric Assessment Unit (GAU) A multidisciplinary team of professionals, which may include physicians, nurses, social workers, pharmacists, and therapists, assesses the elderly patient's medical, psychological, functional, and social status and recommends a comprehensive plan of treatment and/or care.

Geriatric Consultation Service

Consultation by an individual or a team of health professionals specializing in geriatrics. Provided upon request of the patient's physician or mental health professional.

Ambulatory

Physician Care

Medical care to individual patients provided by primary care and specialist physicians in their office or a clinic setting.

Outpatient Clinics

Organized services (or clinics) for the provision of nonemergency medical and/or dental services for ambulatory patients based in hospitals or free-standing facilities.

Geriatric Assessment Clinics

Usually organized by hospitals, outpatient clinics staffed by geriatric specialists who provide a comprehensive interdisciplinary assessment and plan of care for older patients. In some instances, the clinic is the patient's source of primary care; in others, the results of the assessment are referred back to the patient's regular physician.

Day Hospital

A program that provides intensive medical, psychiatric, nursing, and/or rehabilitation services to individuals who spend the day at the hospital and return home in the evening, who do not need 24-hour nursing care, but who would need to be inpatients of the hospital were the day program not available.

Adult Day Care

Centers providing health, recreation, and social services to adults during daytime hours, usually Monday through Friday. May include intake assessment, health monitoring, rehabilitation therapies, minimal nursing care, drug supervision, personal care, a noon meal, and transportation. Health services may be provided but are not as intense as those provided in a day hospital. There are typically two models: the ''social'' model that concentrates on socialization and supervision and serves primarily those with mental conditions, and the ''medical'' model that cares for those with a more severe degree of physical impairment.

Mental Health Clinic

Outpatient mental health clinic that provides services such as mental status assessment, alcohol, drug-abuse control, psychosocial counseling, and psychotherapy.

Satellite Clinics

Outpatient clinics, usually at some distance from the hospital or physicians' offices, that provide limited care to ambulatory patients. With regard to geriatrics and long-term care, such clinics are often located in senior housing complexes or in conjunction with senior centers.

Psychosocial Counseling

Provision of medical care, including diagnosis, treatment, and counseling, for psychiatric outpatients by psychiatrists, psychologists, social workers, and other health care professionals.

Alcohol and Substance Abuse

Services for the provision of medical, psychiatric, rehabilitative treatment, and counseling for patients with a primary diagnosis of alcoholism or other chemical dependency.

Home Care

Home Health (Medicare)

A program that provides, under a physician's orders, medical, nursing, rehabilitation, and social services to patients in their home. Clients are those who are recovering from hospitalization, are homebound, and who require only intermittent care. Service, staffing, and payment are tightly regulated by Medicare.

Home Health (Private)

An organized program that provides medical, nursing, other treatment, social services, personal care, and homemaker services to the patients in their place of residence.

Hospice

A program providing palliative care—primarily medical relief of pain and symptom management—and support services to terminally ill patients and assistance to their families in adjusting to the patient's illness and death.

High Technology Home Therapy

Therapy provided in the home for patients requiring antibiotic infusion, chemotherapy, enteral or parenteral nutrition. The therapy mechanisms involve infusion of liquid solutions by pumps and related equipment.

Durable Medical Equipment (DME)

Products designed to assist individuals needing medical care at home. Including wheelchairs, canes, walkers, electric beds, and respirators. Equipment may be purchased or rented. Many DME items are paid for by the Medicare and Medicaid programs if prescribed by a physician.

Home Visitors

Volunteers act as "friendly visitors" and provide companionship on a regular basis to those who are homebound, especially to those who live alone.

Home Delivered Meals

A service for the preparation and delivery of nutritionally balanced meals (includes special diets) to those who are not able to provide or prepare meals for themselves. "Meals on Wheels" is a nationwide program sponsored by the Older Americans Act. The cost of meals to the patient is $2 to 2.50, with subsidies through government and private programs.

Homemaker and Personal Care

Services include housekeeping, homemaking, personal care, reporting significant observations, teaching client to perform various tasks, and performing limited nursing duties.

Outreach/Linkage

Screening/Outreach

Health education and screening programs offered to the public directly within their communities, sometimes in collaboration with groups (e.g., neighborhood associations or community clinics).

Information and Referral

A special program to provide information about and referral to services available in the community. A formal "Information and Referral" program is sponsored by the Older Americans Act. Many senior centers and related community programs offer this service.

Telephone Contact

A 24-hour answering service that may provide one or all of the following: counseling, information, referral, and checkup services or monitoring for all kinds of health and health-related problems.

Transportation

Providing or arranging for transportation to meet daily needs and to make accessible a broad range of services for the disabled.

Emergency Response System

A program for frail or disabled individuals whereby subscribers have a portable emergency response unit in their residences that will automatically secure a phone line and call for help in an emergency. The program is intended to give older persons who live alone the security that they can get help if needed, and thus the program contributes to enabling the older person to maintain independent living in his/her own home.

Support Groups

Education, therapy, and socialization groups for patients or their caregivers having similar health problems. Groups include those for family members who are caregivers for stroke victims, spouses of patients with Alzheimer's Disease, parents of children with multiple sclerosis, etc.

Wellness/Health Promotion

Educational Programs

Educational programs for patients, families, and community members to provide information on health or social problems. A series may cover different aspects of a single illness or multiple topics. Education may be provided through community forums, one-on-one teaching, videocassettes, or other means.

Wellness Clinics

Health maintenance, disease prevention and management, as well as exercise programs for social, psychological, and physical well-being. Examples include risk reduction (e.g., smoking cessation and weight reduction programs), health and nutrition education, exercise, and stress management programs.

Recreational and Social Groups

Activity programs and social groups sponsored by health care or social service agencies, usually targeted at persons with common interest or problems (e.g., healthy seniors, the developmentally disabled, etc.).

Senior Volunteers

A hospital volunteer program making particular efforts to recruit and involve older adults.

Congregate Meals

Group meals provided by a social service agency, health organization, or housing complex designed both to facilitate socialization and ensure healthy eating.

Meal Discounts

Many hospitals and nursing homes invite seniors in the community to eat in the cafeteria during off-hours. Meals are usually provided at a discount.

Housing

Continuing Care Retirement Communities

A program through which older adults commit to reside in a community complex for the remainder of their lives. The site has the physical facilities and services to provide a spectrum of care including apartments for independent living, accommodations with personal care, and nursing home care. Services may be paid for on a fee-for-service basis, may be included in a monthly fee, or a combination thereof. An entry fee and monthly fee are common.

Senior Housing

Housing accommodations designed specifically to meet the physical and security needs of elderly persons who are capable of living independently. Senior housing ranges from publicly-supported buildings intended for low-income seniors to elite retirement complexes. Senior residential facilities may be licensed by the state.

Congregate Care Facilities

Special housing for physically handicapped, mentally disabled, or frail individuals of any age, but particularly the aged, which includes meals provided in a common area and may provide varying degrees of supervision and personal care assistance. Nursing care is generally not provided. Such facilities may be licensed by the state under health or social service laws.

Adult Family Homes

A program where adults who require supervision or assistance with the basic activities of daily living go to a family in the community either during a transition from the hospital to their own home or as a permanent arrangement. Adult homes may be licensed by the state under health or social service laws.

Chapter 4

Clients of the Continuum
of Care

Connie J. Evashwick, ScD
Laurence G. Branch, PhD

The continuum of care is defined as ''an integrated system of care that guides and tracks clients over time through all levels of intensity of care.'' The purpose of the continuum is to help identify clients' needs appropriately and facilitate access to services through mechanisms such as case management and creative financing.

The primary clients of a continuum of care fall into two categories. The first category comprises those who have complex problems and thus require multi-faceted care over a prolonged period of time. These people tend to have chronic and multiple problems, functional disabilities, conditions that may change in degree of severity, and weak or limited social support systems. Consequently, such persons require formal orchestration of an array of services; the particular services they use will change over time as their needs change. The second category comprises those who have relatively short-term needs, but needs that are complex or rapidly changing and require greater coordination of multiple services than the patient or family can handle without formal assistance.

Clients who can benefit from a continuum of care may have any of a number of health problems, including multiple chronic conditions and health problems complicated by age, birth defects or congenital abnormalities, degenerative neu-rological conditions, stroke, accidents involving major debilitating trauma or disability, mental illness, functional disabilities due to a variety of reasons, social dysfunctioning that can lead to economic and health problems, and recent epi-sodes of acute illness requiring hospitalization, home care, or rehabilitation.

The focus of a continuum of care is those population groups that are most likely to require the breadth and intensity of services offered by a comprehensive, integrated, continuing, formally managed system of care. In general, the pop-ulation is comprised of individuals who have complex problems, functional disabilities, are not able to care for themselves, and cannot depend entirely on their informal support systems. The goal is to help people get the support they need to achieve the highest possible level of health and functional independence. The organization that decides to create a continuum of care must decide which population groups it will target—all of its clients or just select groups? If the latter, which groups?

In this chapter, we provide an overview of the various population groups that benefit from a continuum of care. The groups are broken into the following categories:

1. long-term, chronically ill, and disabled
   - older adults
   - disabled younger adults
   - mentally ill
2. short-term, complex
   - acutely ill
   - comprehensive, capitated

When possible, estimates of the numbers of persons are provided. One of the challenges of planning and operating a continuum of care is that the estimates of the various segments are often vague. For some of the applicable client groups, precise numbers are not available, particularly at the local level. Furthermore, the population groups are not mutually exclusive. Estimating the total population for the continuum of care thus requires compiling and extrapolating from a mosaic of estimates.

DEFINITIONS

Before dealing with the mosaic, however, a clarification of several concepts is necessary.

Need versus Demand

The distinction between need and demand is somewhat academic. However, in the current climate, it is useful to review. A *need* is considered to be the result of a professional judgment that a specific service or treatment should be provided to an individual in order to improve his condition. A *demand* is an individual's overt request for a service or treatment, presumably the result of a perceived deficit and a belief in the benefits of the requested service or treatment. The utilization of a service or treatment, therefore, usually occurs because of a concordance between need and demand—the professional's judgment and the individual's perception coincide.

Heretofore, consumers were not likely to express a demand for a continuum of care. The concept had not become common among the lay public. However, with the considerable publicity that has recently been given to HMOs, Medicare

HMOs, Social/HMOs, PPOs, and a variety of senior linkage programs, more consumers are oriented toward one-stop health care. Moreover, the entire health care field is becoming more market-driven, with consumers, rather than health care professionals, making decisions about the utilization of services. Thus, although it remains unlikely that the typical consumer will call up and ask for "continuum services," it is entirely likely that the consumer and family will seek out health and social service programs that encompass multiple services. The consumer-based demand for the continuum of care is increasing simultaneously with providers' increased awareness that quality care for many clients requires a new level of comprehensive, integrated services.

Dynamic versus Static

At any given time, the clients of a continuum of care reflect varying degrees of need. From a static perspective, some may have no immediate needs because they are functionally independent, have a well-established support system at the time, and their health conditions are stable. Some may have modest needs because of relatively complicated problems requiring more than the informal assistance they get from family and friends. Still others have more severe needs due to more complicated conditions and/or minimal informal support systems. The latter groups may require intense and multifaceted care on a regular basis.

From a dynamic perspective, an individual's need status can range over time from no need, to modest need, to severe need—and back again. An acute episode of a chronic condition may require intervention and rehabilitation before stability and functional independence are regained. The individual who recognizes his or her own potential continuum of needs will tend to seek the efficiencies and service accessibilities offered by a coordinated continuum of care.

Functional Status

Functional ability has several dimensions, and each can be measured in a variety of ways. The general areas of function are physical, cognitive, emotional, and social. Functional ability may be affected by health, mental health, social, or economic conditions, but it is distinct from health or illness.

One of the most frequently used measures of a person's physical function is the ability to perform the activities of daily living (ADL). The most common scale is one developed by Katz.[1] The basic activities are bathing, dressing, toileting, ambulating, continence control, and eating. A person's ability to perform each of these is measured and is rated as (1) totally independent, (2) requiring mechanical assistance, (3) requiring personal assistance, or (4) unable to do the activity.

A second commonly used measure of function is Instrumental Activities of Daily Living (IADL).[2] IADL includes a person's ability to perform activities necessary to maintain independent living in his or her own household, such as preparing meals, shopping, telephoning, paying bills, managing finances, housekeeping, and doing chores.

ADL and IADL abilities decline with age. Of persons aged 64–75, only 2 percent report having chronic conditions that severely limit performing the basic activities of daily living. Of those aged 85 and older, 10 percent report severe limitation in performing ADL functions, and an additional 10 percent report limitations in IADL.[3]

The ability to maintain functional independence may be inhibited by physical, mental, or social conditions, and may also be affected by economic status. For example, an older woman may not be independent in eating because she has:

- a physical condition that temporarily requires enteral or parenteral nutrition
- severe arthritis that makes it difficult to use a fork or knife
- dementia (and simply forgets to eat)
- not enough money to buy an adequate supply of groceries

The role of a continuum of care would be to identify the correct cause, clinical or otherwise, of the woman's inability to eat, to ensure that this woman has access to the appropriate services (e.g., high technology home therapy, occupational therapy, telephone contact, Meals on Wheels, etc.), and to follow-up over time to ascertain that services are being used appropriately in order to deter deterioration of health or functional independence (which would likely result in greater use of health and social services in the future).

CONTINUUM OF CARE POPULATION SEGMENTS

Long-Term, Chronically Ill, and Disabled

The Older Population

The senior population is one of the major target groups for a continuum of care. Older people tend to have multiple chronic conditions and functional disabilities. These result in multiple, multifaceted, changing problems and the concomitant use by seniors of an array of health, mental health, and social services.

Functional ability decreases with age.[4] Of adults under 65, only 1 percent have functional disabilities severe enough to disrupt their ability to perform major functions. By the time age 85 is reached, 20 percent of the population have a major functional disability and 32 percent require at least minimal assistance with personal care. Sensory perception decreases as part of the aging process, contributing to functional disabilities that may be the result of health conditions or accidents.

The prevalence of chronic conditions also increases with age.[5] Those under 65 have an average of fewer than one chronic condition. Once the age of 65 is reached, the number of chronic conditions increases with age. Four out of five persons 65 or older have at least one chronic condition. Those over 85 have an average of almost four chronic conditions.

In addition, older adults are more likely than younger adults to suffer acute episodes of illness. For example, the incidence of heart attacks, strokes, cataracts, and other conditions requiring types of surgery increases with age.[6] The likely presence of several chronic conditions complicates the treatment of and recovery from the acute episodes of illness. Older persons are more subject to iatrogenic illness, have more delicate homeostasis, and are less resilient than younger adults. Thus, when older persons do become ill, they are likely to recover less quickly than younger adults.

Older people use more health care services: those over 65 are hospitalized at a yearly rate of 400/1000, compared to 135/1000 for adults under 65.[7] Those over 85 are hospitalized at even higher rates. Of those aged 65–74, approximately 1–2 percent reside in nursing homes.[8] Among those aged 75–84, the rate increases to 6–7 percent. Among those 85 or older, the rate is 20–25 percent. Older persons visit physicians more frequently than younger adults: six times per year compared to four times per year.[9] And home health care is used predominantly by older patients.[10]

The optimal care for older persons with functional disabilities and chronic illnesses is a continuum of care—an array of services that meets their multifaceted illnesses, even if their needs change over time. The majority of older people, approximately 60 percent, are self-sufficient and independent.[11] For the majority of older persons requiring assistance, family and friends both perform direct services and negotiate for the arrangement of other services. Many other older persons, however, do not have sufficient help or have such severe health problems that they cannot rely entirely on informal sources of support. For the former group, a formal continuum of care facilitates the assistance provided by families and friends; for the latter group, a formal continuum may be the only necessary source of assistance.

The older population is growing rapidly.[12] As it expands, there will be a corresponding increase in the demand for formal continuums of care. In 1900, those over 65 composed 4 percent of the U.S. population and numbered 3.1 million. By 1984, those over 65 composed about 12 percent of the U.S. population and numbered 28 million.[13] This growth in the older population has been dramatic, but it portends changes of even greater magnitude. The U.S. Bureau of the Census projects that by the year 2000, 13 percent of the U.S. population will be over 65, and by 2020 this will increase to 18–20 percent. The number of seniors will reach 51 million.

The growth in the number of persons over 75 and over 85 is particularly noteworthy.[14] In 1980, 3.4 percent of all U.S. citizens were over 75, and 1 percent were over 85. By 2000, these percentages will increase to 4.6 and 1.8, respectively. The number of persons over 85 is estimated to be 5 million, while those over 75 is estimated to be 17.3 million, compared to 17.7 million between 65 and 74. These rapid population increases among the very old impact on the need for continuums of care, because those in older age groups make the greatest use of formal services.

A continuum of care includes housing and wellness services, as well as services to deal with illness. Many seniors, seeking a supportive environment that will help them maintain health and independence, desire select types of living arrangements. Although housing complexes for seniors vary greatly, common features include access to various health and social support services and the security of knowing that a professional, whether administrator or clinician, will be present to help arrange access to needed assistance. Overall, it is estimated that about 2 percent of seniors are interested in living in some type of senior housing or continuing care retirement community. As the number of seniors nearly doubles, from 28 now to 51 million in 2020, the number of candidates for senior housing is expected to increase even more rapidly, because of changes in future cohorts' economic status and life style preferences.

The management principles of a continuum of care apply as much to continuing care retirement communities as to health care systems, and indeed overlap between the two is becoming more prevalent as seniors look for environments that integrate housing and health care services.

The Disabled and Chronically Ill

In addition to seniors, many people under 65 have complex, chronic problems that make them appropriate clients of a system that provides comprehensive, integrated care over an extended period of time.

Each year, hundreds of people are involved in accidents that result in long-term or permanent disabilities. Thousands of persons suffer a stroke or myocardial infarction and must deal with the subsequent disability. Yet others have degenerative neurological diseases such as multiple sclerosis or progressive systemic conditions such as diabetes or kidney failure. Technology has improved the ability to keep very ill persons with very complex conditions alive longer. Many of these persons require multidisciplinary, comprehensive rehabilitation to regain functioning and a network of health and social support services to sustain independence.

The number of persons with chronic illnesses who would be appropriate clients for a continuum of care is difficult to estimate. For some categories of illness, such as *accidents*, there is no uniform information on the outcome. For other conditions, the manifestation of the illness varies significantly from individual to individual, and the contribution of a formal continuum of care is tempered by the ability of family and friends to coordinate and monitor the use of services.

Ninety percent of the long-term care assistance required by persons with functional disabilities is provided by friends and families. Formal organizations are relied upon for only ten percent of such assistance, at least for the present. The most thorough estimate of the total population requiring long-term care (defined by the need for various types of assistance due to functional disability) was done by the Department of Health and Human Services.[15] Weissert and colleagues estimated that a total of 6 million persons require various types of care: 3.6 million community residents require personal care or mobility assistance, 600,000 persons require care in board and care homes, and 1.8 million require care in nursing homes and long-term care facilities. To this are added 800,000 mentally ill or retarded persons living in the community and 2.8 million developmentally disabled persons. In total, persons requiring continuing care due to functional disabilities, based on 1977 data, are estimated to be more than 8 million. About two-thirds of these people are over 65. Children and infants with birth defects or congenital abnormalities were not included in this study; thus these population segments should be added to the total.

Rather than attempt to make precise counts of the number of persons appropriate for a continuum of care, the critical issue from an organization's standpoint is to identify the client groups that will be the target of a continuum of care. A continuum of care may be organized around a well-defined disease (e.g., stroke survivors with permanent disabilities), around the patients of a particular department (e.g., all patients on the rehabilitation floor of the hospital or who are admitted to the rehabilitation program), or around specific demographic or other client characteristics (e.g., seniors or widows without children).

The Mentally Ill and Retarded

A critical dimension of independent physical functioning and the capability of managing one's own affairs involves cognitive or mental status. People with mental disabilities due to somatic or physiological disorders (e.g., older persons with Alzheimer's disease) and mentally retarded individuals are potential candidates for a continuum of care, as are individuals with behavioral disorders (e.g., either chronic or episodic depression) or social inhibitions (e.g., reclusiveness). While a person may be physically capable of performing all activities, he or she may require supervision and professional care for psychological, medical, or medically related problems.

Like the chronically ill and disabled populations, the number of people with mental illness is difficult to calculate. For purposes of estimating the number who would benefit from the use of a formal continuum of care, the focus is on those whose condition is complex, unstable, and severe enough to warrant arrangement of multiple services over time and whose family and informal supports are not able to provide an ongoing array of services.

The President's Commission on Mental Health estimated that 10 million people experience one or more episodes of serious mental illness before age 65 and that 20–32 million people may be in need of some type of mental health services.[16] The prevalence rate for functional psychiatric disorders has been reported as follows (based on a percentage of total U.S. population): schizophrenia, .5–3 percent; manic-depressive psychosis, .3 percent; neurosis, 8–13 percent; personality disorders, 7 percent. More than half (54 percent) of the people with psychiatric disorders are treated in outpatient settings by physicians. Organic mental disorders, particularly primary degenerative dementia, are common in later life. Epidemiologic surveys have found a definite organic mental disorder in 4–6 percent of persons over 65 and in 20 percent of those over 80. The prevalence rate is higher if persons with mild cognitive dysfunction are included.

To translate the estimates of illness into the need for assistance in functioning, the National Institute of Mental Health estimates that 3 million persons have chronic mental conditions that inhibit their ability to perform the basic activities of daily living.[17] Of these, 1 million are in nursing homes or psychiatric hospitals. The others are in the community and various short-term institutional settings.

The population classified as developmentally disabled includes persons diagnosed before age 22 as mentally retarded or as having cerebral palsy, epilepsy, or autism. The minimum estimate is 3.9 million severely disabled, with perhaps two to three times as many with a milder degree of disability.[18] The ability of such persons to function independently varies widely, as does their need for ongoing health services or assistance from formal sources. For some, such as those with mild mental retardation, a supportive family environment is all that is required to maintain a relatively high level of independent functioning. For others, such as children with cerebral palsy and an unstable family environment, continued interaction with formal health and social services may be essential.

Short-Term, Complex Conditions

Formal association with a continuum of care is not necessarily a permanent aspect of a client's life. Many people may benefit from the assistance of an organized, integrated, comprehensive array of services to help them get through a short-term crisis or through a period of rehabilitation. Elderly stroke survivors, for example, may have multiple problems and permanent disabilities, yet may not require indefinite involvement with a formal system. The staff of a formal continuum of care work with the family and friends through the crisis stage of illness and guide or arrange community supports that can be short-term or ongoing, depending upon the person's recovery. Most case management programs carry a limited number of active clients. Many clients require formal assistance for less than a year.

The Acutely Ill

Of the five leading hospital discharges, all are for potentially long-term conditions.[19] For those over 65, the leading hospital discharges are for heart diseases, malignant neoplasms, fractures, pneumonia, and cerebrovascular diseases.

Hospitals are organized to meet needs for acute care—whether the condition is short-term or an acute episode of a chronic illness. Yet, the majority of patients are hospitalized for conditions that continue after the period of hospitalization, and many require professional care beyond a follow-up visit to a physician. To provide quality care for such patients, a comprehensive continuum of care is appropriate.

In 1983, hospital admissions totaled 38,135,000, and patients used 264 million days of care.[20] Recent projections indicate that by the year 2000, the U.S. population will use 348 million days of hospital care per year. This would be an increase of over 27 percent between 1983 and 2000. Of this, almost half will be attributable to the population over 65.[21] This increase in admissions will be due to both an increase in the number of older people and an increase in the rate of admissions,[22] possibly reflecting the increased ability of high-technology to keep very ill, frail people alive.

Simultaneous with the increase in days of care is a decrease in the length of stay in acute hospitals and a rise in the use of home health care and ambulatory services. Due to changes in the payment systems, hospitals are using other services before, after, and instead of hospitalization. Thus, clients of the hospital are becoming clients of the continuum of care.

Comprehensive, Capitated Populations

Health care systems with enrolled or captive populations are increasing rapidly. Such programs include HMOs, S/HMOs, preferred provider organizations, public welfare contracts, and consumer-oriented networks. Some programs are organized for and targeted at consumers; others focus on providers or insurers.

The recent surge in HMOs is indicative of the growth of such programs. Between June 1984 and June 1985, HMOs had their fastest growing year since their inception in the early 1970s.[22] The number of HMOs increased 29 percent to 393.[23] The number of enrollees climbed 25 percent, to reach 18.9 million. Similarly, Medicare allowed HMOs to enroll seniors under new risk arrangement contracts, and senior HMO enrollment climbed from 671,000 to 924,000, or 38 percent, during the first full year of availability.

Such health care systems tend to offer a wide array of services. In most instances, payment is tied to the breadth of the service program, the amount of use, and the number of enrollees. These systems of care incorporate the financial principles of a continuum of care. Thus, the clients of such systems are appropriately considered clients of a continuum.

The majority of enrollees in such programs are healthy and most use very few health services. On the other hand, even if services are not offered by the organization or included in the financial arrangements, consumers (and in many instances providers) will assume that they are or should be. If systems of care are successful in getting consumers to turn to them first whenever they have a health or support problem, then the organization must be prepared to be responsive to the consumers' needs and to develop access to services, provide education, and ensure consumer expectations are consistent with the organization's program.

Similarly, the measure of a successful continuum of care is in directing people to the type and level of care most applicable to their immediate need. The continuum should be structured to triage and coordinate services for clients who have short-term problems as well as for those who have ongoing, changing problems. Thus, appropriate clients of the continuum of care include all those enrolled in formal health care systems.

SUMMARY

In summary, the population that is the heaviest user of health and social services is one that requires long-term, multifaceted, continuing services, not short-term acute services offered by the existing system. Not everyone requires the formal assistance of a continuum of care, even if they use multiple services. Those who require care from formal sources tend to be those with functional disabilities and the inability to care for themselves or to have care provided by informal sources. Seniors are major candidates for the continuum of care. However, once a continuum is established, many of the patients and clients who use one or two of the service components of the continuum are likely to benefit from the efficiency of its organization and operation.

During the next decades, the health care field will become increasingly market-driven. As it does, there will be considerable growth in the demand for a continuum of care approach. Various subpopulations requiring the assistance of a formal continuum of care, particularly the older population, will increase. And as continuums of care are developed, they will serve several distinct population groups. The services of the continuum will vary depending on the particular large audience and whether the clients are long-term or short-term. However, once organized and operating, the continuum will serve diverse population groups.

NOTES

1. S. Katz, T. D. Downs, H. R. Cash, and R. C. Grotz, "Progress in the Development of an Index of ADL," *The Gerontologist* 10, no. 1 (Spring 1970):20–30.

2. M. P. Lawton and Elaine M. Brody, "Assessment of Older People, Self-maintaining and Instrumental Activities of Daily Life," *The Gerontologist* 9, no. 3 (Fall 1969):179–186.

3. Beth J. Soldo and Kenneth G. Manton, "Health Service Needs of the Oldest Old," *Health and Society, Milbank Memorial Fund Quarterly* 63, no. 2 (Spring 1985).

4. Barbara Feller, *Americans Needing Help To Function at Home*, National Center for Health Statistics, Advance Data from Vital and Health Statistics, No. 92 DHHS Pub. No. (PHS) 83-1250 (Hyattsville, Md.: Department of Health and Human Services, 1983).

5. Senate Special Committee on Aging, "Chronic Conditions and Health Problems," in *Aging America: Trends and Projections*, 1985–86 ed., 99th Cong., 1st sess., 1985.

6. National Center for Health Statistics, Division of Health Care Statistics, "Operations for Inpatients Discharged from Non-Federal Short-Stay Hospitals, According to Sex, Age, and Surgical Category: United States, 1979 and 1983," in *Aging America*.

7. National Center for Health Statistics, 1983 Hospital Discharge Survey, *Utilization of Short-Stay Hospitals for Selected Age Groups, 1983*, in *Aging America*, 99.

8. Kenneth Manton and Korbin Liu, "The Future Growth of the Long-Term Care Population: Projections Based on the 1977 National Nursing Home Survey and the 1982 Long-Term Care Survey, 1984," in *Aging America*, 97.

9. National Center for Health Statistics, Division of Health Interview Statistics, "Physician Visits, According to Source of Place of Care and Selected Patient Characteristics: United States, 1982 and 1983," in *Health: United States, 1985*, DHHS Pub. No. (PHS) 86-1232 (Hyattsville, Md.: Department of Health and Human Services, 1985).

10. Health Care Financing Administration, "Medicare Persons Served/Type of Service," in *HCFA Statistics*, HCFA Pub No. 03209 (Hyattsville, Md.: Department of Health and Human Services, 1985).

11. Charlene Harrington, Robert Newcomer, and Carroll Estes, *Long Term Care of the Elderly* (Beverly Hills, Calif.: Sage Publications, 1985).

12. U.S. Bureau of the Census, *Decennial Censuses of Population, 1990–2050*, and *Projections of the Population of the United States, by Age, Sex, and Race: 1983 to 2080*, Current Population Reports, Series P-25, no. 952, May 1984.

13. Senate Special Committee on Aging, *Aging America*, 11.

14. U.S. Bureau of the Census, *Decennial Censuses* and *Projections*.

15. W. Weissert, "Size and Characteristics of the Non-Institutional Long-Term Care Population," in *Project to Analyze Existing Long-Term Care Data, Final Report*, vol. 2, Department of Health and Human Services, July 1983; W. Weissert and W. Scanlon, "Estimating the Long-Term Care Population: National Prevalence Rates and Selected Characteristics," in *Project to Analyze Existing Long-Term Care Data*.

16. *President's Commission on Mental Health: Final Report*, vol. 2 (Washington, D.C.: GPO, 1978).

17. William Oriol, *The Complex Cube of Long-Term Care* (Washington, D.C.: American Health Planning Association, 1985), 34–35.

18. Ibid., 37.

19. National Center for Health Statistics, Division of Health Care Statistics, "Discharges, Days-of-Care, and Average Length of Stay in Non-Federal Short-Stay Hospitals, According to Sex, Age, and Selected First-listed Diagnosis: United States, 1979 and 1983," Table 50, in *Health: United States, 1985*, DHHS Pub. No. (PHS) 1232 (Hyattsville, Md.: Department of Health and Human Services, 1985).

20. Ibid.

21. Dorothy Rice and Arden Wick, *Impact of an Aging Population on Health Care Needs* (San Francisco: Institute for Health & Aging, 1985), II–8 Table 2.4.

22. Janet Schwartz, *Demographic Trends and Hospital Utilization: The Elderly Population*, Office of Public Policy Analysis, Policy Brief No. 41, American Hospital Association (Chicago: American Hospital Association, 1982).

23. Interstudy, *The 1985 Medicare and HMO Data Book* (Excelsior, Minn.: Interstudy, 1986).

Chapter 5

Structural Changes in Health Care

Jeffrey A. Alexander, PhD
Donna G. Vaughan

The American health care system, like all industries, evolves over time. Historically, previous periods of development encouraged the expansion and growth of a fragmented system of isolated, free-standing community hospitals. Recent environmental constraints impinging upon the health care industry have reversed the earlier trends and resulted in a dramatic transformation in the institutional structure of American health care delivery.

THE HISTORICAL DEVELOPMENT OF THE AMERICAN HEALTH CARE INDUSTRY

Period I: Mid-1800s to 1900

Prior to the midnineteenth century, health care in the United States was represented by loosely organized individual services that functioned independently of each other.[1] With the development of the first large hospitals in 1850, such as Bellevue Hospital in New York and Massachusetts General Hospital in Boston, the health care delivery system moved, for the first time, toward organized institutional care.

Period II: 1900 to World War II

The turn of the century brought the introduction of scientific medicine to American health care.[2] The opening of a new medical school at Johns Hopkins University in Baltimore, Maryland, provided the impetus for the development of a solid scientific base for medical practice. Advances in medicine initiated a rapid growth in hospitals and transformed them from custodial to curative institutions.[3]

57

Period III: World War II to Mid-1960s

Until World War II, hospitals were considered institutions primarily dedicated to patient care.[4] Following the war, many hospitals became extensions of research laboratories and universities where new scientific advances and sophisticated technology were utilized daily.

The technology eventually captured the hospitals and became the motivating force for many major decisions.[5] Rising costs persisted unabatedly both for the technology itself and for the specialized personnel required for its implementation.[6] In spite of the cost escalation, the premise of "health care as a right, not a privilege" was generally accepted.[7]

The development of health insurance plans such as Blue Cross and Blue Shield ensured a flow of funds for expansion of facilities and services and increased the demand for hospital care.[8] Hospitals operated on the premise that no service or piece of equipment was too good or too expensive for individual institutions, regardless of the need for it or its overall cost.[9]

Easily obtainable insurance, the availability of public and private funds, and the nation's continuing commitment to high quality care and optimum levels of health led the hospital industry to assume that the health care system would continue to grow in size and complexity and that sufficient resources for expansion would always be available.[10] The basic network for health care delivery continued to be composed of autonomously operated private physicians, group practices, private and public nonprofit voluntary hospitals, proprietary hospitals, teaching and research institutions, rehabilitation facilities, and nursing homes.[11] Some public health and community programs were supported by the government, but these remained out of the mainstream of the health care delivery system.

Paralleling the growing technology and rising costs was a growing interest in the social and organizational structure of health care. In the early 1960s a major battle was won by those advocating a greater societal role in the organization of health services.[12] The passage of Medicare legislation, directed primarily at the nation's elderly, had two major implications. Financing for health care was provided for all persons over the age of 65 regardless of need; and the federal government assumed responsibility for planning, financing, and monitoring a significant portion of the health care services in this country. This shift of financial responsibility for health care would later prove to be a pivotal turning point in the industry's history.

Period IV: Mid-1960s to Present

Torrens has called the most recent period of hospital development the era of "limited resources, restriction of growth, and regulation of effort."[13] The changing composition of the population, with the accompanying chronic problems of the elderly, created new demands for hospital care, thus continuing the upward pressure on health care expenditures. [14] A decline in births, the trend of population shifts to the suburbs, and increased consumer advocacy also presented serious challenges. [15]

Free-standing hospitals found it impossible to use their specialized equipment, personnel, and facilities to capacity. [16] Private group practices increasingly competed with hospitals by escalating the number of ambulatory and emergency care ancillary services to vie with services previously provided in inpatient settings.

Hospitals turned to debt financing as a primary source of capital due to a decline in public financial support and reduced contributions from philanthropists. [17] As the bond market strained to keep pace with the new debt requirement, it soon became clear that continued access to the market would only be provided to the most financially sound institutions. Thus, the dilemma facing many hospitals became one of obtaining funds for modernization and maintenance of facilities.

At the same time, the rapid escalation of costs between 1965 and 1975, coupled with the dominant financial role of private and public insurance programs, made variations in hospital costs a subject of expanding public scrutiny. [18] Hospitals were increasingly subjected to legislative activities. [19] While some of the legislation was favorable, such as the 1970 Hill-Burton amendments, which added new provisions for federal loans and loan guarantees for construction, much of the legislation was regulatory.

During the mid-1960s, 46 states enacted certificate of need laws that required health facilities to obtain approval for building plans from state health departments. [20] In 1972, a Social Security amendment mandated the establishment of professional standards review committees (PSRCs) for the purpose of reviewing services provided to Medicare and Medicaid patients to assure suitable quality and a cost-effective manner of provision.

With the passage of the National Health Planning and Resource Development Act of 1974, state laws gained the support of the federal government. [21] At various governmental levels, formal planning mechanisms were defined that established well-publicized national health priorities. [22] Priorities articulated in the Act called for the development of multi-institutional collaboration for coordination, consolidation, and geographic integration of health services; the sharing of support services necessary to all health service institutions; improvement of productivity and quality; prevention of unnecessary duplication; and better access. [23]

Other health care organizations grew in number and in the proportion of resources consumed. After the passage of Medicare and Medicaid, the number of nursing homes mushroomed and they soon outnumbered hospitals by threefold. Home health agencies expanded. Free-standing rehabilitation centers and hospices, approved by Medicare, began to appear. Health maintenance organizations (HMOs) and preferred provider organizations (PPOs) also emerged during this period as major alternative providers.

The increasingly complex and demanding environment of the 1970s set the stage for structural changes that health care organizations would make in an attempt to cope with the new laws and regulations, socioeconomic pressures, and demands from union and consumer groups, as well as the rapid advances in medical science and technology.[24] The passage of prospective payment in 1982, accompanied by the development of new health care financing mechanisms such as HMOs and PPOs, accelerated the need for health care organizations to consider structural alternatives to unrestricted growth and expansion. As a solution to their multifaceted problems, health care organizations increasingly turned to a variety of multi-institutional arrangements, new diversification strategies, and corporate reorganization.

MULTI-INSTITUTIONAL ARRANGEMENTS

Health care organizations have the option of participating in a variety of collaborative multi-institutional arrangements ranging from simpler, less committed arrangements such as affiliation agreements and shared services to the more complex models of contract management and complete ownership by a separate organizational entity. Several authors have developed taxonomies of organizational affiliations in an attempt to differentiate model complexity by level of commitment, corporate ownership and management, influence on policy decisions, reaction of personnel, time commitment requirements, and difficulty of termination.[25]

DeVries' classification schema, for example, shows shared service arrangements falling on the low end of the commitment continuum and complete ownership and management of the individual organization by a multi-institutional system at the high end (see Table 5-1).[26] Starkweather has developed a similar typology for hospital mergers.[27] Using seven dimensions, he classifies hospitals along a continuum from complete pluralism (involving no relationship with other hospitals) to complete fusion with other hospitals through mergers. Reynolds and Stunden use centralization of management to characterize systems, with the degree of centralization a function of the geographical dispersion of the system and the level of competition in its market.[28]

However, more recent literature indicates that such typologies, while of some value, do not fully capture the similarities and differences among multi-institutional systems.[29] Each type of system descriptor or category, e.g., complete ownership or contract management, is an aggregation of a number of organizational characteristics as well as hospital types.

For example, Lewis and Alexander recently identified 15 distinct subgroups of systems through an analysis of 16 organizational characteristics of 160 multihospital systems.[30] Although all clustering variables were significant, the following six were found to be of particular importance: system ownership;

Table 5-1 Classification of Multihospital Arrangements

Characteristics \ Types or Categories	*I Formal Affiliation*	*II Shared or Cooperative Services*	*III Consortia for Planning or Education*	*IV Contract Management*	*V Lease*	*VI Corporate Ownership but Separate Management*	*VII Complete Ownership*
	Less commitment, more institutional autonomy ◄——— Continuum ———► More commitment, more system control						
Descriptions, Definitions, Terms	Patient transfer agreements, house officer affiliations, referral agreements	Financial, political commitment over time for selected products for services	Voluntary health planning council for a specific geography; area health education centers (AHECs)	Corporate management; full management without ownership	Policy as well as management provided by a single board	Owners do not interfere in the management of hospitals even though they have legal authority (absentee ownership)	1. Mergers, consolidations 2. Satellites, branch operations 3. Authorities, chains 4. Holding companies
Corporate Ownership	No	No	No	No	No	Yes	Yes
Corporate Management	No	No	No	Yes	Yes	No	Yes
System Influence on Major Policy Decisions	No	No	Yes	Minor	Yes	Maybe	Yes (Absolute)

Source: Reprinted by permission from *Hospitals*, Vol. 52, No. 6, March 16, 1978. Copyright 1978, American Hospital Association.

centralization of governance; hospital-related decision making; medical staff organization; proportion of hospitals contract managed; and extent of corporate involvement in medical affairs. Contract management arrangements also include a wide range of health care organizations, including rural, urban, public, private, financially ailing, and financially solvent institutions.[31]

More recent classification schema suggest that multi-institutional arrangements are more complex than the earlier typologies indicated. Differences may occur in allocation of responsibility for decision making, the degree to which medical professionals are involved in policy-making activities, the scope and range of services, and geographical concentration. Thus, rather than using simple categories to distinguish among multi-institutional systems, it is more appropriate to focus on the arrangements that link individual organizations to multi-institutional systems and to identify prevalent types of organizations and systems that share similar organizational, operations, and governance characteristics.[32]

Due to the availability of empirical research, the following focus is on hospitals. However, the principles are applicable to the broader health care field.

Multihospital Systems

The American Hospital Association (AHA) defines a *multihospital system* as "two or more hospitals owned, leased, sponsored, or contract managed by a central organization."[33] In the more complex models of multihospital systems, additional layers of management (e.g., the corporate office and system governing board) necessitate sharing of decision making between headquarters and hospital units. Although centralization of decision making appears to decrease with system complexity (geographical dispersion and product diversification), the absence of complete autonomy of the hospital units differentiates them from free-standing hospitals.[34]

The Growth of Multihospital Systems

The growth of multihospital systems began to escalate rapidly during the middle to late 1960s and continued unabated until approximately 1980. By the early 1980s, 267 systems contained 30.7 percent of all nonfederal community hospitals and 35 percent of their beds. Based on the initial phenomenal growth, speculation abounded that the majority of hospitals would be a part of systems by 1990.

However, since 1980, system growth has begun to moderate. From 1980 to 1985, the number of hospitals in systems grew at an average rate of 4.5 percent annually, with the growth in the number of hospital beds averaging 3.3 percent. In 1985, systems contained 38.4 percent of all nonfederal community hospitals and 39 percent of their beds.

The slowing growth rate has been accompanied by a period of system consolidation, with the number of total systems declining from 267 to 250 (6.4 percent); however, the numbers of system hospitals and beds have increased 22.9 percent and 16.9 percent respectively (see Table 5-2). For the past five years, the other nonprofits have demonstrated the greatest growth in total number of systems (14.8 percent), with the Catholic church-related systems showing the largest decrease (21.8 percent). The greatest growth in multi-institutional system hospitals and beds has occurred within the investor-owned systems (42.2 percent and 42.5 percent respectively).

A number of variables differentiate contract-managed hospitals from those that are owned, leased, or sponsored. Management of contract-managed hospitals has more input over control issues, the contract is for a limited period of time, and the hospital maintains authority over its assets. The remainder of this section is devoted to an in-depth analysis of these two popular and complex models of system arrangements.

Owned, Leased, and Sponsored Systems

Complete ownership is considered to be the most complex system model, since it requires a substantial commitment of organizational resources and administration.[35] Investor-owned and voluntary systems tend to differ in the structure of these linkages with other hospitals.[36] Investor-owned systems favor acquisition or buying assets, while voluntary chains favor merger, where little cash or other financial assets change hands.

In a lease arrangement, general policies, as well as daily management, are provided by an outside organization.[37] These arrangements are typically found among hospital chains operated by religious communities and are similar to contract-management, except that policy making as well as management is provided by a corporate board.

Sponsorship is a relationship between a religious organization and a health care institution that sets limits on activities initiated within the health care institution or is intended to further the objectives of the sponsoring organization. This type of arrangement does not involve ownership or other legal relationships.[38]

Overall Growth

In 1980 the number of owned, leased, and sponsored systems represented 23.9 percent of all nonfederal community hospitals and 30.5 percent of their beds. By 1985, these systems contained 29.2 percent of all nonfederal community hospitals and 33.5 percent of their beds.

Between 1980 and 1985, the largest increase in the number of owned, leased, and sponsored hospitals and beds occurred in investor-owned systems (64.2

Table 5-2 Number of Multihospital Systems and Their Owned, Leased, or Sponsored and Contract Managed Beds by Ownership Control 1980 and 1985 (as a percentage of all systems in parentheses)

| Ownership Control | Number of Systems | | | Hospitals and Beds in Systems | | | | | | |
	1980	1985	% Change 1980–1985	1980 H	1980 B	1985 H	1985 B	% Change 1980–1985 H	% Change 1980–1985 B
Catholic Church-Related Systems	124 (46.4)	97 (38.8)	– 21.8	533 (29.7)	139,767 (40.9)	527 (23.8)	137,734 (34.7)	– 1.1	– 1.5
Other Church-Related Systems	20 (7.5)	21 (8.4)	+ 5.0	137 (7.6)	20,590 (6.1)	152 (6.9)	28,647 (7.2)	+10.9	+39.1
Other Nonprofit Systems	88 (33.0)	101 (40.4)	+14.8	426 (23.7)	91,356 (26.7)	532 (24.1)	102,799 (25.9)	+24.9	+12.5
Investor-Owned Systems	35 (13.1)	31 (12.4)	– 11.4	701 (39.0)	89,635 (26.3)	997 (45.1)	127,745 (32.2)	+42.2	+42.5
All Systems	267	250	– 6.4	1797	341,382	2208	396,925	+22.9	+16.3

Note. H = Hospitals   B = Beds

Sources: Data Book on Multihospital Systems 1980–1981, American Hospital Association, © 1981; *The Directory of Multihospital Systems, Multistate Alliances and Networks*, 6th ed., American Hospital Association, © 1985.

percent and 55.3 percent). As a result, for the first time they surpassed the growth of secular nonprofits and were second only to the Catholic church-related systems in the number of hospitals and beds.

During the same time period, other church-related systems increased the number of their hospitals by 17.3 percent and beds by 36.2 percent. The secular nonprofit systems demonstrated only modest growth in the number of hospitals and beds, while the Catholic church-related systems showed a decrease in both categories (see Table 5-3).

System Strategies

Throughout the 1970s, horizontal integration (the purchase or acquisition of hospitals) accounted for the bulk of growth in system assets for both investor-owned and nonprofit systems. For the past five years, horizontal growth for the latter has been modest, while there has been a marked increase in growth for investor-owned systems, generally attributable to their superior access to capital.

The recent impact of prospective payment, coupled with an increasingly competitive health care environment, is expected to have major implications for system strategy during the upcoming decade. A recent study, combining an analysis of AHA survey data with interviews of seven multihospital system executives, reported that growth for growth's sake will no longer be pursued by the majority of systems.[39]

Table 5-3 Number of Owned, Leased, or Sponsored Beds and Hospitals in Multihospital Systems by Ownership Control 1980 and 1985 (as a percentage of all OLS beds and hospitals in parentheses)

| Ownership Control | Owned, Leased, or Sponsored | | | | % Change 1980–1985 | |
| | 1980 | | 1985 | | | |
	H	B	H	B	H	B
Catholic Church-	510	134,293	475	130,063	− 7.3	− 3.3
Related Systems	(36.4)	(45.2)	(28.3)	(38.4)		
Other Church-	104	18,722	122	25,503	+ 17.3	+ 36.2
Related Systems	(7.4)	(6.3)	(7.3)	(7.5)		
Other Nonprofit	373	85,103	405	90,966	+ 8.6	+ 6.8
Systems	(26.6)	(28.6)	(24.1)	(26.9)		
Investor-Owned	413	59,324	678	92,143	+ 64.2	+ 55.3
Systems	(29.6)	(19.9)	(40.3)	(27.2)		
All Systems	1400	297,447	1680	388,675	+ 20.0	+ 13.8

Note: H = Hospitals   B = Beds

Sources: Data Book on Multihospital Systems 1980–1981, American Hospital Association, © 1981; *The Directory of Multihospital Systems, Multistate Alliances and Networks*, 6th ed., American Hospital Association, © 1985.

Future acquisition strategies of systems will be directed toward enhancing a system's range of services and obtaining hospitals located in favorable market conditions except when the system's mission dictates otherwise.[40] Thus, a substantial portion of system acquisition dollars will be diverted into nonhospital vertically integrated services such as insurance, PPOs, joint ventures with multigroup physicians, and pre- or postcare facilities.

Evidence of this trend is already well documented. Surveys by *Modern Healthcare* over the last five years show rapid vertical integration into nursing homes and psychiatric hospitals for both investor-owned and nonprofit systems.[41] The growth of the investor-owned systems in these arenas has been five times that of their nonprofit competitors. Health insurance has also become an important form of vertical integration, particularly for the investor-owned systems.[42]

Multiclustering, the latest system strategy, involves concentrating resources into vertically integrated health care services clustered in predetermined geographic areas, both regional and local.[43] For example, National Medical Enterprises (NME) is forming clusters in areas where it owns a number of primary care facilities. Around each cluster it will develop at least one skilled nursing facility, a durable medical equipment center, a home health care agency, and hospital-based or free-standing psychiatric, substance-abuse, and rehabilitation units.

The move by systems to focus their markets due to declining utilization and increasing competition will also result in strategic disinvestment of unprofitable services and hospitals.[44] A full range of services will continue to be provided in targeted markets, but they will be offered through joint-venture or other contractual arrangements with a variety of providers. American Medical International (AMI) already has made plans to sell up to 26 facilities that do not fit its clustering strategies, and Hospital Corporation of America (HCA) expects to sell up to $500 million worth of hospitals before its divestiture strategy is completed.

System Performance

As system development escalated, many prophesied that the following benefits would occur, providing solutions to both institutional problems and cost containment pressures:[45]

- increased access to capital markets
- reduction in duplication of services
- economies of scale
- improved productivity and operating efficiencies
- access to management expertise
- increased personnel benefits (career mobility and recruitment)

- improved patient access through geographical integration of various levels of care
- improvement in quality through increased volume of services for specialized personnel
- increased political power to deal with planning, regulation, and reimbursement issues.

In general, the empirical literature to date has documented few differences in quality and access between system and nonsystem hospitals.[46] There also is little or no evidence supporting differential care for the disadvantaged or differences in case mix.

Except for greater access to capital markets and greater efficiency in the use of personnel, research has been unable to demonstrate many advantages of systems over free-standing hospitals. Moreover, there is increasing evidence of higher costs in system hospitals, particularly investor-owned, whether measured on a per diem or per case basis.[47] Explanations for the higher costs in system hospitals include (1) a capital advantage that provides opportunity for diversification and increased services, (2) higher markups and general services costs (attributable mainly to home office costs), and (3) higher capital costs.[48]

While profits of systems appear to be increasing yearly, *Modern Healthcare* reports that assets currently are being used less efficiently because of DRGs and the impact of price competition, both of which are negatively impacting hospital utilization.[49] In 1985, lower earnings were reported by 24.2 percent of the surveyed systems.[50]

The following precautions must be taken into account when evaluating system performance data:

1. Most available empirical data comparing the performance of free-standing and system hospitals comes from the period before the implementation of prospective payment.
2. Systems generally tend to self-select into favorable market areas, making comparisons of free-standing and system hospital data methodologically difficult to analyze.
3. Approximately one-half of existing systems contain three or fewer hospitals, substantially lessening major advantages in economies of scale or collective financial resources.
4. Systems have been treated as homogeneous rather than heterogeneous organizations for the purpose of empirical analysis.

Contract Management

The AHA defines *contract management* as "the general day-to-day management of an entire organization by another organization, under a formal contract."[51] The managing organization reports directly to the board of trustees or owners of the managed organization; the managed organization retains total legal responsibility and ownership of the facility's assets and liabilities.

Brown and Money report that management contracts also include the following elements:[52]

- An administrator is appointed by the managing organization, subject to board approval; the administrator's salary is usually paid by the managing organization, although in some cases the cost may be reimbursed by the managed hospital.
- Operation of the hospital is managed by the appointed administrator under a budget subject to board approval; the administrator obtains approval of key decisions from the board.
- The managing corporation provides specialized services and personnel to the managed facility; new information systems may be implemented and feasibility studies may be performed; the administrator appointed by the managing corporation takes daily management responsibility for the institution and suggests changes in services typically enacted with the approval of the board.

Reasons for Entering a Contract Management Agreement

Recent data suggest that financially pressured organizations in weak markets, regardless of management strength, tend to enter into management contracts.[53] Until recently, providers of contract management services have been predominantly large, for-profit, investor-owned multihospital systems, and clients have been mostly small nonprofit, free-standing hospitals.[54]

Hospitals tend to choose contract management over other forms of multihospital arrangements for a variety of reasons, including the following:[55]

- Contract management provides a closer contractual relationship for support services than can be obtained from shared services or consortium arrangements.
- Facilities selecting management contract services can choose between competing investor-owned firms and nonprofit organizations offering services in their regions.
- Management contracts have numerous advantages over merger in that they are easier to accomplish, the physicians and other personnel feel less threatened, the hospital's commitment is clearly specified and for a shorter period of time, and the board generally retains complete control of decision making (i.e., highly valued institutional independence and identity is preserved).
- Contract management has the advantage of providing the hospital with an

onsite-trained administrator who has easy access to the managing corporation's specialists in finance, planning, development, nursing, labor relations, marketing, etc.

The reasons underlying the managing institution's decision to enter into management contract agreements are not completely understood. It has been suggested that managing organizations may wish to influence major policy decisions and impact corporate management among health care facilities in their region.[56] In this scenario, contract management would be preferred over other less committed forms of multihospital arrangements such as consortia, affiliation agreements, and shared service arrangements. Management contract services may also be viewed as a diversification strategy for revenue-generating shared service programs that an organization may already be providing.

Others view contract management as a transitional organization form that offers the managing system the opportunity to obtain in-depth information about the managed organization for the purpose of ultimately acquiring the institution from a strong bargaining position.[57] However, a preliminary analysis of data provided by Morrisey and Alexander[58] indicates the following:

1. From 1976 to 1982 only 24 hospitals were converted from being contract managed to system-owned, suggesting either that contracts are of long duration or that acquisition is not a primary motivation of management contracts.
2. Systems tend to acquire hospitals with weak management but located in favorable markets, while management contracts generally exist in unfavorable markets. If the preliminary findings are correct, this suggests that the range of management contracts likely to result in system acquisition is small.
3. Finally, the research findings suggest that management contracts are stable organizational forms designed to provide operational efficiency without sacrificing the unique mission of the managed organization.

The Growth of Contract Management

During the 1970s, investor-owned systems were in the forefront of the contract management movement. By 1980, they managed 288 hospitals with 30,311 beds, compared to 53 hospitals with 6,248 beds managed by their closest competitors, the other nonprofits. During the past five years, the number of hospitals and beds contract managed by all systems have increased by 33 percent and 32.7 percent, respectively.

In 1985, although investor-owned systems retained their lead with 319 contract-managed hospitals and 35,602 beds, their percentage of all system contract-managed hospitals and beds declined due to an increase in contract management by the nonprofit systems (see Table 5-4). The largest five-year increase occurred in the other nonprofit systems, followed by the Catholic church-related systems, although growth during the past three years has remained relatively stable for both ownership categories. Growth in other church-related systems has remained relatively stable for the entire five-year period.

Structural Models of Contract Management

The three basic structural models of contract management include (1) the operating division model, (2) the wholly-owned subsidiary model, and (3) the shared or joint management model.[59] Over 90 percent of the hospital and health care facility contract management market is represented by the operating division model.

The operating division model can be developed using either a centralized or decentralized approach, although the former is the most popular.[60] Most investor-owned chains and some nonprofit chains employ the centralized approach, where the hospital contract management function is administered through the central corporate headquarters. While some of the largest firms place management responsibility on regional or district personnel, the managers are typically corporate office employees. Also, the management agreement is signed between the hospital corporation and the managed facility. An example is the Nebraska Methodist Hospital in Omaha, which manages 11 voluntary hospitals in three states.

In the less popular decentralized model, member hospitals of a system are responsible for the management of hospitals and other health care facilities in their geographic area.[61] In this approach, the management contract is signed

---

Table 5-4 Number of Contract Managed Beds and Hospitals in Multihospital Systems by Ownership Control 1985 (as a percentage of all contract managed hospitals and beds in parentheses)

Ownership Control	Contract Managed 1985	
	Hospitals	*Beds*
Catholic Church-	52	7,671
Related Systems	(9.8)	(13.2)
Other Church-	30	3,144
Related Systems	(5.7)	(5.4)
Other Nonprofit	127	11,833
Systems	(24.1)	(20.3)
Investor-Owned	319	35,602
Systems	(60.4)	(61.1)
All Systems	528	58,250

Sources: Data Book on Multihospital Systems 1980–1981, American Hospital Association, © 1981; *The Directory of Multihospital Systems, Multistate Alliances and Networks*, 6th ed., American Hospital Association, © 1985.

between a member hospital and the managed institution. An example is the Dakota Midland Hospital in Abeedeen, South Dakota, a corporate member of Health Central, which has offered management contract services to hospitals in North and South Dakota.

In the wholly-owned subsidiary model, nonprofit hospitals and health care systems establish wholly owned for-profit subsidiaries to handle the management contract. The subsidiary is governed by the board of trustees and the management team of the sponsoring organization, and the subsidiary's profits are used exclusively for the nonprofit corporation's benefit.

Shared or joint management models are developed when hospitals and other health care facilities in a region join together to sponsor a managing corporation (investor-owned or nonprofit entity) that manages each of the participating institutions. The governing board of the management corporation is composed of a representative of each participating institution.

While little evidence is available to recommend one model of contract management over another, Lowe suggests the following issues for consideration:[62]

1. The degree of management control is higher in both the operating division and wholly owned subsidiary than in the shared or joint management model.
2. The degree of medical staff and trustee acceptance is moderate in all models, although it probably increases with the decentralized version of the operating division model, since the managed facility deals with a local institution instead of a remote corporate headquarters.
3. Opportunities for vertical integration are more promising under the shared or joint management model, since participants are considered "equal" and purchase management services from an organization that they partially own.

Performance Indicators for Contract Management

Most of the information available about contract management performance is descriptive or antecdotal. The few excellent studies that have been conducted on performance outcomes have not been replicated, and much of the remaining empirical data is fraught with methodological problems, including small sample size, poorly specified models, lack of adequate theoretical framework, and limited generalizability. However, the contract management area is attracting a promising number of excellent researchers who undoubtedly will advance the knowledge base of this important system model.

CORPORATE REORGANIZATION

For many years, business organizations in other fields have coped with regulatory, liability, tax, and competitive pressures through the utilization of multicorporate ventures.[63] Health care organizations are beginning to follow their lead by restructuring in a manner that diversifies the health care corporation into provider and nonprovider organizations. Many of the newly formed organizations perform functions that were previously the responsibility of the hospital. While an extensive reorganization provides both benefits and risks for the health care organization, often the process of restructuring meets the free-standing organization's needs better than affiliations with systems or other multi-institutional arrangements.

A recent study on corporate reorganization by Ernst and Whinney indicates that corporate reorganization is widespread in hospitals of all sizes in urban, suburban, and rural settings, although it is most prevalent among larger and medium-sized urban hospitals.[64]

Exhibit 5-1 provides a summary of proposed benefits for corporation reorganization. The Ernst and Whinney study found that when hospitals with fewer than 400 beds first decided to reorganize, the primary benefits expected were related to government regulation or reimbursement. The larger hospitals, over 400 beds, considered reorganization because of the belief that a reorganized corporate structure would enable them to improve operational flexibility and diversify revenue-generating functions.

Exhibit 5-1 Proposed Benefits of Corporation Reorganization

Economic

    Increased potential revenue sources; diversification of revenue base

    Insulation of assets/revenues from current and future federal and state regulations

    Protection of assets from contract and tort liability

    Minimization of tax liability for nonpatient care activities

    Improved third-party reimbursement

Diversification and Flexibility

    Provision of vertical integration of services to control patient demands and referrals (improve competitive position)

    Increased flexibility for future expansion of existing activities (health care and nonhealth-care development, service, and investment activities)

    Improved certificate of need status

    Establishment of vehicle for attracting, retaining, and compensating executive management personnel (expansion of management authority and responsibility into other corporations would provide justification for high salary demands)

Sources: Corporate Reorganization Modules by P. Brasher, School of Public and Tropical Medicine, Tulane University, © 1984; *Corporate Reorganization: A Survey of Hospitals That Have Restructured*, Ernst & Whinney, © 1982.

Interestingly, as the reorganization process evolved, many hospital executives found that they had initially made the reorganization decision for the wrong reasons. While they still were pleased with the decision to reorganize, it became increasingly clear that revenue diversification and asset protection were the areas that reorganization would most improve, not third party reimbursement.

Structural Options of Corporate Reorganization

Although restructuring is relatively new to the health care industry, several structural forms of corporate reorganization have emerged. These include establishment of a parent holding company, a separate asset holding company, a separate development foundation (related or unrelated), and multihospital relationships.[65] The Ernst and Whinney survey found that the majority of surveyed hospitals chose the parent holding company model (63 percent), with the second most popular choice being the related foundation (23 percent).[66]

The Parent Holding Company Model

A parent holding company can be established by a spinoff or transfer of existing function or asset or by the acquisition of an existing entity through transfer of control or purchase of assets or stock.[67] The parent corporation can conduct activities itself or through other created subsidiaries (see Figure 5-1).

Both the parent organization and the hospital are tax-exempt, but other parental subsidiaries may be for-profit. Significant assets and activities do not necessarily pass to the parent. The hospital may choose to retain its autonomy or may surrender the power to appoint the board, select the CEO, etc.

The advantages of this structure include the following:[68]

- Better utilization of board and management expertise occurs due to the separation of business, fund raising, and patient care activities.
- New for-profit corporate entities can be added with minimal disruption of existing activities.
- The boards are of a limited and efficient size, and board members and management are not overworked.
- Operational decisions can be made at the operating corporation level while policy direction is provided at the parent organization level.
- Losses, to some extent, can be offset by profits.

Potential problems or hazards of the holding company model include the following:

- Political problems may develop within the organization because of the complexity of the necessary structural changes.

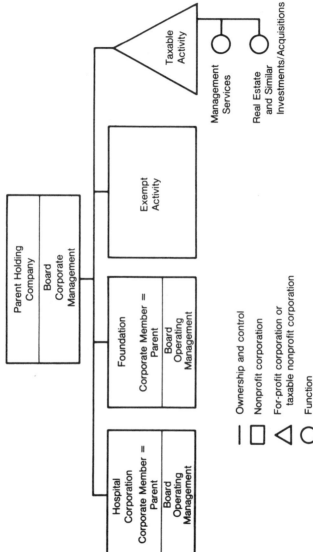

Figure 5-1 Parent Holding Company Model

- Governance can become confusing unless authority is clearly defined by the parent organization.
- New qualified directors must be obtained who are capable of understanding the problems of both the subsidiary and parent organization.
- The Medicare-related party rule is difficult to avoid, and the parent organization's records may have to be disclosed if it provides $10,000 worth of services for which the hospital seeks Medicare reimbursement.
- Creation of tax-exempt 501(c)(3) parent or public charity 509(a) status may require a private IRS ruling. The parent company may have to serve charitable purposes other than those of a hospital to protect tax status. Nontaxable "internal" transfers of revenue may become taxable if a for-profit subsidiary is formed.
- State licensure approval may be required if the parent is created by transferring hospital assets to the new entity.

Ernst and Whinney reported that there are two popular legal forms for establishing control in a parent-subsidiary relationship.[69] A charter and bylaws arrangement, favored by 36 percent of those surveyed, gives total control of the hospital to a named holding company. Under a sole member arrangement, the hospital's board of directors becomes the board of the holding company. The hospital becomes a membership corporation whose sole member is the holding company; thus the latter controls the operations of the hospital. This arrangement was favored by 30 percent of the respondents.

The survey also reported that 86 percent of all hospitals forming parent companies also formed subsidiaries or controlled entities other than the hospital. The most common types of organizations formed were general service corporations, professional office buildings, nursing homes, funding-raising foundations, real estate companies, and ambulatory care centers. Entities most likely to be formed as tax-exempt corporations include electronic data processing (EDP) service centers, general service corporations, professional office buildings, HMOs, and management companies.

The Foundation Model

Foundation structures (controlled, symbiotic, or wholly independent) consist of two corporations (hospital and foundation) with varying degrees of control exercised by the hospital and varying degrees of common membership in boards and management.[70] Both entities are usually tax-exempt, but additional subsidiaries of the foundation can be created for taxable or nonprofit activities. Advantages include[71]

- enhanced fund-raising success resulting from the separation of business and fund development activities

• increased eligibility of favored tax treatment of charitable donations for foundation
• for wholly dependent foundations, avoidance of the Medicare-related organization principle

Hazards of the foundation model include

• lack of formal, direct control
• increased conflict between cultural values of hospital and foundation (minimized by symbiotic, quasi-independent foundations)
• lack of credit worthiness, particularly for wholly independent model
• the necessity of obtaining a private IRS ruling to ensure public charity status and avoid unfavorable private foundation treatment

The Ernst and Whinney survey reported that related foundations (the second most popular model utilized by respondents) were most often used by hospitals attempting to broaden their philanthropic or community support base.[72] In most cases, the hospital transferred funds to start the corporation and selected new board members (usually not members of the hospital board), but the hospital retained control of the funds.

The parent company and independent foundation models are not necessarily mutually exclusive.[73] Often multiple entities are created using both models.

Corporate Reorganization Performance Outcomes

Other than the Ernst and Whinney survey, little or no data exists on performance outcomes of corporate reorganization. However, the Ernst and Whinney data documented some interesting observations on the part of hospital executives.[74]

For example, during the reorganization process, executives reported that a number of obstacles had to be overcome, including

• lack of hospital management support
• lack of board support
• unprojected increases in the length of time and costs to reorganize
• lack of church or community acceptance
• legal and contractual issues

Some 40 percent of the hospitals surveyed also reported that the reorganization process had caused problems not present prior to reorganization. The major issues cited were:

1. communication problems
2. employee or medical staff dissatisfaction
3. management-related problems, including lack of adequate staff to handle the restructured entity and management resentment over loss of authority

Very similar problems were cited following reorganization. Communication and human resource problems were found to be far more prevalent than technical or cost considerations. Not unexpectedly, hospitals with 200 or more beds cited communication problems as the major difficulty, while hospitals under 200 beds cited human resource problems among others.

When executives of reorganized hospitals were asked to what extent the reorganization had solved designated problems, 40 percent responded that reorganization completely solved problems, 62 percent that reorganization partially solved problems, and 12 percent that it was too early to judge. An analysis of these responses led Ernst and Whinney to conclude that the smaller rural hospitals were most satisfied with their reorganization efforts, probably because their objectives—improving financial or competitive position—were easier to achieve than the broader goals set by large hospitals. The larger hospitals' goals of achieving increased flexibility and diversification were more sophisticated, more general, and oriented toward the long-term.

CONCLUSIONS

The American health care industry is undergoing a major structural transformation. The rapidity of the change process makes predictions regarding the future very difficult and merely speculative. The conclusions of the authors given below are based on available empirical and anecdotal data as well as guesswork.

Increased consolidation is predicted for the health care industry in the form of system mergers, consortia and alliances among nonprofit systems, and continued movement of independent hospitals into systems.[75] Some system executives prognosticate that 25 to 50 large health services organizations will dominate the health care industry in the near future.[76]

These organizations can be expected to contain primary, secondary, and tertiary care at the core, in addition to vertically integrated, extended services for ambulatory, home, and long-term care, all covered under system insurance. The term that is emerging to refer to these all-encompassing organizations is *managed care system*. In a managed care system, patient care is supervised in some manner from pre-admission through hospitalization of postcare.

Increasing system divestiture of unprofitable services, coupled with the trend toward vertical integration and market selectivity, has profound implications for free-standing hospitals and other health care organizations. Fewer system buyers are anticipated in the more restrictive financial environment, yet more health care organizations will be available for sale. Some of the hospitals, unattractive to systems, will survive as free-standing institutions, others will be converted to long-term care or ambulatory care facilities, and others will close.

Similarly, nursing homes may be converted to step-down, respite, hospice, or Alzheimer's units to improve financial networks. Home health agencies that had planned on being bought out by hospitals may close or merge with their competitors.

The closure of an increasing number of small hospitals (under 100 beds), both rural and urban, community and speciality, has already been documented. In 1985, AHA reported that 49 community hospitals closed (up from the 1980–1984 average of 33), together with 12 speciality hospitals.[77] The vast majority of the closed community hospitals were owned by nonprofits and the investor-owned sector, while the majority of closed specialty hospitals were owned by state and local governments.

The recent experiences of hospitals are indicative of forces affecting home health, nursing homes, HMOs, and all other health care organizations. All of these trends suggest that health care organizations must continue to consider innovative structural changes that will assist them in addressing the increasingly competitive health care environment. However, any structural reorganization must be predicated on a thorough analysis of the organization's programs, services, and capital resource needs. Careful consideration must also be given to an analysis of tax and reimbursement considerations, flexibility for adapting services for future needs, resources and time required for implementation, legal issues, and the potential for success.

NOTES

1. Paul R. Torrens, "Historical Evolution and Overview of Health Services in the United States," in *Introduction to Health Services*, Stephen J. Williams and Paul R. Torrens, eds. (New York: John Wiley & Sons, 1980), 3–4.

2. Ibid.

3. William L. Dowling and Patricia A. Armstrong, "The Hospital," in *Introduction to Health Services*, Williams and Torrens, 126–132.

4. Ibid.

5. Robert M. Cunningham, "More Than a Business—Are Hospitals Forgetting Their Basic Mission?" *Hospitals* 57 (January 1, 1983):88–90.

6. Steven Portnoy, "The Swelling Tide: Services and Management in Systems," *Hospitals* 51 (April 1, 1977):63–67.

7. Torrens, "Historical Evolution and Overview," 4.

8. Paul J. Feldstein, "The Demand for Medical Care," in *Health Care Economics* (New York: John Wiley & Sons, 1979), 74–102.

9. Stephen R. Walker, "Corporate Restructuring of Hospitals," in *Issues in Health Care* II-1 (Philadelphia: Laventhol & Horwath, 1981), 54–57.

10. Ibid.

11. Diana Barrett, "Multihospital Systems: The Process of Development," *Health Care Management Review* 4, no. 3 (Summer 1979):49–59.

12. Feldstein, "Demand for Medical Care."

13. Torrens, "Historical Evolution and Overview," 4.

14. Robert E. Schlenker, "The Future Health Care Organization," *Health Care Management Review* 5, no. 2 (Spring 1980):69–74.

15. David H. Hitt and Michael P. Harristhal, "Financing Health Care in the 1980's," *Hospitals* 54 (January 1, 1980):71–74; Montague Brown, "Current Trends in Cooperative Ventures," *Hospitals* 48 (June 1, 1974):40–44; Robert A. DeVries, "Strength in Numbers," *Hospitals* 52 (March 16, 1978):81–84.

16. Donald C. Wegmiller, "Corporate Restructuring of Hospitals and Multi-Institutional Arrangements," in *Issues in Health Care*, 12–16.

17. Hitt and Harristhal, "Financing Health Care"; Michael D. Hernandez and Arthur S. Henkel, "Need for Capital May Squeeze Free-Standing Institutions into Multi-Institutional Arrangements," *Hospitals* 56 (March 1, 1982):75–77.

18. Martin Feldstein and James Schuttinga, "Hospital Costs in Massachusetts: A Methodological Study," *Inquiry* 14 (March 1977):22–31.

19. Buford B. Longest, "A Conceptual Framework for Understanding the Multi-Hospital Arrangement Strategy," *Health Care Management Review* 5, no. 1 (Winter 1980):17–23.

20. Jeffrey C. Goldsmith, "The Health Care Market: Can Hospitals Survive?," *Harvard Business Review* 58, no. 5 (September-October 1980):100–112; Steven Portnoy, "The Swelling Tide: Services and Management Systems," *Hospitals* 51 (April 1, 1977):63–67.

21. Joseph S. Coyne and Leslie C. Young, "Multihospital Bed Transfers: Strategic Approach for Multi-Institutional Planners/Managers," *Health Care Management Review* 8, no. 1 (Winter 1983):25–37; Longest, "Conceptual Framework."

22. Howard S. Zuckerman, "Multi-Institutional Systems: Adaptive Strategy for Growth, Survival," *Hospital Progress*, 62, no. 5 (May 1981):43–45; James Reynolds and Ann E. Stunden, "The Organization of Not-for-profit Hospital Systems," *Health Care Management Review* 3, no. 3 (Summer 1978):23–35.

23. Scott Mason, "The Multihospital Movement Defined," *Public Health Reports*, 94, no. 5 (September-October 1979):446–453; Montague Brown, "Contract Management: Latest Development in the Trend Towards Regionalization of Hospital and Health Services," *Hospital and Health Services Administration*, 21 (Winter 1976):41–55; Robert A. Vraciu and Howard S. Zuckerman, "Legal and Financial Constraints on the Development and Growth of Multiple Hospital Arrangements," *Health Care Management Review* 4, no. 1 (Winter 1979):39–47; Marilyn Mannisto, "For-Profit Systems Pursue Growth in Specialization and Diversification," *Hospitals* 55 (September 1, 1981):71–76.

24. DeVries, "Strength in Numbers"; Portnoy, "The Swelling Tide."

25. DeVries, "Strength in Numbers"; Myron D. Fottler et al., "Multi-Institutional Arrangements in Health Care: Review, Analysis and a Proposal for Future Research," *Academy of Management Review* 7, no. 1 (January 1982):67–79; David B. Starkweather, "Health Facility Mergers: Some Conceptualizations," *Medical Care* 9 (November-December 1971):467–478.

26. DeVries, "Strength in Numbers."

27. Starkweather, "Health Facility Mergers."

28. Reynolds and Stunden, "Not-for-profit Hospital Systems."

29. Bonnie L. Lewis and Jeffrey Alexander, "A Taxonomic Analysis of Multi-Hospital Systems," *Health Services Research* 21 (April 1986):29–56.

30. Ibid.

31. Jeffrey A. Alexander, James G. Anderson, and Bonnie L. Lewis, "Toward an Empirical Classification of Hospitals in Multi-Hospital Systems," *Medical Care* 23, no. 7 (July 1985):913–932.

32. Ibid.

33. *Glossary of Multi-Institutional Terms* (Chicago: American Hospital Association, 1982).

34. Jeffrey A. Alexander and Mary L. Fennel, "Patterns of Decision Making in Multihospital Systems," *Journal of Health and Social Behavior*, 1986:14–27.

35. Jeffrey C. Goldsmith, "Horizontal Consolidation: The Multihospital System." In *Can Hospitals Survive the New Competitive Health Care Environment?* (Homewood, Ill.: Dow Jones-Irvine, 1981), 100–112.

36. Jeffrey Alexander, Bonnie Lewis, and Michael Morrisey, "Acquisition Strategies of Multihospital Systems," *Health Affairs*, 14, no. 3 (Fall 1985):50–66.

37. Fottler et. al., "Multi-institutional Arrangements."

38. *Glossary of Multi-Institutional Terms*.

39. Alexander, Lewis, and Morrisey, "Acquisition Strategies."

40. Ibid.

41. Donald E. L. Johnson, "Investor-Owned Chains Continue Expansion, 1985 Survey Shows," *Modern Healthcare* 15 (June 7, 1985):75–125.

42. Karen Sandrick, "Multi's Enter Health Insurance Field," *Hospitals* 59 (February 1, 1985):M14–M17.

43. Terri Shahoda, "Multi Clustering: A Natural Evolution," *Hospitals* 60 (March 5, 1986):56–62.

44. Terri Shahoda, "Disinvestment to Surface as Multi Strategy," *Hospitals* 60 (June 5, 1986):38–39.

45. Myron D. Fottler and Donna G. Vaughan, "Multihospital Systems." In *Hospital Organization and Management* Lawrence F. Wolper and Jesus Peña, eds. (Rockville, Md.: Aspen Publishers, In Press).

46. Dan Ermann and John Gabel, "Multihospital Systems; Issues and Empirical Evidence," *Health Affairs* 3 (Spring 1984):50–64.

47. Ermann and Gabel, "Multi-Hospital Systems"; Lawrence S. Lewin, Robert A. Derzon, and Rhea Marquiles, "Investor Owned and Not-for-profits Differ in Economic Performance," *Hospitals* 55 (July 1, 1981):52–58; Bernard Ferber, "An Analysis of Chain Operated For-Profit Hospitals," *Health Services Research*, Spring 1971:49–60; Gary S. Levitz and Paul P. Brook, Jr., "Independent versus System Affiliated Hospitals: A Comparative Analysis of Financial Performance, Cost, Productivity," *Health Services Research* 20, no. 3 (August 1985):315–37; Thomas Treat, "The Performance of Merging Hospitals," *Medical Care* 14 (March 1976):199–209.

48. Treat, "Merging Hospitals"; Ermann and Gabel, "Multi-Hospital Systems"; B. Newmann, "A Financial Analysis of a Hospital Merger: Samaritan Health Services," *Medical Care* 12 (December 1974):983–98; Levitz and Brooke, "Independent versus System Affiliated Hospitals"; Lewin, Derzon, and Marquiles, "Investor Owned and Not-for-profits"; Lewin and Associates, "A Study of Investor Owned Hospitals" (Unpublished report to Health Services Foundation, 1976); Robert Pattison and Howard Katz, "Investor Owned and Not-for-profit Hospitals," *The New England Journal of Medicine* 309, no. 6 (August 1983):347–53.

49. Johnson, "Investor-Owned Chains."

50. Donald E. L. Johnson, "Multi-Unit Health Care Providers Continue to Diversify in 1985," *Modern Healthcare* 16, no. 12 (June 1986):49–59.

51. *Glossary of Multi-Institutional Terms.*

52. Montague Brown and William H. Money, "Contract Management: Is It for Your Hospital?" in *Multihospital Systems*, ed. Montague Brown and Barbara McCool (Rockville, Md.: Aspen Publishers, 1980), 154–55.

53. Michael A. Morrisey and Jeffrey A. Alexander, "Hospital Entry into Management Contracts," (Working Paper, University of Alabama at Birmingham, 1986); Lynn Kahn and Mark Harju, "Contract Management: More Buyers, Smarter Shoppers," *Hospitals* 58 (February 1, 1984):53–60.

54. Kahn and Harju, "Contract Management"; Johnson, "Investor-Owned Chains."

55. John Lowe, "Contract Management of Health Care Facilities," *Health Care Management Review* 6, no. 3 (Fall 1981):17–24; Montague Brown and William H. Money, "The Promise of Multi-Hospital Management," *Hospital Progress* 56 (August 1975):36–42; Errol L. Biggs, John E. Kralewski, and Gordon Brown, "A Comparison of Contract Managed and Traditionally Managed Non-Profit Hospitals," *Medical Care* 18 (June 1980):585–96; Jeffrey Alexander and Thomas G. Rundall, "Public Hospitals Under Contract Management," *Medical Care* 23, no. 3 (March 1985):209–19.

56. Lowe, "Contract Management."

57. Morrisey and Alexander, "Hospital Entry."

58. Ibid.

59. John Lowe, "Contract Management."

60. Ibid.

61. Ibid.

62. Ibid.

63. William H. Roach, "Hospitals Re-organize to Survive the 80's," *Hospitals* 56 (March 1, 1982):78–81.

64. Ernst and Whinney, *Corporate Reorganization: A Survey of Hospitals That Have Restructured* (Cleveland, Ohio, 1982), 1–55.

65. Phyllis Brasher, *Corporate Re-organization Modules* (New Orleans: Tulane University, 1984), 1–2.

66. Ernst and Whinney, *Corporate Reorganization.*

67. Brasher, *Corporate Re-organization Modules*, 2.

68. Ibid., 25.

69. Ernst and Whinney, *Corporate Reorganization.*

70. Brasher, *Corporate Re-organization Modules*, 2.

71. Ibid., 23–24.

72. Ernst and Whinney, *Corporate Reorganization.*

73. Walker, "Corporate Restructuring."

74. Ernst and Whinney, *Corporate Reorganization.*

75. Alexander, Lewis, and Morrisey, "Acquisition Strategies."

76. Ibid.

77. Ross Mullner, "Speciality Hospitals—Closings Continue to Hit Smaller Hospitals," *Hospitals* 60 (April 5, 1986):93.

Part II

Structure and Organization

The basic tenets of this section are drawn from the field of organizational behavior. The fundamental assumption underlying the structural approach to organization theory is that organizations exist in order to accomplish goals. The three basic components of organizations are tasks, structure, and people. And, of course, organizations exist in an environment that may be stable or changing and that may have a greater or lesser impact on day-to-day operations.

The chapters of this part present an extensive assessment of the structural issues of managing a continuum of care. They examine the goals and objectives, the details of structure, and the tasks involved in creating and operating a continuum. Part III describes key operating systems that must accompany the structural changes. Part V focuses on the human aspects of an organization. From the perspective of the pragmatic manager, as well as from that of the organizational theorist, the basic structures and operating systems are prerequisites for accomplishing the continuum of care goals of client service and employee satisfaction.

Chapter 6

Goals and Objectives

Connie J. Evashwick, ScD

Careful delineation of a health care organization's goals and objectives is critical to building and operating a continuum of care. Diversification, expansion, and integration can accomplish several distinct purposes. The objectives have different implications for action and subsequent evaluation, and thus should be clearly specified in advance. Based on the experience of a number of organizations, we have identified the possible goals and objectives as presented in Exhibit 6-1.

Many health care organizations are expanding or diversifying without the intended purpose of providing a comprehensive, integrated system of patient care. Some, for example, are focusing only on the increasing demand for efficient, short-term outpatient treatment for transient populations. However, as competitive forces continue to grow and as the demographic imperative impacts all health care delivery organizations, the organizations that offer access to a continuum of services will be most likely to survive and prosper. Thus, the assumption underlying this book is that one of the primary long-range goals of an organization should be to develop a continuum of care as defined in Chapter 3, i.e., a comprehensive, coordinated, continuing system of patient care.

Building a continuum of care however, is a long-term process. Thus, an immediate goal may be as specific as expanding a home care program or converting beds for heavy-care patients. Even for a single service, a precise statement of goals and evaluation criteria is essential. The goals of a single service must be devised and their implementation carried out in the context of the longer-term goals.

The following common example involving the range of goals within an institution is illustrative of one likely kind of misperception about the rationale for expanding into the continuum and adding a new service program.

CASE EXAMPLE: HOSPITAL HOME CARE

A hospital proposed starting its own home health agency. Everyone was in favor of it.

Exhibit 6-1 Goals and Objectives of Expanding To Provide a Continuum of Care

To Meet Changes in Consumer Demand
- To increase capacity to absorb growing senior population
- To reorient care to focus on chronic illness and functional ability
- To increase sensitivity
- To appeal to changing consumer preferences

To Enhance Quality
- To apply expanding biomedical knowledge
- To provide comprehensive, continuing care
- To develop collaborative relationships with community agencies
- To optimize use of advanced technologies
- To deal with patient rights and ethical issues

To Improve Financial Status
- To generate new revenue streams
- To maximize payment
- To offset fixed overhead
- To spread or minimize risk
- To gain economies of scale
- To gain greater access to capital

To Maximize Market Position
- To capture new clients
- To enter new markets
- To enhance financial competitiveness
- To attract physicians
- To outpace competing organizations

The hospital administrator assumed that this would be one way to discharge patients within the time and financial constraints imposed by Medicare's diagnostic related group (DRG) reimbursement system without alienating patients by sacrificing quality of care.

The chief financial officer did not expect the home care program to affect DRG experience greatly, but envisioned the spreading of overhead by reallocating certain costs to the home health program. It would also enable higher productivity to be gained from the therapy staff, who were not busy full-time.

The nursing department was pleased that they would have greater ability to maintain contact with patients and families. However, they recommended that the agency should be owned by the hospital but be free-standing, so that it could serve other clientele in addition to the hospital's inpatients. They felt that the benefits of cost allocation would be far outweighed by the potentially larger market share.

The public relations department saw the new service as something they could promote to attract patients. They also thought it would help in competing with the other hospital across town, which advertized a "full-service" range of services.

The human relations department saw the new service as a way of offering alternative employment to staff whom they were forced to let go because of dramatic and continuing drops in inpatient census. They did not consider the different practice patterns or staff preferences of home versus hospital nursing practice as major deterrents.

The pharmacy department anticipated that the new home care program would also offer high-technology home therapy: antibiotic therapy, chemotherapy, and enteral and parenteral nutrition, provided to patients in their home. The pharmacy expected to accrue the financial benefits of this potentially lucrative program.

The women's auxiliary perceived that their community had a high demand for homemakers and supportive services. They thus envisioned that the home care program would have a homemaker and personal care division, with services provided at minimum cost to clients.

Financially oriented members of the board expected new services to be profitable. They were subsequently dismayed to learn that $100,000 in start-up monies would be needed, and then that the Medicare-certified component of the home care program would be only cost reimbursed. The socially oriented members of the board felt that home care was important for quality of care and for the hospital's image. They were thus prepared to absorb direct financial losses for the indirect gains in image.

The local Visiting Nurses Association viewed the hospital's home care program as a threat, and promptly negotiated a contract with the competing hospital.

It is evident that each of the parties had a different perception of the purpose of a new home care program. Although many of these issues might be faced in any type of expansion, creating a continuum of care adds exponentially to the complexity. Each service of the continuum differs in what it can accomplish, and the degree of understanding about many of the services is often quite limited. For these reasons, careful delineation of goals and objectives is critical. Below, we summarize four basic goals sought by many expanding health care organizations.

GOALS AND OBJECTIVES

The motives underlying a health care organization's expansion or diversification are as numerous and complex as the environment that prompts the change. Four basic goals seem to be common; each has its own set of objectives and potential achievements.

Goal I: To Meet Changes in Consumer Demand

A growing senior population and the recognition of the different nature of seniors' health conditions, as well as changes in society's attitude toward aging, are forcing health care organizations to change their orientation toward the care provided to seniors. Health care in general is becoming a market-driven industry. Trends among consumers to become more responsible and active in regard to their own health and to expect more from a health care delivery system make it essential that health care organizations be more responsive to consumer demand.

Objective: To Increase Capacity

Older persons, who tend to have several chronic problems, use nearly three times as many health care resources as younger adults. As the older population doubles in number (to as many as 55 million people by 2040) and grows in proportion (to include almost one of every five U.S. residents), health care organizations face increased demand in terms of the sheer volume of services to be delivered.

Objective: To Focus Care on Chronic, Multifaceted Problems and Functional Ability

Most health care organizations are oriented toward curing acute illnesses. Yet, advances in biomedical technology keep those with severe and permanent disabilities alive longer, as well as enable persons with less severe problems to go home and become independent more quickly. The client population of any health care organization increasingly consists of clients and families confronted with chronic, complex conditions and functional disabilities. Clients include not only older adults, but also infants, children, adolescents, and adults with chronic or trauma-related conditions. To provide the type of care appropriate for its clients, health care organizations must stay with clients over time and must provide and orchestrate use of an array of health, mental health, and social services.

Objective: To Increase Sensitivity

Based on the traditional orientation to acute care, many health care organizations are not designed or operated with sensitivity to the special needs of clients who are older, chronically ill, or functionally disabled. To offer an ambiance atuned to the needs of such clients, health care organizations may alter physical design and decoration, staff education and attitudes, and operating procedures such as scheduling.

Objective: To Appeal to Consumer Preferences

Consumer values are also changing, and there is a greater expectation that a health care organization will provide all types of services and be cost-effective.

The hospital that provides only acute care; the home health agency that cannot provide durable medical equipment, high-technology home therapy or home-maker services; the clinician who is insensitive to the special problem of seniors; the insurance company or HMO that charges too high premiums for too little coverage—all of these will lose clients over the long run.

Goal II: To Enhance Quality

Major advances in biomedical technology and biomedical knowledge have directly affected patient care. They have also led to the emergence of specialists in geriatrics, who in turn bring changes to the organizations they work with. Simultaneously, the combined growth in population and expansion of technology have brought societal attention to ethical issues. New definitions and expectations of quality of care and quality of life are being promoted by professionals and lay people alike. These trends then prompt health care organizations to assess the quality of care they provide and to move in the direction of creating a continuum of care.

Objective: To Apply Biomedical Knowledge

After more than ten years of gestation, geriatrics has received national rec-ognition as a subspecialty within the field of medicine. This is indicative of the increased understanding of the special needs of older adults, which, as noted elsewhere, include comprehensive, integrated, continuing care. The focus on geriatrics has brought attention to the need to change practice patterns, utilize new types of practitioners, and initiate or alter clinical services to incorporate new biomedical knowledge in geriatrics, chronic illness, and functional dis-ability.

Objective: To Provide Comprehensive, Continuing Care

The growing number of seniors, as well as younger clients, with chronic conditions exacerbates the inconsistency between the acute care orientation of health services and the chronic needs of many clients. Prompted by clinicians, administrators of health care organizations are recognizing that to provide the top quality care required by the majority of their clients, they must broaden the orientation of their service, making it less highly delineated and discrete and more comprehensive and ongoing. The traditional fragmentation of health, men-tal health, social services, and insurance does not result in the optimum quality of care.

Objective: To Develop Collaborative Relationships with Other
Community Agencies

Services for seniors, as well as ones aimed at other specific target groups, abound in most communities. However, each tends to operate independently.

This fragmentation results in an inefficient use of societal resources. More important, the lack of exchange and continuity between providers does not maximize the potential quality of care that is rendered separately or collectively. One objective of the continuum is to formalize collaborative relationships among community agencies to the benefit of all involved. Often, an official declaration of the intent to create a continuum of care is required to give administrators the mandate to create such relationships. Otherwise, the focus on external activities does not receive priority attention in the face of administrators' numerous daily internal tasks.

Objective: To Optimize Use of New Technologies

The continuum of care approach opens access to many new technologies, all designed to enhance the quality of health care and of life. An emergency response system (ERS) located in the home is now offered by major hospitals, not because of its financial benefits, but because health care providers are aware that the psychological security provided by an ERS enhances a client's emotional well-being, and thus can be seen as an integral part of providing high quality health care. New home care programs can provide chemotherapy and enteral, parenteral, and antibiotic therapy in the home to patients who formerly had to remain in a hospital or nursing home. However, the involvement of a hospital keeps the client linked with the necessary sophisticated medical back-up. To provide top quality care using the latest technologies, health care organizations are finding it increasingly obligatory to link up with other components of the delivery system.

Objective: To Deal with Patients Rights and Ethical Questions

Ethics, values, attitudes, and understanding of patient rights are changing. Consumers are becoming increasingly cognizant of the potential and limitations of health care and of their own potential to make decisions regarding the type of care they want to receive over an extended period of time. As organizations expand into new service lines, they are involved with more and more aspects of the rights of patients to decide upon treatment modalities. Some health care organizations have added new programs, such as a hospice, because they believe this not only increases the options for technical medical care but also enhances patients' ability to control the quality of their own lives. Others have started ethics committees to help clinicians in dealing with the difficult ethical aspects of patient care.

Goal III: To Improve Financial Status

Expansion into a continuum of care can improve a health care organization's financial status in several ways.

Objective: To Generate New Revenues

New services can produce new revenue streams. Private home care agencies, for example, average an operating margin of about 15 percent of revenues above expenses. However, new revenue streams are accompanied by new expense streams, and the net revenue may not always be as great as expected!

Objective: To Maximize Payment

Under Medicare's DRG payment system, hospitals can realize financial gains or minimize losses by moving patients out of inpatient services to lower levels of care. To the extent that the health care organization has organized a continuum of care, it will have greater control over patient flow. Under capitated systems, health care organizations may (or may not) enjoy a greater profit margin by assuming responsibility for multiple services, such as physician primary care, home health care, and hospital care. The more services are aggregated under the organization's control, the more the opportunity to maximize efficient use of expensive resources.

Objective: To Offset Overhead

For organizations that have underutilized resources, new services of the continuum of care can often be added at low marginal cost, thereby offsetting fixed overhead as well as generating new revenues. Some services make it possible to save by reallocation of costs. A hospital that starts a hospital-based home care program, for example, can allocate part of its fixed costs to the home care cost center.

Objective: To Gain Economies of Scale and Efficiencies of Operation and to Minimize Risk

If the administration is organized appropriately, efficiencies and economies of scale can be gained by simultaneously operating several complementary service programs. Similarly, risk can be minimized if it is spread across several departments or entities.

Objective: To Gain Access to Capital

Some services bring opportunities for new sources of capital financing. Construction of housing or nursing homes, for example, give access to bond and private monies under auspices different from those available for the capital financing of nonprofit hospitals or public community service agencies.

Goal IV: To Increase Markets and Market Share

Health care organizations are facing ever-tighter utilization criteria and ever-increasing competition. In the long-term, the growing number of older adults will generate increased total demand for health care services. However, in the immediate future, getting and keeping an optimum number and mix of clients is a major challenge. Offering an expanded array of services can enhance market penetration.

Objective: To Capture Clients

Some new clients will come because they are attracted to the idea of a single organization that can meet all of their needs. Clients might include individual patients and major companies such as private insurers or HMOs. In addition, each of the individual services will have its own distinct client population, and once in a continuum, clients are likely to use other services of the same organization (particularly if internal referral mechanisms are working effectively). Similarly, health care organizations that offer a continuum of services targeted at meeting a full spectrum of a client's needs as they change over time are less likely to lose clients because they had to refer them to an external organization that did not refer them back.

Objective: To Enter New Markets

Entirely new markets might be discovered, such as provider organizations that want to purchase consultation, data processing, or management services. Once a health care organization provider of one type of service begins to work with and understand another provider, opportunities for collaboration, synergy, and exchange of resources arise. Client markets can be shared, and collaborative strength may give organizations that are functioning together as a continuum a competitive edge over organizations acting individually.

Objective: To Compete Financially

Offering multiple services in the continuum of care should result in financial economies of scale and efficient utilization of resources. This will enable the health care organization to charge lower rates or, in a capitated program, to offer more services for the same price. This will enhance the financial attractiveness of the organization. Clients—individuals or payers—who choose on the basis of price per value are thus more likely to select the organization with a multiple service or continuum of care approach and good prices.

Objective: To Attract Physicians

Physicians have also come to expect access to an array of services and efficient financing mechanisms. The health care organization that facilitates cost-effective access to services for a physician's patients is likely to attract the physician. The health care organization that actively attracts clients into its network for a variety of services will also be able to attract physicians who seek to become providers of medical care for these clients.

Objective: To Outpace the Competition

With the flurry of expansion currently seen in all sectors of the health care and social service fields, many organizations are feeling the necessity of starting a new program simply to counter competition. In some instances, a provider may offer a product to another provider on an exclusive contract or franchise basis, with the understanding that if the provider does not accept, the competition might. Recent attention to marketing has increased consumer awareness of the services and benefits offered by many health care organizations, thereby heightening competition among organizations and stimulating the expansion of services.

CASE EXAMPLE: MISSION AND GOALS

In articulating its rationale for creating a continuum of care, an organization may have multiple goals. To operationalize, some priority must be established. However, planning a farsighted, comprehensive program that will emerge over a three- to five-year period is not unrealistic. Below is a statement of mission, including goals and objectives, prepared by one health care organization. This is representative of the breadth of scope that must be considered in implementing a continuum.

Mission

The mission of the continuum of care program is to enhance and maintain the highest quality of care of seniors, other patients, and the families of the community. We seek to provide effective, sensitive, and affordable care that will help clients maintain their well-being and functional independence. To accomplish this, we will develop education, research, and service programs focused on a comprehensive continuum of care approach.

The specific goals of the continuum of care program are:

1. to provide high-quality, family-oriented care that reflects the most current biomedical and social knowledge
2. to provide comprehensive, ongoing care that reflects the multiple, multifaceted, chronic needs of our clients
   - to create a continuum of care—through collaboration, new programs, joint ventures, and all other means—to enable our clients to have access to a full spectrum of services

- to develop interdisciplinary clinical service programs to complement the services offered by individual physicians and other specialty programs of the organization
- to develop the integrating mechanisms that will enable the continuum of services to operate as a coordinated system of care

3. to collaborate with community agencies to provide comprehensive, continuing health and social service care and community-oriented education, and to avoid duplicating resources already available
4. to develop and conduct education and training programs for health care professionals, patients and families, and the community
5. to pursue clinical health services research efforts that will advance the knowledge about chronic illness, geriatrics, and the continuum of care
6. to contribute to the financial viability of the overall organization through efficient and creative operation of existing and new businesses
7. to establish the internal and external organizational structures for the continuum of care
8. to establish a local and national reputation for excellence

SUMMARY

Creating a continuum of care can accomplish several distinct goals and objectives for a health care organization. As is evident, however, not all of the goals may be achieved by the addition of a single service or set of services, and, indeed, adding some services may be in conflict with certain goals.

For these reasons, the goals and objectives must be clearly specified and understood by all involved from the outset. An initial white paper or workplan should delineate proposed goals, objectives, and evaluation criteria. This should be circulated, revised, and approved by all of those who will ultimately be involved: the board, senior administrators, mid-level managers, physicians, and clinical staff.

Each service or program must be examined for its independent contribution to the long-term, broader goals and objectives of the health care organization. Then, the interrelationship of the service to other existing or new services can be determined.

Ongoing evaluation should be incorporated in the design and implementation of a new continuum of care program or individual service. In this way, the goals and objectives serve a real purpose of addressing the questions, "*Why* are we doing this?" and "*How are we doing?*"

Chapter 7

Structure and Organization

Thomas E. Terrill, PhD
Connie J. Evashwick, ScD

The purpose of an organizational structure is to enable the people within the organization to perform the tasks necessary to accomplish the specified goals and objectives. If "form follows function," then what is the appropriate structure for a continuum of care?

In this chapter we review basic organizational issues affecting or affected by the operation of a continuum of care. We give examples of organizational structures that have worked and some that have not. As the early students of organization theory concluded about organization in general, "There is no one best way." Yet, as health care organizations expand into continuums of care, attention to basic management principles may prevent direct experience with the corollary, "There are many possible wrong ways."

The basic assumption underlying the discussion is that the long-range goal is to develop a continuum of care as defined in Chapter 3 (i.e., a comprehensive, coordinated, continuing system of patient care). This assumes that the target population is composed of individuals who need multifaceted, ongoing care, and thus will benefit from the integration offered by a continuum approach. It also assumes that the existing structure and operations of the organization and the orientation of the clinicians emphasize short-term, discrete service and that contact with other departments or agencies is sporadic. The immediate goal of the organization may be as specific as a hospital starting a home health program or a social service agency opening a day health center. As services are added, the structure and organization appropriate for the long-term goals should be considered, as well as the short-term experiences often required to get a program started. As with the services and integrating mechanisms, the structure may grow and evolve over time.

CASE EXAMPLE: COMPREHENSIVE CAMPUS MEDICAL CENTER

Due to heavy market competition, Comprehensive Campus decided to expand into an array of services, many targeted at seniors. This was proclaimed as a broad organizational mandate. A year later, the hospital had numerous programs in various stages of development. The organization chart with relevant programs is presented in Figure 7-1. The circles trace the path that a patient had to follow as his condition changed and he successively used the available services.

The confusion of the diagram is indicative of numerous problems. From the patient's perspective, the services were not well organized for facilitating continuity of care or ease of access. The clinicians felt a lack of control, were threatened by a loss of power to an amorphous organizational web, and were frustrated by the complicated referral patterns and lack of coordination among staff of various services. Administrators at all levels were equally frustrated. They were confused by competing goals and felt a lack of control over patient flow; they had difficulty in meeting projected patient load staffing, allocation, and budget.

This hospital violated the basic principles of congruent lines of authority, accountability, and responsibility. Except for the president of the overall holding company, there was no single locus of control for all of the related programs. There was no parity in administrative or clinical responsibilities. There was no mechanism for communication or coordination among administrators or clinical staff. There were omissions in the performance of some tasks and duplication in the performance of others. Moreover, there was no integrated budget. Each of the programs functioned entirely independently. In some instances, the programs and services actually competed or conflicted with each other. Staff manifested a high degree of uncertainty, frustration, anger and defensiveness. The enthusiasm and hard work that should have been generated by expansion into new areas was absent; instead there was unhappiness, uncertainty, and hesitation to take the initiative.

One effect the organization had on operations was that more than 50 percent of the patients appropriate for the hospital's own services were referred externally. Financial status was diminished in lost revenues from patient referrals and by missed opportunities for economies of scale and for maximized use of resources employed in caring for an individual patient. The marketing advantages specifically desired by the hospital did not materialize because there was no single product to market. Moreover, productivity decreased because staff were confused and frustrated.

After examining its problems, Comprehensive Campus became more focused and formulated a plan to implement structural changes over time. The new organization is shown in Figure 7-2. The reorganization made each basic service a distinct unit, with two additional units for crosscutting administrative functions. Two levels of management were created from existing staff. Senior administrators of each unit met as an executive management committee. Responsibilities included monitoring referrals among services and negotiating annual budgets. The second level consisted of managers of direct day-to-day operations. The responsibilities of this group included establishing and monitoring the patient

Figure 7-1 Comprehensive Campus Medical Center Organization Chart

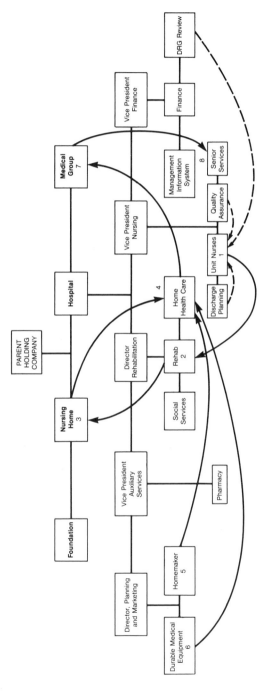

1. Patient is on acute floor. Discharge planning, quality assurance, and DRG coordinator each review patient progress toward discharge separately.
2. Patient transferred to rehabilitation floor.
3. Patient transferred to nursing for more rehabilitation.
4. Patient transferred to home with home health care.
5. Patient receives homemaker from community agency.
6. Patient receives durable medical equipment at home.
7. Patient scheduled to see physician in his office.
8. Patient recommends contacting senior services to arrange Meals on Wheels and friendly visitor.

Figure 7-2 Comprehensive Campus Medical Center Reorganization Chart

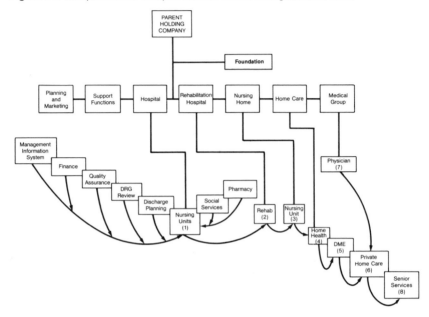

1. In hospital, all clinical support and monitoring programs are coordinated.
2. Transfer to rehabilitation arranged by acute hospital case manager.
3. Transfer to nursing home arranged by case manager.
4. Durable medical equipment ordered and demonstrated prior to discharge.
5. Transfer to home health arranged by case manager.
6. Continuation of private home health arranged by case manager and coordinated with Medicare home care.
7. Physician visit; M.D. apprised of status by case manager; records forwarded from all services.
8. Client recovers; referred by case manager to senior services for social activities.

referral process and developing appropriate methods for interaction among clinical staff. In addition, the integrating systems common to all services were grouped together to enable them to assist all units.

The patient flow in Figure 7-2, albeit oversimplified, shows that as the patient progressed from one service to the next, he followed a rational pattern of receiving care: The administrators and clinicians in charge of the services had parity of position, and communication mechanisms enabled clinicians to coordinate care.

ORGANIZATIONAL ISSUES

The following discussion assumes the existence of an organization that has decided on a long-term plan to develop a continuum of care and has established a clear definition of what the continuum is and what it is intended to accomplish. The long-term view recognizes that the continuum will be built over a realistic period of time, with changes made gradually. Each continuum will be unique, and is adapted to the existing structure, resources, and environment. In all instances however, the issues below should be addressed.

Structure

One of the first steps should be to decide where the program is to be located within the organizational structure, identify who is in charge, decide which service and support units are direct components of the continuum, and thus determine which managers report directly to the administrator in charge. Similarly, it is also critical to identify and clarify the reporting relationships of the management systems that support the continuum and the clinical service units that relate to but are not direct parts of the continuum.

At the present time, the operationalization of a continuum of care is still relatively new, and the idea of implementing one is being promoted by various organizational units, including departments of social service, geriatrics programs, and divisions of marketing and public relations. Too often, the organizational unit that promotes the idea of a continuum of care does not have sufficient power, authority, and control over resources to achieve implementation.

A continuum of care requires coordination of numerous services and support systems, some of which may be owned and operated by the parent organization and some of which are arranged through contracts or affiliations with external organizations. The level of coordination and authority requires that the locus of the program be at a high level in the organizational structure, with a senior administrator who has a position at least equal in authority to the senior administrators of the other key services involved.

One prerequisite in determining the locus of the program is to establish the program's identity. (This is discussed in more detail in Chapters 3 and 11, where the definition and marketing of a continuum of care are dealt with.) In addition to administration agreeing on the locus and lines of responsibility, staff must be informed of changes in lines of authority and accountability, as well as any new responsibilities inherent in providing a comprehensive, ongoing continuum of services. It is essential that the lines of responsibility, accountability, and authority be congruent and be clearly and specifically described—and adhered to.

Health care organizations have as great a need as any to structure routine administrative tasks and the highly individualized work done by clinical professionals. The result has been a matrix approach to management with administrators responsible for standardizing policies and procedures, and a clinician administrator responsible for supervising the quality of care provided by the clinical staff. The medical staff has had yet another line of authority over the clinical staff in directing the care of the individual patient.

There are examples of nascent continuums of care that have been built on traditional hospital matrix structures. There are also social service agencies that have, over time, added successive pieces of the social service range of the continuum. However, in the instances where such structures have seemed to function well, most of the relevant departments were under the same senior administrator.

The successful and emerging organizational structures seem to emphasize product line management. Product line management is the structuring of an organization around a product, with the production, staff expertise, and marketing efforts concentrated on a single functional or clinical focus (product). As health care organizations become increasingly broad and complex—and as the clinical practice is increasingly regulated by external, nonclinical policies—lines of authority, accountability, and responsibility are converging. Organizing along a product line accomplishes both administrative and product identification needs, as well as permitting the ability to provide care and to control patient flow in an integrated manner.

Figures 7-3, 7-4, and 7-5 show examples of three medical center organizations, all of which have the same business activities. Based on experience, such extreme organization forms do exist. Yet, as health care organizations evolve into pro-

Figure 7-3 Historical Medical Center Organization Chart

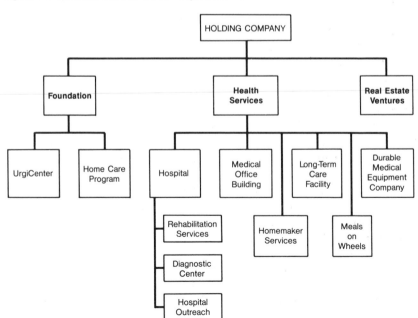

Figure 7-4 Progressive Medical Center Organization Chart

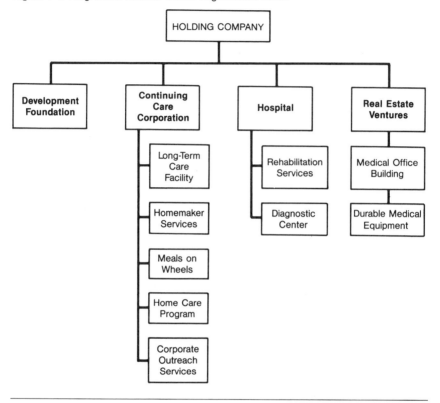

viders of comprehensive, continuing care, the increasingly common structure involves grouping services offering related types of programs.

The system represented by Figure 7-3 reflects the historical patterns of growth of a hospital, the politics and agendas of interested and well-meaning trustees, and the creative pressures arising internally from the professional staff. The organization is a hotbed of intrigue, miscommunication, and discontent. The organization represented in Figure 7-4 is not dissimilar in history, but has progressed. This medical center has worked hard at planning and implementing structural change and is beginning to use some of the mechanisms described below. Figure 7-5 shows the structure both organizations would want to establish as they evolve.

Formal structure is obviously only one aspect affecting the operations of the continuum. However, the appropriate lines of authority, responsibility, and accountability inhibit or enhance the effective use of communication and integration mechanisms and the consideration of human factors, all of which are critical in maintaining and supporting the operation of a continuum of care.

Figure 7-5 Continuum of Care Organization Chart

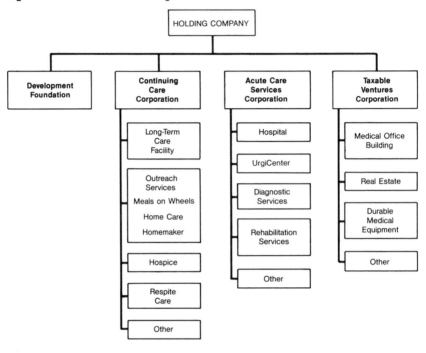

Physician and Medical Staff Structure

The roles of the physician and the organized medical staff in a continuum of care vary greatly and are heavily dependent upon the type of organization developing the continuum, the population groups targeted, the services and integrating mechanisms that are included, and the sequence in which services are added.

For example, a Medicare-certified home health agency may decide to add new services: a private home care service, durable medical equipment, case management, high-technology home therapy, and select social services. No formal medical staff will be involved in the initial decision or the implementation. Individual physicians will only be aware of differences as the home health agency promotes the availability of its additional services. In contrast, if a hospital hires a geriatrician and starts a geriatric assessment unit and outpatient clinic, the medical staff will have to vote on appointment to the staff and will be heavily involved in determining patient referral criteria, follow-up procedures, etc. If a group practice of physicians contracts with an HMO to provide a package of ambulatory, inpatient, and home care services, the physicians might find that they are heavily involved in negotiating with home health agencies about the quality, range, and price of the services. The impact of a continuum is more likely to affect the individual practitioner. Some of the salient issues are described in more detail in Chapter 18. In brief, the physician may find that he is constrained in the care of individual patients because of a loss of authority or discretion in making referrals: encroachment by other practitioners such as case managers; tighter utilization and practice restrictions imposed by external forces such as PROs; new duties such as ethics committees membership and risk sharing in use of capitated services; and increased demands from consumers as they know more and are promised more by the health care provider organizations and insurers. Alternatively, the physician may find that through the continuum he is able to offer more services to his patients: a case manager will arrange community social services; an HMO financing mechanism will cover services that the patient formerly would have paid out-of-pocket; the physician may trust more to be done in the patient's home because he is familiar with the home health agency staff. Thus, practicing medicine within the context of a continuum of care may enhance or inhibit the physician's role—or do both in different respects.

Within the health care organization structure and operations, the same principles apply to medical staff involvement as apply to the involvement of other clinicians and administrative decision-making bodies. Physicians maintain ultimate control over the use of most health care services and have a major influence, if not authority, in the ordering of many social services. Thus, it is critical to include the physicians and the organized medical staff in the planning and operation of a continuum of care.

Integrating Mechanisms

Once a structure is in place, appropriate supporting management systems must also be established. These include

- communications
- information systems
- budgeting and financial reporting
- clinical services management (care coordination or case management)
- human resources
- quality assurance and ethics
- marketing

Subsequent chapters of this book address some of these specific areas. The tasks of coordination, communication, and control are presented here.

Mechanisms for Coordination and Communication

The tasks performed by the staff of a continuum of care are highly differentiated. Clinical services range from biomedical technology for severely ill patients in the acute hospital setting to strong emotional support for hospice patients or to recreational activities as part of wellness programs. Support services in the continuum range from sophisticated management information systems to interpersonal case management. Yet, to make the continuum function smoothly, all of the staff must have means of communicating and coordinating their many and diverse activities.

From the perspective of organization theory, Lawrence and Lorsch have described the phenomenon of "differentiation and integration." Based on their studies of organizations, they conclude that the more complex the environment of an organization and the more differentiated the tasks, the more attention must be given to integration. A continuum of care, even in its elementary stages, involves a complex array of activities and potentially threatens the power of many departments and individuals within an organization, not to mention those outside of it. Intense effort at involvement is essential to ensure that the many who are part of the day-to-day operation of the continuum become committed to it by being involved in planning, problem identification, resolution, and ongoing communication, as well as by constant attention to the simple question "How are we doing?"

In many organizations, senior administrators are moving rapidly to expand their organization's scope of service by negotiating contracts, establishing affiliation agreements, and purchasing existing services. Often there is little communication with midlevel managers, and only vague or minimal contact with physicians or other care providers. Yet, staff are expected to deal appropriately in referring patients and advising them about available services. The more rapidly an organization is moving to diversify, expand, and publicize new services, the more essential it is to make specific efforts to educate and involve all those who will be participating in the delivery of services in the continuum.

Integrating mechanisms must be put in place to educate, increase commitment, and maintain ongoing coordination of the activities of clinical staff, the support system staff, and the interface of clinical and administrative staff and their respective responsibilities. There are a variety of standard and creative techniques to accomplish this.

Liaison Staff

Many community-based home health agencies, for example, have placed liaisons on hospital floors to bridge the transition from inpatient to home care for both staff and patient. Geriatric assessment teams that do comprehensive workups for older patients often send a nurse or nurse–social worker team into the patient's home to enhance the assessment and to provide continuity for the patient and family.

Committees

Every organization cringes at the suggestion to add yet one more committee. On the other hand, committees serve a valid purpose in bringing together staff from different units (or organizations) to work together for a specific purpose. A continuing care committee could be composed of administrators of various services for the purpose of discussing and resolving management issues, or it could be composed of clinicians for discussing and acting on clinical issues. If given the correct charge, this combined group can be effective in cutting through existing bureaucracies.

Task Forces

For many organizations, adding a new service, attempting to integrate several services, or implementing a comprehensive information system are unfamiliar activities. The potential problem areas and the range of solutions may not have been previously considered. Moreover, many employees may not be aware of management's objectives in initiating the new actions. Task forces can serve both as means of educating staff about changes and as mechanisms for problem identification and resolution.

Regular Management Meetings

The heads of the services involved in a continuum of care might be designed as a management group and brought together regularly to review performance and plan future actions.

Patient Care Conferences

Based on the assumption that the primary purpose of a continuum is to be a *system of patient care*, it is essential that the clinicians involved with a single patient have the opportunity to get together. This may require a formal mechanism, partly because it takes up staff time and thus must be sanctioned by the organization. Nurses have conferences to transfer information from one shift to the next. The idea is the same, except that the patient may be transferred from one service and/or facility to another. A regular patient care conference brings together the key staff of the acute floor and the home health care, extended care, and rehabilitation departments. The patients discussed are those who are expected to use one or more services after acute discharge. A slightly different approach is used by rehabilitation departments, which have regular patient care conferences to bring together staff of different disciplines simultaneously involved with patients. This model is appropriate for weekly or biweekly conferences of the multidisciplinary staff of the home health program, case managers, and staff of rehabilitation, pharmacy, and any other department that might be contracting staff to home health, as well as representatives of community agencies that might be providing social support or meals to the patients or family.

Newsletters and Written Communication

The above mechanisms are likely to involve a relatively small number of staff. However, all staff of the organization should be aware of the existence of a continuum, as well as of the individual services. Newsletters, whether incorporated in the organization's existing news bulletins or created new, should be used to achieve widespread communication with staff, physicians, and perhaps with community agencies.

Policies and Procedures

Operating policies will need to be written or revised. Certain procedures that have been accomplished informally and to a certain extent subjectively will most likely need to be formalized.

Many organizations do not manage change, let alone expansion, very effectively. This is particularly true when many new services are being added simultaneously. During the process of change, use of the above mechanisms is all the more important.

Mechanisms for Control and Coordination

Communication techniques foster the exchange of information and the coordination of activities. Control mechanisms may perform these functions, but in addition they are tied to evaluating the performance of the organization and its individual staff members and departments in accomplishing the organization's objectives.

Management Information Systems

Historically, health and social service organizations have most often had separate record-keeping systems for clinical and financial data, some computerized and some maintained as paper records. During the past ten years, with the development of computer technology and the pressures of cost-containment, many managers have invested heavily in information systems in order to control the use of resources.

The need to integrate a number of service components in a continuum of care raises the issue of multiple information systems and how they should interact. The use of several different systems that do not have the ability to communicate with each other should be avoided. A single, comprehensive management information system will be less costly to the users in the long run, minimizing financial and human resource costs and errors. However, as discussed in Chapter 14, very few data systems exist that even begin to integrate the clinical, financial, utilization, and administrative information for one patient in a single service setting, let alone integrate the information from multiple service settings.

Comprehensive and integrated data systems will evolve as the continuum of care does. In the meantime, organizations that are orchestrating integration of multiple services should give as much attention to the creation of integrated, accurate information bases as to the integration of other aspects of the organization. Only with valid information will the organization be able to assess the effectiveness of the continuum of care and make the refinements necessary to achieve its goals of quality patient care, market responsiveness, and financial viability.

Budgeting

A second major area of control is budgeting and financial reporting. Each operating entity must consider the interrelationships of the continuum services in preparing its budget and assessing its financial status. The maximization of revenues of one service may negatively impact the revenues of another profit center, with the net effect of reduced revenues for all entities operating in the continuum.

The converse may also hold. For example, a nursing home on the same campus as a hospital may take heavy-care patients with no additional charge to the clients. The nursing home may show excess costs over revenues due to extra staffing. Yet, the hospital may save money under DRG reimbursement by moving its stable but heavy-care patients to the nursing home. The system as a whole will have a profit. If the nursing home refuses to take heavy-care patients, it may show net revenues in its profit center, but the hospital and the total corporation may show a loss due to losses on the DRG heavy-care patients.

The budgeting process, then, must be an ongoing management task involving all of the departments involved in the continuum of care system. Budgeting must not be a process that is assigned to the finance department and delegated to department managers to prepare without sufficient time for negotiation among the managers of related departments. In order for budgeting to be effective as a short-range management control tool, an ongoing, participatory process must be in place. This process requires the department managers to have an understanding of account structure, exception reporting mechanisms, and of the impact each department's operations has on other departments. Organizations that have recently added services, changed to a continuum of care approach, or restructured will find that the budgeting process during the first year or two will be time consuming and challenging until appropriate systems for intraservice negotiations and appropriate inter-entity transfer pricing can be formulated and accepted by the managers.

Numerous problems of accountability raised during the budgetary process can reduce a budget's credibility and use as a management tool, and these may be exacerbated by the complexity and interrelationships of the continuum. Costs attributable to a department may be subject to significant controversy (e.g., accounting for float pool personnel; personnel loaned, borrowed, or shared by departments and other entities; and requisitions costed to departments). Just as organizational differences exist among hospitals that make comparisons of costs and quality difficult, inadequate costing mechanisms and consensus building by management in the budgeting process can limit a budget's effectiveness. This situation has become so severe in some institutions that participatory budgeting techniques have been abandoned in favor of the budget being produced by a finance department engaged solely in financial analysis. This situation should be avoided if an institution expects its managers to support the continuum of care and operate their departments for the good of the total system.

The tradeoff's incorporated into the budget should be acknowledged by senior management and should be consistent with the overall goals of the organization. Moreover, as regular finance reports are produced, it is essential that managers be given sufficient information about the performance of the total system in order to evaluate the degree of benefit (or detriment) of their activities and that the financial tradeoffs among departments be recognized and sanctioned. In organizations in which promotion or bonuses are tied to financial performance, a manager would not suffer showing a loss in his profit center unless such a loss were accepted, expected, and approved by his superiors and accommodation made in the promotion and bonus criteria. Thus, the creation of a total system of patient care and the operation of a continuum may require changes in the incentive system, as well as its manifestation in the budget. Such a transition from traditional budgeting and financial controls may be all the more complex if part of the organization and some proportion of its clients are oriented toward a continuum of care and part are oriented toward the current fee-for-service approach to care and performance evaluation.

Beyond the budgeting process, the management system should make reports available to all managers on a regular basis (monthly or quarterly), showing the performance of their department and the overall organization. Ongoing measurements of utilization, productivity, and financial status that are shared among departments will facilitate problem identification and refinement of the continuum of care operations.

CASE EXAMPLE: HOME HEALTH

Home health provides a good example of the need to establish communication, coordination, and control mechanisms in order to translate and formalize at the operational level the basic agreements made at the senior management level.

Between 1980 and 1985, the number of hospitals having formal home health programs increased from 12 percent to more than 20 percent. Like many hospitals, the administrator of Central Hospital decided to collaborate with Community Home Health (CHH) in joint-venturing a home health program. CHH did not have the best reputation among the providers of the area, but it promised the management of Central Hospital significant financial benefits. Because of the restrictions of Medicare regulations, exclusivity in referral could not be specified in the contract. The administrator of Central Hospital and the director of CHH mutually assumed that all patients requiring home health care would be referred to CHH.

As in many hospitals, the discharge planners of Central Hospital had been accustomed to deciding to which community home health agencies they would refer patients. Several home care agencies were used, the choice depending upon geographic coverage, particular expertise, availability, and the personal relationships developed between discharge planners and the staff of the community agencies. The majority of referrals, however, went to the local Visiting Nurses Association, an historic pattern which had existed for years and with which everyone was quite satisfied.

When the hospital administrator decided to move into the home care arena, the discharge planners were not consulted. The administrator responsible for the discharge planning department interpreted the administrator's decision as a criticism of her management of discharge planning and as a threat to her power. She also felt slighted that she had not been asked to participate in examining home care options. Thus, when finally consulted, she expressed modest concern to the administrator that CHH was not the home health agency preferred by the staff; however, she did not raise specific management issues. The administrator proceeded to sign the contract with CHH.

Subsequently, the hospital faced the problem of ensuring that patients were referred to CHH. Unless there is a formal policy and the implementation includes educating and involving the discharge planning staff, patients requiring home care may continue to be referred to other agencies. Without the procedures for operational implementation specified and protected by the nonexclusivity requirement of Medicare, the discharge planners simply ignored the existence of the contract signed by management. The discharge planners found many subjective criteria for deciding that another agency was more suitable to meet the patient's needs: geography, previous use, or designation by a physician citing a specific name (rather than a generic name, as should have been encouraged by the discharge planners and, through education, by management). The discharge planners also complained about the paperwork required as part of the new system, so they simply did not complete it. The results were as follows:

- Patients continued to be referred elsewhere, and thus were lost to the hospital's system.

- Due to inadequate information, the amount of revenue and the numbers of patients lost could not be evaluated.
- Discharge planners were defensive and angry at administration; they also continued to question the quality of CHH, although with no concrete positive or negative evidence.
- Physicians did not understand why suddenly some patients were being referred to one home health agency and some to another.
- The staff of CHH were angry and frustrated because they had added staff in the expectation of additional referrals, only to sit day after day wondering where the patients were.
- The projected financial return, rather than positive, was negative; this was due to start-up costs and lack of offsetting revenues.
- The administrator was frustrated with the discharge planning staff, but did not know how to deal with the staff directly; the director of the department continued to behave in a passive-aggressive fashion, but did not take steps to resolve the management issues.
- Community good will and the reputation of both Central Hospital and CHH suffered.

After six months of negative operations, the administrators of Central Hospital and CHH met and jointly determined what was necessary to remedy the ineffective operations. A task force was created composed of representatives from discharge planning, CHH, the medical staff, hospital administration, and information systems (medical records). The task force accomplished the following:

- prepared referral policies specifically identifying the criteria for determining who would be referred to CHH and who could be referred to another home health agency (e.g., distance, unique staff expertise required, family request for a particular agency, etc.).
- presented an information and educational session on the home care program, including referral criteria and procedures at staff meetings of nurses, department heads, and medical staff.
- formatted new home health referral authorization forms to be included in the patients' charts in order to facilitate referral by physicians.
- assigned a liaison person designated by CHH to be based at the hospital and work with the discharge planners to assess referral to home care and, similarly, expedite the home health agency's receipt and assignment of the patient.
- held periodic meetings with all discharge planners to discuss concerns about quality, providing an opportunity to develop specific evaluation criteria. It also held subsequent meetings with CHH staff to discuss quality performance

issues and evaluation criteria, and then established a joint hospital-CHH quality assurance committee that would meet regularly and interface with the hospital's quality assurance program and resources.

- published an article on the new home care program in each of the hospital's newsletters and in the CHH newsletter.

- conducted a special follow-up survey of patients referred to all home health programs to gather information on patient and family reactions to home health. The results were shared with the discharge planning and CHH staff, and subsequently published in the hospital's newsletters.

- incorporated specific codes into the discharge summary to identify patient referral to home health, naming the exact agency.

- set up monthly monitoring of referrals to home health and evaluation based on specified policies and procedures and referral criteria.

The administrator of Central Hospital and the director of CHH agreed to meet quarterly to review the success of these actions and to analyze in detail the data on the operations of the joint venture.

The Human Component

Power, authority, leadership, motivation—all of these are subjective aspects of organizations that may maximize or inhibit the relationships delineated in the formal structure. Particularly in service organizations and those involving professionals of multiple disciplines, management of the human component of the organization is essential. This is discussed in Chapter 10 and in Part IV.

Principles of the Internal Organization of a Continuum of Care

In summary, the organization of a continuum of care must reflect the following principles:

1. There should be in the organization a designated locus of responsibility for the continuum of care that has the ultimate authority to coordinate and arbitrate among the various clinical and support services and programs.
2. Fragmentation of services, clinically or administratively, should be avoided.
3. For multiple services of the continuum, congruent lines of authority, accountability, and responsibility should be aligned to create managerial and staff parity.
4. Mechanisms should be created to facilitate coordination and communication among the services, both at the management and clinical levels.
5. Formal policies and procedures will need to be established to clarify the operation of the continuum and to provide criteria to enable evaluation.

6. Budgeting and financial reporting systems should identify and account for tradeoffs between services.
7. Control and support systems should relate to all services and not be duplicated for each service.
8. Staff communication, education, and incentive programs should create and encourage an orientation toward a continuum of care.
9. Roles, responsibilities, and rewards should be continually revised to reflect the change in service from narrow tasks to the broad spectrum of services and ongoing patient care.
10. New services should be planned as an integral part of the continuum of care.

COLLABORATION AMONG COMMUNITY AGENCIES

Realistically, no single organization will be likely to directly provide all services of a continuum of care for all clients. Cooperation and collaboration with other providers will be necessary. For many years community based systems of long-term care have been in the process of experimentation and development.

Most health and social service provider organizations, as well as insurers, HMOs, and physicians, have had some experience with collaborative ventures. Furthermore, most of the steps in establishing joint arrangements are common sense. Yet, all too often, collaborative arrangements go awry or simply never materialize. Thus, it is helpful to review the basic principles of collaboration as applied to a continuum of care.

Get To Know Who's Out There

Most service providers are relatively unfamiliar with the providers of other types of services, including potential competitors and collaborators. (This is the very fragmentation that requires a continuum of care to be *designed* rather than to develop naturally. The insular orientation is closely related to the distinct financing and regulatory history of each service.) Before any attempts can be made to link up with other organizations, it is necessary to identify those organizations and get to know them. This includes getting to know its leaders (senior administrators, board members, physicians), its mission and goals, and the environmental pressures or opportunities that it might be facing.

Many organizations are threatened by the growth of others and have a rampant, (and usually unwarranted) fear of a takeover or the stealing of patients. These anxieties must be overcome and basic trust established before collaboration can occur. A clear statement of purpose by the initiating organization will help appease the fear of other organizations: At least they will know if the organization is a competitor or not.

Go Informal before Formal

A hasty decision to join up with the first collaborator who walks in the door may not be a good decision in the long-run. The current trend of hospital-nursing home contracts and hasty PPO alliances that never materialize into service use are good examples. Because of the many clients with diverse needs, there are ample opportunities to get to know an organization on an informal basis before formal contracts are signed. Indeed, staff may know more about the organization, based on following clients, than the administrators know. Tracing experiences on an informal basis should be done internally to avoid pursuing administratively rational but subjectively ill-informed formal relationships.

Other organizations have been overly cautious in negotiating relationships, for example, engaging in formal and formidable bidding processes and thereby creating immediate adversaries. Informal discussions and agreement of principles done with potential affiliates can result in greater mutual understanding of perspectives and needs. Then, if formal competitive bidding is done, all parties involved will have a better understanding of the goals, and the final agreement is likely to be implemented more easily and achieve its purposes more fully.

Hosting meetings of potential affiliates is one avenue for gaining this informal knowledge in an informal way. For example, an adult day care center might hold quarterly luncheons for home health agency staff, or an urban hospital might invite the administrators of all the local nursing homes to attend an annual reception.

Involve the Staff

Administrative and clinical staff have a great deal to contribute in exploring the feasibility and benefits of collaborating with other organizations in developing criteria and implementation plans, and in assessing collaborators. Moreover, if the staff responsible for the day-to-day enactment of policy are not involved, an agreement made by two senior administrators may never be implemented.

Specify Goals, Measurable Outcomes, Evaluation Processes, and Cancellation Conditions

The purpose of a collaborative relationship should be clearly articulated by all organizations involved. Goals and specific measurable evaluation criteria should be included in the final agreement, as well as a timetable for regular evaluation and joint assessment of success. Terms and conditions of cancellation should be precisely specified.

The goals of the collaborators need not be the same to produce a mutually satisfying arrangement. A hospital may see a bed reservation contract as a means to empty filled beds; the nursing home reserving the beds may see it as a means to fill empty beds. Nonetheless, each is clear that ten beds will be reserved. In addition to specifying price and quality issues, the evaluation criteria should specify the number of patient days, or percent of occupancy, to be accepted as the minimum criterion of ''success.'' Both short-term and long-term evaluation criteria might be appropriate. Regular evaluation meetings should be scheduled, perhaps monthly at first, then quarterly or annually. Cancellation terms should be agreed upon at the outset in case evaluation indicates that the arrangement is not working out as expected and the situation apparently cannot be rectified. This will enable discontinuation (if necessary) to occur with a minimum of alienation.

Specify Tasks and Implementation Procedures

Agreements in principle, particularly if made by the heads of two organizations, may either not be implemented or be implemented in such a way that they result in problems rather than achieve the mutual benefits initially envisioned. Implementation procedures should include (as appropriate)

- characteristics of clients to be referred or accepted
- policies and procedures of the referral process (who calls whom, written and verbal exchanges, timeliness of response, etc.)
- reporting mechanisms, including documents, data requirements, time schedules, etc.
- staff responsibilities and authorities
- communication mechanisms (e.g., weekly meetings of joint staff)

Clarify Lines of Authority, Accountability, and Responsibility

Each organization should identify the person with ultimate responsibility for the collaborative agreement. The role and authority of other staff should be clarified for both organizations. Liaisons should be established at all appropriate administrative and clinical levels. In particular, control over patient flow should be identified and patient scenarios tested with staff of all organizations prior to actual implementation of the agreement. The responsibilities of the staff of each organization in interacting with physicians should be included.

Anticipate Conflicts

Problems may arise due to unanticipated competing agreements. Prior to establishing an arrangement with another provider, an organization should find out what other arrangements the provider has with yet other agencies in the community. If an organization has multiple collaborative agreements, it may have worthwhile cooperative experience. However, there may also be the potential for conflict. This should be discussed and dealt with in the initial contract, before an actual case of conflict occurs. A formal contract may include noncompetition clauses.

Communicate and Publicize

Any agreement to collaborate made between organizations should be explained internally to staff and externally to other organizations and to the community. Such publicity enhances the success of the collaboration, for staff are made aware of, and can therefore make use of, the opportunities for collaboration. It may also facilitate the implementation: As the agreement is publicized, staff may express concerns or questions that will need to be dealt with in order to implement the collaboration. Also, in needing to explain the agreement to others, those establishing it will need to be precise about what they intend to do and to accomplish.

Structure the Financing Fairly and Precisely

If financial exchange is involved, the terms should be precise. How are extra expenditures handled? What if utilization is higher or lower than expected? What are the legal and financial obligations, if any, to the other parties?

As market competition heightens and as the concept of the continuum of care evolves, more organizations will wish to engage in collaborative programs. Consumers will consequently come to expect greater access and coordination among agencies. Ongoing mechanisms for exchange of information and for fostering cooperation among agencies may be warranted. In some communities, the area agency on aging or the hospital council has formed a long-term care or continuing care committee as a public forum for communication. In other communities, providers of the same type of service continue to meet with each other but not with providers of other services. Committees and other forms of communication among multiple agencies are essential in order to find partners in the community suitable for informal or formal collaboration.

Case Examples: How Not To Collaborate

The president of a large East Coast hospital met the director of a community social service agency at a cocktail party. He was impressed with the concept of case management and with the program offered by the agency, and he invited the director to send him more information and a draft letter of affiliation. The president reviewed the idea and materials with his vice-president for patient care and returned a signed letter of affiliation stating that, on a trial basis, the hospital would refer patients needing case management to the community agency.

The director of the agency was delighted and promptly added another case manager to handle the patients expected from the hospital. After two months, the agency had not received a single referral.

In principle, the agreement was mutually understood and the goals were even specified. The letter of affiliation was an informal arrangement with no formal obligations on the part of either organization, and thus an easy pilot test. However, the agreement neglected to delineate how the affiliation would be implemented. Moreover, the day-to-day staff had not been involved. The agreement lacked the following:

- *Identification of appropriate patients.* The staff of the hospital did not know which patients were to be referred to the case management program; the agency did not know which patients it was expected to accept. No delineation had been made of the characteristics of patients for whom case management would be appropriate.

- *Specification of referral procedures.* Was the hospital discharge planner, the social worker, or the nurse to call the case management agency? Was a telephone referral adequate or was written referral required? Who was responsible for contacting the patient's physician?

- *Financial implications.* The case management agency charged patients on a sliding scale. Did the hospital intend to subsidize the community agency for at least the initial evaluation of its patients in exchange for more rapid discharge and continuity of care? Were patients apprised that they would be billed for the service? The financial considerations were not clearly identified.

- *Marketing.* How was the case management affiliation being explained to the consumers and to individual patients? Was it being advertised as a program offered by the hospital, as a program of the community agency, or as a collaborative effort? Was any public attention at all given to the collaboration?

The earlier sections in this chapter stressed the importance of creating coordinating mechanisms internally in order for a continuum of care to be operated effectively and efficiently. Because the continuum usually involves several agencies, the same attention must be given to establishing communication and coordination with agencies in the organization's external environment.

Principles of the External Organization of a Continuum of Care

1. Get to know who's out there.
2. Go informal before formal.
3. Involve the staff in planning affiliations.

4. Specify goals, measurable outcomes, evaluation processes, and cancellation conditions.
5. Specify tasks and implementation procedures.
6. Clarify lines of authority, accountability and responsibility within and between organizations.
7. Anticipate conflicts.
8. Communicate and publicize.
9. Structure the financing fairly and precisely.

BUSINESS PLAN

Successful corporate reorganization efforts, in both the planning and implementation phase, include the development of business plans for each of the suggested corporate entities to be created and the product lines to be developed in each entity. Elements of a business plan are presented in Exhibit 7-1.

During the planning process, it is useful to have an inter-disciplinary task force composed of the heads of departments of the services that will be involved

---

Exhibit 7-1 Key Elements of a Business Plan

Goals and Objectives
- Meet changes in patient demand
- Enhance quality
- Improve financial status
- Maximize market position

Product Definition
- Characteristics of new product/service
- Pricing

Target Population
- Seniors, families, friends, physicians, community agencies
- Demographic and demand trends
- Existing/New
- Segment market

Service Characteristics
- Target population
- Regulations
- Financing
- Staffing
- Space and equipment
- Complementary programs

Exhibit 7-1 continued

Environment
- Demographics
- Community orientation
- Provider trends
- Market context
- Financial climate
- Regulatory trends

Market Analysis
- Demand
- Community context
- Existing providers
    Competitors
    Collaborators
- Market share

Internal Structure
- Commitment and leadership
- Program identity
- Organizational locus
- Interdisciplinary team
- Inter-entity committee

Internal Resources
- Commitment
- Staff expertise
- Space and equipment
- Organizational structure
- Capital

Management Systems
- Interdisciplinary planning
- Product line crosscutting management structure
- Appropriate personnel policies
- Integrated, automated records
- Case management (service coordinator)
- Comprehensive financing

Financial Feasibility
- Capital requirements
    Fixed
    Start-up
    Operating

Exhibit 7-1 continued

- Revenue and expense projections
- Budget process
- Performance indicators
- Interactive implications

Marketing Strategy
- Internal
- Current patients
- New patients
- Community
- Written techniques
- Verbal techniques

Evaluation
- Evaluation criteria
- Evaluation plan
- Timetable

---

in the continuum. This may evolve into the ongoing management committee for the continuum. In addition, because of the importance of collaboration with agencies in the community, a community liaison committee may be formed of representatives of relevant provider, consumer, and government agencies.

As corporate leadership moves toward reorganizing the current health system to address "the demographic imperative," use of outside advice and counsel might be both prudent and useful, or even necessary. Consultants, accountants, and legal counsel should be used where organizations are moving toward reorganization or merger and affiliation agreements.

Futurists such as Russell Coile have suggested that health delivery systems companies will proliferate during the coming decade and then consolidate into fewer than five to ten major health delivery entities. If the forecasts are correct, those companies that survive the growth, competition, and changing regulatory environment will be those that recognize that the provision of health care is perceived by the customer or patient as a local matter. Successful continuums can be sponsored by almost any entity—national, regional, or local—but the focus of successful efforts will continue to be on local community coordination and on services provided in a high quality, cost-effective, and caring manner.

Chapter 8

Legal Issues in Restructuring To Provide a Continuum of Care

Peter N. Grant, Esq.
Koreen Kelleher, Esq.

Major trends in the health care industry are pressuring health care providers to adjust to a changing and competitive marketplace. Shifts in demographics indicate that the American population is aging. By the year 2050, one out of every four persons will be a senior citizen[1] Twelve percent of the population will be 75 or older.[2] The family support system that traditionally provided informal health care to the elderly is also expected to diminish as families continue to disperse geographically and more women are employed outside the home. Thus, there will be an ever-increasing demand for providers to serve the long-term, chronic health care needs of the growing elderly population.

At the same time, financial resources to pay for long-term care are diminishing. Financing such services is already straining federal, state, and private budgets, while the future costs of providing care for the older population will only increase.

Traditionally, health care systems utilized fee-for-service payment mechanisms. Individually owned public and private facilities provided distinct levels of acute, intermediate, or skilled nursing care. Due to the changing demographics, diminishing financial resources, and enhanced competition, hospitals are currently moving toward providing a comprehensive array of services to the elderly. Such services include combinations of acute, intermediate, and skilled nursing facilities, long-term care beds, swing beds, ambulatory and outpatient clinics, hospices, home health units, and health maintenance organizations. Thus, hospitals are increasingly able to provide patients with a long-term continuum of care. The expanding of services is sometimes characterized as diversification or vertical integration of health care systems. Such diversification involves dramatic corporate restructuring of existing facilities and service agencies. Providers should be aware that numerous legal and regulatory issues arise as a result of this diversification.

LEGAL ISSUES THAT ARISE DURING VERTICAL INTEGRATION

The legal methods of implementing vertical integration are varied. They range in complexity and magnitude from acquisitions and mergers of health facilities and service agencies to progressively lower degrees of affiliation. Legal and regulatory issues that arise during the process of vertical integration are also varied. The major issues are discussed below. Related tax and accounting issues are presented in Appendix 8-A. Providers should carefully analyze all of these considerations.

Corporate Laws

There are several methods by which one health corporation can acquire or obtain ownership of another health corporation. These methods may vary, depending on the applicable state corporate and common law procedures and whether the corporations in issue are organized as for-profit or nonprofit entities.

For example, under California law a hospital corporation has several alternatives in structuring health care mergers and acquisitions. First, it may purchase, for cash or for a combination of cash and promissory notes, all of another corporation's assets. Second, the hospital may purchase, for cash or for a combination of cash and promissory notes, all of another corporation's outstanding shares. Third, the hospital may combine with another corporation, using the "statutory merger" procedure whereby the hospital may exchange its equity securities, in whole or in part, for shares of another corporation if, immediately after the acquisition, the hospital has control of the other corporation. Finally, the hospital may exchange its equity securities, in whole or in part, or certain of its debt securities, or both, for all, or substantially all, of another corporation's assets. In addition, a hospital corporation may acquire a nonprofit health corporation by becoming the sole corporate member of the nonprofit entity. If there are no memberships in the nonprofit corporation, the hospital may acquire the nonprofit corporation by purchasing, or otherwise obtaining, the right to appoint the nonprofit entity's governing body.

Alternatives to health facility or health corporation mergers and acquisitions include less complex forms of affiliation. Medium degrees of affiliation between facilities and service agencies include joint ventures, partnerships, leasing of all or substantial portions of facilities, and long-term management contracts. Lower degrees of affiliation include shorter-term management contracts, "bed reserve" agreements, networking, and cooperative efforts to coordinate specific activities such as equipment, supplies, and services purchasing (see Table 8-1).

The complexity of the processes of diversification will vary according to the type, combination, and number of legal alternatives used. For example, a for-profit hospital or hospital subsidiary and a for-profit, long-term care corporation

Table 8-1 Alternative Methods for Health Facility Vertical Integration and Diversification

Corporate Mergers and Acquisitions	*Medium Affiliation*	*Lesser Affiliation*
statutory merger	joint ventures	short-term management contracts
purchase of another corporation's assets	partnerships	bed reserve agreements
	lease arrangements	
purchase of another corporation's outstanding shares	long-term management contracts	networking
exchange of shares between corporations and gain of control of another corporation		cooperative efforts, such as joint equipment, supplies and services purchasing
exchange of shares for another corporation's assets		
become sole corporate member of another nonprofit corporation		
obtain right to appoint another nonprofit corporation's governing body		

might form a general partnership to own and operate a long-term care facility. Each partner provides 50 percent of the necessary funds to establish the long-term care facility. Each partner receives 50 percent of the profits. The long-term care corporation manages the facility. In a second example, an acute care hospital might merge with or acquire another acute care hospital that has a vacant wing. The acquiring hospital might decide to convert the acquired facility's vacant wing to long-term care beds. The hospital might then either lease or sell the wing to a company that owns and operates long-term care facilities. In the alternative, it might engage the company to manage the long-term wing or enter into a joint venture with the company to share ownership of the wing.[3] In both examples, numerous legal and regulatory issues might arise, as will be discussed in this chapter.

The possibilities for diversification activities are substantial. Thus, it is difficult to estimate what costs are involved in the various processes and how long each may take to carry out. Providers should make themselves aware of what is required for each venture and whether potential delays in the formation process could result. Furthermore, providers should determine whether or not such delays could adversely affect the market share that the project or venture is aimed to capture.

Securities Laws

Whether integration occurs by acquisition, merger, lower degrees of affiliation, or combinations of these approaches, providers should be aware of and consider the number of legal issues that impact on the process. For example, corporate securities registration requirements and exemptions apply to certain diversification transactions.

State securities laws, commonly known as "blue sky" laws, regulate the offer, subscription, sale, and issuance of shares of stock and other securities by corporations, associations, business trusts, public partnerships, joint stock companies, and certain individuals. These laws seek to ensure that adequate disclosure is made and that issuances of securities are fair, just, and equitable. They also seek to protect purchasers from investing in unsound or fraudulent enterprises. The laws require registration or qualification of the issuance of securities with the appropriate state corporations department, unless exemptions apply. Blue sky laws may also require the qualification of transfers of securities by shareholders and changes in the rights and preferences of outstanding securities in recapitalization and reorganization transactions.

Federal securities laws, such as the Securities Act of 1933, also apply to certain diversification transactions.[4] The Act requires issuers of securities and underwriters to register with the Securities and Exchange Commission, unless an appropriate exemption applies. Disclosure under the Act involves correctly filing registration statements, forms of prospectus and offering circulars, advertising, and notices of intent to sell. Liability may result from misrepresentation or omission of facts.

Registering or qualifying under federal and many state securities laws is burdensome and can result in significant expense and delay. Depending on the project, securities registration or qualification will generally result in additional expense for state or federal filing fees and legal fees for preparation of the appropriate application to comply with the state or federal requirements. Additional delay may result in order to obtain review and approval of the application by the state corporations department or the Securities and Exchange Commission. Often vertical integration activities can be structured to avoid securities laws registration and qualification requirements. Whether exemptions to registration or qualification apply may therefore impact on the types of transactions providers choose to participate in for implementing vertical integration.

Tax Laws

Other issues that arise as providers design health systems to provide long-term continuums of care are specific to the nature and the relationship of the entities involved. For-profit, nonprofit, and governmental health systems have different legal restrictions that must each be considered in any diversification activity. The tax consequences of such activities are ever-present and should be given thorough consideration in the earliest stages of planning. For example, a for-profit entity's participation generally causes tax issues to be a significant aspect of a transaction or agreement. The principal goal is often state and federal income tax minimization or elimination. Other major considerations may include the impact of sales, property, and employment taxes on the entity.

On the other hand, a nonprofit entity's participation in a transaction or agreement may be limited by its stated charitable purposes, which must be adhered to in order to maintain tax-exempt or nonprofit foundation status. This requires consideration, before a transaction is entered into, of the restrictions that may be present in the organization's articles of incorporation, by-laws, and major endowments. Such consideration may help avoid later actions alleging breach of charitable trust. Some flexibility may result in situations where a trustor gives property in trust to a nonprofit entity for a specific charitable purpose that has become impossible, impracticable, or for some reason cannot be carried out. A court may apply the *cy pres* doctrine under certain circumstances. In doing so, the court directs the disposition of the property for a related charitable purpose that carries out the trustor's intention as nearly as possible. The entity may therefore be held to be able to participate in an otherwise prohibited activity that is a necessary step in the vertical integration process. It should be noted, however, that courts use the *cy pres* doctrine very sparingly.

In addition, if a venture involves both a tax-exempt entity and a for-profit entity, there should be concern about structuring the arrangement to ensure that the tax-exempt entity does not lose its status as such. The Internal Revenue Code generally prohibits the tax-exempt entity's assets or earnings inuring to the benefit of private entities or individuals.[5]

A tax-exempt corporation may also find itself subject to taxation at ordinary corporate rates for "unrelated business income" it receives from its participation in a regularly carried trade or business that is not substantially related to its exempt purposes.[6] Tax-exempt health facilities should consider whether certain diversification activities, such as joint ventures and other affiliation arrangements, are sufficiently related to their exempt purposes before they agree to participate. Thus will they be able to fully assess the tax implications.

Hill-Burton Issues

The federal Hill-Burton Act provided a system of financial assistance for the construction of certain health care facilities.[7] The Act's imposition of obligations to provide a reasonable volume of services to those unable to pay for such care are additional considerations for nonprofit entities. It is therefore necessary for providers to determine whether the entities involved, or the nature of any proposed diversification transaction or activity, will prevent or inhibit the performance of such obligations by a facility that has received loans or grants under the federal program. Another Hill-Burton concern arises when a nonprofit entity combines with a for-profit entity. An acquisition of a nonprofit entity that has received Hill-Burton grants or loans by an entity that did not qualify under the program may trigger a "recapture" of funds from the nonprofit entity. Under certain circumstances, the federal government may recapture the current fair market value of the Hill-Burton benefits that the nonprofit entity originally received. There are several methods used to calculate the current value of the original benefits. Providers should be aware of this possibility and plan for its occurrence accordingly.

Governmental Entity Considerations

When governmental entities, such as district, municipal, and county hospitals, are involved, there are additional relevant issues to consider during the vertical integration process. These include the permissible corporate structures and affiliations of the governmental entities, the restrictions on their power to affiliate with religious entities, and their obligations to provide special indigent care under the applicable local and state statutes, charters, and constitutions. Any of these restrictions may limit or prohibit a governmental entity from participating in a diversification agreement or transaction.

Antitrust Laws

A number of legal and regulatory issues arise during the vertical integration process regardless of the nature of the entities involved. Among other issues, federal and state antitrust laws remain extremely important and providers must be aware of their impact.

Federal antitrust laws, including the Sherman Antitrust Act, generally prohibit anticompetitive commercial activities.[8] Under these laws, as interpreted by numerous court opinions over the years, any contracts, combinations or conspiracies in restraint of trade, monopolization, division of markets, price-fixing agreements, price discrimination, and other unfair methods of competition are illegal. As shown by the United States Supreme Court's decision in *Arizona v. Maricopa County Medical Society*, certain antitrust prohibitions may apply to the health care industry.[9]

Therefore, joint planning or other vertical integration cooperative projects between competing hospitals, whether a hospital acquires or merges with other facilities or merely affiliates to a lesser degree, may raise antitrust concerns. Providers should carefully structure such transactions and agreements in consultation with an antitrust counsel in order to avoid or at least minimize any potential antitrust risks.

Health Planning Laws

Health planning issues are also relevant to the diversification process. Providers should consider whether, under the applicable state laws, prior certificate of need approval is necessary for a health facility's acquisition, merger, or affiliation with other facilities or health services.

As an illustration, under federal guidelines and some state laws, a hospital's acquisition of an existing health facility generally does not require a certificate of need unless the purchaser fails to notify the regulating state health department of the proposed acquisition within a specified time period before it occurs. Even if the notification is given, a certificate of need may be required if the state department finds that in acquiring the facility the purchaser will change the number of beds or the health services the acquired facility currently offers.[10] In addition, a purchasing hospital should determine whether any applications for a certificate of need are being prepared, are pending, are on appeal, or have previously been denied or withdrawn from the facility it plans to acquire. The hospital should further determine if the facility has prepared, filed, supported, or presented opposition to a certificate of need application by another facility. The hospital should determine if there are any applications pending or likely to be filed by others that would affect the acquired facility. The hospital should also confirm that all improvements, capital projects, changes in services, construction, and equipment purchases of the facility were made, if necessary, with certificate of need approvals. This is important because any resulting exposure or disabilities for the facilities noncompliance may carry over to the hospital after the acquisition.

Licensure Laws

A health facility must determine whether its acquisition, merger, or affiliation with other facilities or health services requires prior approval by the state licensing authorities. A facility should also review the licenses of any facility that it merges with, acquires, or otherwise affiliates with. The review should encompass whether the particular license is complete. The review should also include the licensed bed count, bed service categories, bed classifications, and special services of the facility. If a facility acquires or merges with another facility, the purchaser should determine whether approval has been obtained by the facility to be acquired for all its services requiring special licensing or permit under local law and regulations. The purchaser should determine if any administrative proceedings are threatened or pending. It should also identify whether any beds risk loss of licensure. Finally, the purchaser should review state and federal surveys or inspection reports, existing statements of deficiencies, fire marshal reports, Occupational Safety and Health Administration reports, and any other governmental agency reports or notices concerning the facility.

Labor and Employment Issues

Another important legal issue that arises during the vertical integration process is whether and to what extent federal and state labor and employment issues apply to a particular acquisition, merger, or affiliation. For example, if a hospital acquires or merges with another facility, the hospital, as the new employer, may also inherit existing labor relations and equal opportunity obligations under the doctrine of "successorship."

When a health facility's acquisition or merger involves unions, the most important question is whether the purchaser is bound to its predecessor's bargaining obligations, which may include observing the terms of an existing union contract. The conditions under which such successorship occurs remains a point of controversy before the courts and the National Labor Relations Board. Major factors in establishing successorship obligations currently include the terms of any existing collective bargaining agreement, the continuity in the facility's work force after the acquisition or merger, the continuity of identity in the facility's business enterprise after the acquisition or merger, and the appropriateness of the facility's bargaining unit after the acquisition or merger. A purchaser should also be careful when, as the new employer of the facility, it selects its work force. A new employer may not discriminate against union members and may not use coercive tactics, such as interrogation or surveillance of union activities, when it decides who it will rehire after a merger or acquisition.

In addition, whenever a nonunion employer acquires or merges with a unionized facility, or if a purchaser's efforts to avoid successorship fail, the nonunion employer should be aware of certain legal doctrines. Under such doctrines, a union may claim rights to cover some or all of the nonunion employees in the nonunion institution with which it joins. These include the "single employer," "accretion," and "alter ego" doctrines. Whether any of the doctrines apply and will result in an expansion of the union facility's bargaining obligations to cover employees in the nonunion facility, including obligations arising under the collective bargaining agreement, depends on a number of factors. These include the form of the acquisition or merger, the corporate structure of the emerging facilities, and a number of other determinative considerations pertinent to each doctrine.

Other collective bargaining issues that arise include a facility's duty to bargain in advance and in good faith with its existing union over the effects of a planned merger or acquisition. Yet another issue is the effect of the merger or acquisition on, and a new employer's obligation and liability under, existing pension plans arising under a collective bargaining agreement.

A succeeding employer may also inherit, from the preceding employer, equal employment opportunity obligations under state and federal law. Finally, it may inherit certain implied contractual obligations, under state law, between an employer and individual employees based on written employment policies, the preceding employer's practices and representations, and even the employee's longevity.

Thus, the legal issues that arise in implementing vertical integration are numerous and varied. Providers should carefully examine and consider them as they consider and implement diversification options.

LEGAL ISSUES THAT ARISE WITH FINANCING THE CONTINUUM OF CARE

Capital Finance Issues

There are many mechanisms available to finance the creation of long-term care systems. Alternative methods include conventional arrangements such as bank loans, issuance of capital stock, issuance of public or private debt securities, equity financing (by for-profit entities), and seller financing (in acquisition transactions). Any mechanism chosen is likely to be subject to the general contractual and regulatory restrictions on most financing schemes. However, further legal restrictions that pertain particularly to the health care industry may also apply. For example, restrictions in a health facility's bond financing documents may prohibit its later sale or acquisition of another facility without the consent of the holders of the bonds. Therefore, providers should be aware of such restrictions when choosing the method of financing for a particular project.

Payment and Reimbursement Systems

In contrast to the available methods of financing the vertical integration process, the mechanisms of reimbursement for the provision of health services in long-term care systems are in a state of flux and are continuing to evolve.

Medicare

Currently, the benefits of Medicare's diagnostic-related-group–based prospective payment system (PPS) are generally limited to covering care rendered in connection with acute illnesses. Some studies predict that Medicare will expand its coverage of skilled nursing care and continue to allow waivers for certain capitation-financed, long-term care services such as social/health maintenance organizations. However, many believe that Medicare's future role in financing long-term care will most likely remain small. Political pressure to limit or reduce its budget continues to increase, because of concerns about the solvency of its trust fund.

Medicaid

In contrast to Medicare, Medicaid currently assumes the bulk of responsibility for financing long-term care. Benefits generally include skilled nursing and intermediate care and certain home health services. However, Medicaid protection is limited. Eligibility depends on the exhaustion of personal financial resources. The nature and extent of its benefits also depend on a state's willingness to pay. It has been predicted that Medicaid will convert to a PPS or capitated system in order to help control its spiraling budget. It is generally anticipated that different approaches to Medicaid reimbursement will be taken in a number of states. It is also predicted that Medicaid's ability to absorb the growing cost of long-term care may decline. Like Medicare, political pressure to limit or reduce Medicaid's budgets at the state and federal levels continues to increase.

Private Sector Developments

As a result of the public sector's reduced role in financing long-term care, there may be a commensurate growth in private sector financial participation. The development of private long-term care insurance policies, life care communities, continuing health care communities, social/health maintenance organizations, and other evolving financing programs will cause a number of federal and state legal and regulatory issues to arise. These issues will range from licensure and disclosure requirements to specific insurance industry restrictions.

In fact, states have already increased their regulation of long-term care insurance policies. Since long-term policies are still relatively new, many states group these policies with Medigap policies and apply the same regulations. This forces the insurer to cover such things as Medicare copayments or requires that the policy be offered in combination with hospital and physician coverage. Medigap regulations also frequently require very broad definitions of covered long-term care services in order to protect the elderly from overly narrow interpretations of covered benefits. This can act to restrict long-term care policies that offer very specific catastrophic coverage of nursing home care. Some insurers argue that state-regulated minimum loss ratios, which are designed to ensure that subscribers receive a reasonable return on their premium dollars, do not recognize the lag between the initial purchase and the potential use of the benefits when applied to long-term care insurance. State health maintenance organization acts may be applicable to certain long-term care benefit packages. State regulations may also prevent marketing the same long-term care policy in several different states, since each policy must be written to conform to specific state requirements.

LEGAL ISSUES THAT ARISE WITH RENDERING THE CONTINUUM OF CARE

Ethical Issues and Patients' Rights

Once vertical integration of long-term care is implemented and financed, legal and regulatory issues continue to arise as patients receive care through the new systems. Numerous ethical-legal and liability issues arise that pertain to the special needs of a long-term care or elderly patient. An in-depth discussion of these issues is beyond the scope of this chapter. However, providers should inform themselves about them. Such issues include patients' consents, medical information disclosures to patients, administration of antipsychotic drugs, uses of patient restraints, elder abuse, patients' rights, withholdings of treatments, withdrawals of life support systems, and allocations of scarce resources.

Scope of Practice

Another issue to consider is the growing role that certain nonphysician, specialized health care practitioners are playing and will continue to play in providing long-term care in vertically integrated systems. This larger role is due, in part, to medical and technological advances and, in part, to the increased medical focus on chronic, long-term illnesses. Thus, the standards and conditions under which a health facility grants credentials to health care practitioners to practice in the organization will have great importance. Such practitioners useful in the long-term care health system include psychologists, podiatrists, chiropractors, physician assistants, nurse practitioners, and nurse anesthetists.

Providers should therefore be aware of a health care practitioner's defined scope of practice under the appropriate state licensure laws. In addition, other sources such as case law, Joint Commission on Accreditation of Hospitals (JCAH) accreditation standards, and the Medicare Conditions of Participation may assist providers in this regard. These sources may help set limits or provide guidelines for the practice of certain practitioners in connection with their right to practice within health facilities, their required supervision by physicians, the care they may render to hospitalized patients, and whether they may admit and discharge patients.

Referral Restrictions

Finally, providers should be aware of fraud and abuse provisions of certain state laws that prohibit the medical staff members of health facilities from referring their patients, without appropriate disclosure, to other health facilities or health-related providers in which the referring facility has a financial interest. Similarly, laws exist that prohibit health facilities from referring patients to other health facilities or health-related providers in exchange for money or some other form of consideration given to the referring facility.

The federal Medicaid and Medicare statutes also prohibit offers or acceptances of remuneration in exchange for patient referrals for treatment that is wholly or partially paid for by either Medicare or Medicaid benefits. These statutes are drafted very broadly. Thus, providers should be very careful to examine activities and transactions to determine whether they offend these referral statutes. Problems may arise as treatment is provided in vertically integrated systems in which health facilities have significant financial or joint-venture interests in, or affiliations with, other facilities or corporations to which they refer patients and receive direct profits in return. Violations of these statutes can result in severe civil and criminal penalties. For example, punishment under the Medicare and Medicaid federal statutes may include imposition of fines up to $25,000 per violation and imprisonment up to five years.[11]

CONCLUSION

The trend toward creating vertically integrating health care systems to provide long-term care to the growing elderly population is likely to continue. This chapter attempts to name only some of the legal and regulatory issues that therefore will continue to arise. In addition, such legal issues will increase both in number and in complexity. As discussed, diversification is accomplished by combinations of related or joint entities, partnerships, and sole proprietorships that may operate on for-profit or nonprofit bases. These organizational and legal changes result in changes in the types and forms employed to provide various levels of health services to long-term patients.

Therefore, providers should make themselves aware of the legal issues as vertical integration and the application of the laws change and develop. Although many of these legal doctrines may seem to act as impediments to industry restructuring, often activities leading to the development of a continuum of care may be crafted to avoid the legal pitfalls described above.

This chapter is not intended to constitute legal advice. Readers should seek legal counsel regarding specific questions about vertical integration and diversification as they arise.

NOTES

1 Senate Special Committee on Aging, *Aging America: Trends and Projections*, 98th Cong., 2nd sess., 1984.

2. Lifson and Lieberman, "Financial Planning for the Future," *Business and Health*, December 1984:14–16.

3. Cook, "Legal Aspects of Nursing Home-Hospital Arrangements," *American Health Care Association*, January 1986:20–23.

4. 15 U.S.C. §§ 77a–77aa.

5. 26 U.S.C. § 501(c)(3).

6. 26 U.S.C. §§ 511–513.

7. 42 U.S.C. § 291 *et seq.*

8. 15 U.S.C. § 1 *et seq.*

9. 457 U.S. 332 (1982).

10. 42 C.F.R. §§ 123.404(a)(5), 123.406(b).

11. 42 U.S.C. §§ 1395nn, 1396h.

Technical Notes on Corporate Reorganization

Thomas E. Terrill, PhD

Corporate reorganization may be the result of the precursor of development of a continuum of care. The legal issues involved in corporate reorganization are discussed in Chapter 8. A brief presentation of tax and accounting issues is presented here. Although these considerations detailed below are most applicable to hospitals, many of the specifics pertain to other types of health care entities as well, and the general issues should be examined by all health and social service organizations involved in formal reorganization.

HEALTH CARE HOLDING COMPANIES

As health care organizations move to meet the competition and reorganize, a popular approach has been to create a holding company at the top of the structure and in some circumstances to create a ''shell'' corporation as a voluntary not-for-profit entity.

At the present time, the IRS is not issuing favorable determination letters to hospital holding companies unless they meet the ''support tests'' under Internal Revenue Code, Section 509(a). This regulation requires that such holding companies exist in part to raise funds to support the other activities of the entity. Therefore, it is necessary that the holding company foundation *plans* on fund raising and really does carry the plan out.

LOANS FROM ONE HEALTH CARE ORGANIZATION TO ANOTHER

In New Jersey, there is current litigation involving consideration whether the board members of a hospital have met their fiduciary responsibility by loaning funds from its endowment to the hospital and other subsidiaries on a noninterest-bearing basis. To avoid unfavorable scrutiny, such transactions among the new corporate entities should be conducted as ''arms length transactions'' and in a proper business fashion, and fair market interest rates should be charged for intercompany loans.

HOSPITAL ASSOCIATION MEMBERS

In some circumstances where the ownership of the hospital is vested in an association, the circumstances surrounding the reorganization can become very delicate. In successful reorganizations involving associations, there have been numerous educational sessions held for association members prior to the meeting when a final vote is taken. The educational sessions have usually focused on the desirability of the reorganization and the role of the association in the future; they have included presentations from management, legal counsel, and the hospital's auditors or special consultants assisting in the reorganization.

TAX ISSUES

The major tax matter concerning a proposed reorganization will usually be the IRS determination of the proposed holding company as identified by counsel. A minor issue, but one that may be subject to scrutiny in the future operations of the system of companies, is the nature of the transactions among the companies. The IRS will most likely review transactions where a not-for-profit entity in the system is selling products or services to a profit-making entity at profit levels above fair market value. In instances where "excessive profits" are charged to the for-profit entity by the not-for-profit entity in order to reduce tax obligations of the for-profit entity, the IRS may rule that those profits be retroactively reallocated to the for-profit entity for tax purposes.

In 1986, major changes were made in the tax statutes and regulations. Investments and forms of organization that were attractive to institutions under the prior tax code may no longer be desirable. Health care entities involved in reorganizing should consult with their accountant both to evaluate proposed changes and to review past actions for their appropriateness under current regulations.

MORTGAGE OR BOND COVENANTS

The mortgage or bond documents that are involved in a health care organization's debt need to be reviewed to determine whether or not there are any restrictive covenants that would prohibit the reorganization. In most instances, modifying these covenants to accommodate the reorganization can be accomplished quite easily. It is important that this be done, however, in order to prevent the institution from being in technical default of its debt obligations.

REGULATORY AND REIMBURSEMENT CONSIDERATIONS

There are several reimbursement issues that should be addressed by corporate reorganization:

Overhead Cost Allocation Formulae

In many cases the Medicare regulations prescribe the overhead cost allocation methodologies to be used for attributing costs to hospital-based programs. Very often these formulae are grossly simplistic and result in unfairly high allocations to departments that are not significantly used by third party patients (e.g., maternity services) or to nonreimbursable activities (e.g., a medical office building). The effect of keeping certain of these programs within the hospital corporate structure is, therefore, to unfairly reduce reimbursement from third party payers.

Investment or Other Income Offset

The Medicare regulations require that, except in very specific cases (i.e., those involving funded depreciation), unrestricted investment income must reduce otherwise reimbursable interest expense for purposes of cost apportionment. However, during the 1985 federal budget reconciliation process and the 1986 changes in the tax code, the funded depreciation shelter was attacked. It is anticipated that this issue will again arise during future budget sessions. In addition, there are other offsets, such as those for restricted gifts and bequests, income from certain sales of ancillary services to nonpatients, and revenues generated by parking garages, that may be included as offsets for purposes of cost reporting and borrowing.

Unnecessary Borrowings

The underlying philosophy of the federal health program is that a not-for-profit provider will only be reimbursed the "reasonable" cost of providing services. The regulations interpreting this congressional philosophy require that interest expense incurred for unnecessary borrowings not be reimbursed. In that regard, it has been interpreted that a provider must expend virtually all available cash and liquid assets before borrowings are deemed necessary. Corporate reorganization can, under certain circumstances, provide a vehicle for protection of these liquid assets from this interpretation.

PROSPECTIVE PAYMENT SYSTEM

Title VI of the Social Security Amendment of 1983, entitled "Prospective Payment for Medicare Inpatient Hospital Services," has substantially modified the way institutions are reimbursed by Medicare. The prospective payment system (PPS) pays a prospectively determined amount as adjusted for casemix intensity, thus placing a hospital at risk for the cost of providing these services.

Corporate reorganization provides a health care delivery entity with opportunities to mitigate the impact of the ever-increasing regulatory and reimbursement constraints, as well as to create new revenue sources to supplement its financial needs. Various services or programs can be established in separate entities, and as a result these alternative health care delivery modes can generate profits, accumulate capital, operate more efficiently, and free previously committed institutional resources.

However, the corporate restructuring process must also consider the Medicare program's regulations concerning related organizations. Medicare defines *related organizations* as two or more entities of which there is common ownership or control (direct or indirect). An interlocking of boards of trustees of a hospital and another corporation is an example of direct control. Similarly, approval of all hospital board actions by a separate parent corporation board is an example of indirect control. Once two entities are determined to be related under Medicare regulations, reimbursement is limited to reasonable and necessary costs. Inasmuch as capital costs under PPS may continue to be reimbursed on a retrospective cost basis, at least for awhile it is probable that the Medicare program will attempt to offset investment income of another corporation against hospital interest expense or treat the cash and liquid assets of the other corporation as available to offset debt if the two entities were deemed related organizations under Medicare regulations.

In addition, the Medicare program has issued new regulations that consider two entities to be related under certain circumstances even in the absence of common governing bodies or common ownership (e.g., both entities are not-for-profit, nonstock issuing corporations). A hospital or other health care organization, for example, may establish a separate, special purpose organization to conduct certain of the hospital's patient care–related or nonpatient care–related activities (e.g., a development foundation assumes the hospital's fund-raising activity). These two entities will be considered related organizations for Medicare purposes if either of the following occurs:

1. The hospital controls the special purpose organization through contracts or other legal documents that give the hospital the authority to direct the special purpose organization's activities, management, and policies.

2. The hospital is, for all practical purposes, the sole beneficiary of the special purpose organization's activities. The hospital should be considered the special purpose organization's sole beneficiary if one or more of the following circumstances exist:

- A special purpose organization has solicited funds in the name of and with the expressed or implied approval of the hospital, and substantially all the funds solicited by the organization were intended by the contributor or otherwise required to be transferred to the hospital or used at its discretion or direction.
- The hospital has transferred some of its resources to a special purpose organization substantially all of whose resources are held for the benefit of the hospital.
- The hospital has assigned certain of its functions (such as the operation of a dormitory) to a special purpose organization that is operating primarily for the benefit of the hospital.

Once again, if the above criteria are applicable, the Medicare program may look to the assets of a separate uncontrolled foundation in determining the necessity of a hospital's capital borrowings. Accordingly, great care must be exercised during the corporate reorganization process to avoid the regulatory definition of *related organizations*. Special attention must be given to organizational structure and lines of responsibility, governance (board composition), articles of incorporation, and by-laws. Otherwise, possible resultant reimbursement benefits of corporate reorganization can be largely negated.

FINANCIAL REPORTING CONSIDERATIONS

The question of whether or not to combine the financial statements of affiliated corporations with those of the hospital has been discussed extensively for some years. The American Institute of Certified Public Accountants addressed the question formally in "Statement on Audit Standards, Number 6," issued in July 1975, and in "Statement of Position (SOP) 81-2," issued August 1, 1981.

The criteria for consolidations are complex; however, we present a brief summary here. If a hospital is related to a separate organization and meets the criterion of having a controlling financial interest in such an organization (over 50 percent) under Accounting Research Bulletin (ARB) 51, consolidation is generally appropriate. If the ARB criterion is not met, the criteria from Chapter 10 of HMI-15 is applied (see "Regulatory and Reimbursement Considerations" above). If the hospital meets these conditions, the hospital should present summarized information about the assets, liabilities, results of operations, and charges in fund balances of the related organization in the notes to the hospital's financial statements and describe the nature of the relationship.

If this test is not met, one of the following SOP 81-2 tests may apply. If a related organization holds material amounts of funds that have been designated for the benefit of the hospital, or if there have been material transactions between the hospital and the related organization, the hospital's financial statements should disclose the existence and nature of the relationship between the hospital and the related organization. Further, if there have been material transactions between the hospital and the related organization during the periods covered by the hospital's financial statements, the following should be disclosed:

1. a description of the transactions, summarized if appropriate, for the period reported on, including amounts, if any, and any other information deemed necessary to an understanding of the effect on the hospital's financial statements
2. the dollar volume of transactions and the effects of any changes in the terms from the preceding period
3. amounts due from or to the related organization, and, if not otherwise apparent, the terms and manner of settlement

The guidelines in SOP 81-2 allow substantial room for judgment concerning whether or not consolidated statements should be issued. Final decision must be made by the auditor on a case-by-case basis.

If the organization is determined to be related to another organization, according to SOP 81-2, it is probable that these two entities would be considered related organizations under Medicare principles of reimbursement. The reimbursement implications are discussed in ''Regulatory and Reimbursement Considerations'' above.

In addition to the technical accounting requirements, health care organizations that reorganize, particularly those that have numerous services within their corporate structure, must develop ways of budgeting and managing financial operations to make accommodations for a managed continuum of care system. The economies and efficiencies of operating a continuum are realized for the total organization. Yet, if each of the individual services is operated only with its own financial status in mind, some of the financial benefits of the continuum may be lost. For example, assuming health status permits, it is less expensive to the system to discharge long-stay Medicare clients from acute beds and continue the stay in a skilled nursing facility. The skilled nursing facility, however, may need additional resources to maintain heavy-care patients, and it may show less of a profit if it accepts heavy-care patients than if it does not. Thus there must be internal mechanisms for coordinating clinical care and dollar flow among the various services and for showing the financial implications for the total system as well as the financial impact of each individual service. Industry has developed complicated methods for ''inter-entity transfer pricing.'' The health care field, which is not only developing cost-accounting for specific services, still has a long way to go to develop this level of sophistication in its accounting and budgeting processes. Nonetheless, such details of financial operations must be considered in reorganization and in ongoing management.

Chapter 9

Health Care Joint Ventures*

Ernst & Whinney

CREATING A WINNING JOINT VENTURE

Our experience with health care clients and the survey results described below show that a successful joint venture requires matching the new business with the environment to create a "no-lose" situation for the coventurers. In the short run, a joint venture can attract new patients, create new revenue sources, or reduce costs. From a broader strategic perspective, the venture can differentiate the organization from its competitors or help establish it as a cost-effective producer. The test of success will be the strength, pre-eminent competitive position, and value of the joint venture as the structure and economics of the health care industry change in response to market forces and governmental regulation.

Although diversity appears to be the one factor that all joint ventures have in common, successful joint ventures generally follow these rules:

- *Cooperate to compete better.* Joining the forces of natural allies, such as a hospital and its medical staff, can strengthen market position and effectively combat the competition. Joint ventures can be a mutually beneficial response—if coventurers are willing to cooperate to achieve shared objectives.
- *Gain a strategic advantage.* The leading joint ventures will tend to be those that achieve a favorable cost position over the long-run or find a market that is either poorly served or growing quickly. Others will develop a

---

*This chapter was adapted from *Health Care Joint Ventures: Survey Results* with permission of Ernst & Whinney, © 1985. Ernst & Whinney, a nationwide accounting, tax and consulting firm, conducted a survey in 1985 of all nongovernmental not-for-profit hospitals and all investor-owned hospitals in the United States to determine their current interest and activity in joint ventures. This chapter reports the results of that survey. Although hospitals formed the sample (and the text thus refers only to hospitals), the findings of the survey are relevant to all organizations involved in the development of continuums of care through joint venture arrangements.—EDS.

distinguished reputation among patients and consumers. A strategic advantage will become especially critical as health care consumers become more knowledgeable, discriminating, and powerful in their buying decisions.

- *Prepare for competitor reaction.* The actions of competitors in response to a joint venture should not be underestimated. Successful joint venturers will study possible reactions of competitors in their local markets before proceeding and will formulate a strategy with competitors in mind.

- *Balance risks and rewards.* The rewards of a joint venture can be significant; so can the risks. Coventurers must be able to deal with the risks associated with a loss of control—and autonomy—in conducting business, as well as the potential risk of business failure. However, the rewards, both monetary and nonmonetary, can be substantial. Winning ventures will balance risks and rewards to add value over the long-run.

For a hospital, joint ventures can offer opportunities for financial risk sharing or for increasing patient referrals. For physician group practices or hospital medical staffs, joint venturing can provide access to capital or management expertise. For many health care providers the volatile, competitive health care environment may require a strategy of interdependence in order to succeed.

Checklist for Reaching a Go/No-Go Decision

The extensive decision and evaluation process that precedes a successful joint venture was emphasized by survey participants. The following checklist shows some of the important steps in evaluating a potential joint venture. At each step, the concept and viability of the joint venture should be challenged for feasibility.

- Determine the business purpose of the joint venture.
- Evaluate the market and competitors to determine if the product or service concept is realistic and feasible.
- Search for and screen candidates for a joint venture.
- Analyze tax implications from both a tax-exempt status and investor-owned standpoint, if appropriate.
- Evaluate, with a lawyer, the options and pros and cons of the various legal forms of business, as well as such issues as antitrust and corporate practice of medicine laws.
- Review payment and other regulations, including the role of third party payers and possible certificate of need (CON), licensing, and accreditation requirements.
- Evaluate capital investment requirements and financing options.
- Prepare financial projections and what-if analyses.
- Prepare a business plan for review and use by investors.

- Obtain necessary funds.
- Analyze accounting and related system issues.
- Address operational requirements, including management, staffing, procedures, and controls.
- Develop a realistic implementation plan and timetable.

As the checklist suggests, joint ventures require a careful analysis of tax implications and legal issues, as well as a thorough review of marketing, operating, and any other issues critical to launching a new business. Many joint ventures never make it off the drawing board. Unfortunately, some that do should never have reached completion. Nonetheless, if carefully planned and executed, a joint venture can be an excellent vehicle for taking advantage of market opportunities and achieving mutually beneficial objectives.

Spotting Sure-Fire Failures

Joint ventures can offer many benefits to health care providers; at the same time the cost of failure can be substantial. Often an unsuccessful joint venture fails because coventurers have made some of the following mistakes:

- *Copying the competition.* A joint venture developed because the competitors have entered into one that is doomed to fail. The joint venture must be the organization's own and tailored to its market.
- *Distrusting the coventurer.* The risks of the business will be amplified and success jeopardized if the coventurers neither trust nor respect each other.
- *Taking a shot in the dark.* Relying solely on intuition in a market that is volatile and characterized by uncertainty will likely result in failure. A carefully conceived plan can help keep an organization out of marketing, legal, and tax trouble.
- *Expecting a miracle.* A joint venture between two ''unhealthy'' partners will not necessarily cure either of them. Before adding a layer of complexity by joint venturing, partners should realistically assess the expected outcome.
- *Not knowing when to quit.* Although market analyses, numerous meetings, and several thousand dollars of investment reveal that, while the venture seems like a good idea, the market is simply not there. Proceeding will only increase losses; there is no reason to continue investing in a joint venture unlikely to survive.

Needless to say, these mistakes should, and can, be avoided or their effects minimized by carefully planning for, assessing the feasibility of, and implementing the joint venture.

Joint Venture: A Viable Option

Joint ventures are one of the many viable options available to health care providers in adapting to and even changing the relevant environment. Mergers or horizontal integration are other possible vehicles for achieving a strategic goal. Each option is capable of increasing a provider's ability to survive and prosper in the next decade, and each offers different rewards, degrees of control or freedom, and associated risks.

Each joint venture is unique in its complexity, participants, target markets, and investment arrangements. Bringing together, to start the new business, two organizations with different cultures, systems, and objectives provides significant decision-making and implementation challenges. The key to success is combining the organizations' elements effectively to suit the particulars of the situation.

OVERVIEW OF SURVEY RESULTS

In April 1985, Ernst & Whinney sent a letter to the chief executive officer of every nongovernmental nonprofit hospital and every investor-owned hospital in the United States. The letter asked about each hospital's involvement in joint ventures and solicited volunteers for telephone interviews. More than 700 executives volunteered to participate in the survey. Of these, 33 percent already were involved in at least one venture and 64 percent were interested in pursuing joint ventures. Details of the methodology are given in the full report.

Survey respondents represent a broad cross section of hospitals. Joint ventures appear to be used as diversification or investment vehicles regardless of such variables as location, size, or ownership, and the responses of the 400 chief executives, presidents, and administrators whose organizations were either already involved or interested in joint ventures suggest that such ventures will continue to be so used.

SURVEY RESULTS

Besides providing a broad overview of the level of activity presently underway, the types of ventures undertaken, partners selected, location and acquaintance of the coventurers, and the reasons for joint venturing indicate the potential for future activity. The results of the survey are summarized below. In order to identify potential changes in the market, distinctions are presented between those already involved in joint ventures and those interested in pursuing them in the near future.

What Types of Ventures Are Most Prevalent?

The types of ventures were divided into five broad categories for discussion and classification purposes. The categories were:

- ambulatory care
- alternative delivery systems (ADS)
- acute inpatient facilities
- long-term or postacute care
- other facilities

Ambulatory care was the most popular category of joint venture, particularly among multihospital system participants. Thirty-seven percent of respondents were involved and 36 percent were interested in ambulatory care joint ventures. Within this category, surgery centers, magnetic resonance imaging (MRI) and other diagnostic facilities, and urgent care centers were the most common ventures underway. For those interested in joint ventures, surgery centers and MRI and other diagnostic facilities were again mentioned most often, with urgent care centers closely following.

Of special note is the increasing interest in alternative delivery systems (ADS)—30 percent were interested and 16 percent were already involved. For hospitals with more than 400 beds, the percentage interested increased significantly to 55 percent. For both involved and interested groups there was a fairly even split between health maintenance organizations (HMOs) and preferred provider organizations (PPOs). This finding is not surprising given the recent renewed emphasis on HMO and PPO development.

Twenty-four percent were involved in some other type of facility, such as medical office buildings, laboratories, laundry facilities, or alcoholic rehabilitation centers, among others. Within this category, medical office buildings constituted more than 50 percent of the ventures among both groups of participants. Other facilities were mentioned much less frequently.

Within the long-term or subacute care category (13 percent involved and 9 percent interested), home health services accounted for the majority of all ventures for both groups, with a smaller number of responses for durable medical equipment and nursing homes.

There was little activity or interest in joint venturing to develop an acute, inpatient facility—which again is not surprising in the context of the current health care environment.

Who Are Joint Venture Partners?

The joint venture partners of choice for hospitals—by a wide margin—were physician group practices. Forty percent of those involved and those interested in joint ventures named physician groups as their existing and potential partners, respectively. Among hospitals with more than 400 beds, 50 percent of those involved and 65 percent of those interested named physician groups as partners. Individual physicians (most likely the medical staff) were mentioned next by 24 percent of those involved and 30 percent of those interested. Short-term hospitals were mentioned the third most often—although there is a clear decline between those involved and those interested.

These findings probably are a reflection of the current interest in diversifying services from inpatient offerings to other forms of care. It also correlates strongly with the results on types of ventures. The most likely partners for an ambulatory care or ADS venture would be physicians.

Other types of partners were mentioned infrequently. Corporations (other than health care providers) were mentioned by 9 percent of those involved and 7 percent of those interested. Of note is the lack of involvement or interest in joint venturing with home health providers or nursing homes. Although participants had expressed a moderate amount of interest in long-term or postacute care (13 percent of those involved and 9 percent of those interested), they apparently do not plan to undertake such a venture with an existing provider of these services.

The choice of partner differed by type of venture. For ambulatory care and alternative delivery systems, physician partners were mentioned most often. In addition, physician group practices were mentioned more often than individual physicians in both cases. Participants already involved in ADS were venturing with physician groups more than 75 percent of the time.

Survey participants who were just becoming interested in ADS showed a relatively greater inclination toward individual physicians (32 percent) and a correspondingly lower interest in physician groups (44 percent) than did those already involved. This may signal a higher degree of interest in identifying opportunities for coventuring with hospital medical staffs.

Respondents reported that the joint venture tended to be a local market endeavor and to be based on already established relationships between local health care providers. However, approximately 53 percent had a specific partner in mind, compared to 44 percent who had several partners in mind. This would suggest that carefully evaluating and selecting the appropriate partner is an important part of the process.

What about Time and Distance?

Coventurers tended to be located near each other, with almost 70 percent within 10 miles, and more than 90 percent within 50 miles. Not surprisingly, almost 40 percent of those involved in a joint venture had known their partner for more than five years. At the same time, a somewhat surprising 21 percent had known their joint venture partner for less than six months. More than 70 percent of the existing joint ventures in the survey had been in operation less than two years. Only 9 percent had been in operation for more than four years.

What Joint Venture?

Participants most often said they were joint venturing to increase market share. In fact, market-oriented reasons were given by 72 percent of participants already involved in a joint venture and by 84 percent interested in joint ventures. The percentage of market-oriented reasons among the interested group were even higher for multihospital system participants (92 percent), medium-sized hospitals of 200 to 399 beds (91 percent), and those who named ADS as their proposed venture (97 percent).

Participants were asked their primary reason for joint venturing. Their answers can be grouped generally into two categories: market-oriented and financially-oriented reasons, as shown below.

Market-Oriented Reasons	All	Involved	Interested
Increase market share	37%	27%	46%
"Lock-in" utilization	20%	23%	17%
Improve competitive position	13%	12%	14%
Diversify services	9%	10%	7%
Subtotal	79%	72%	84%
Financially-Oriented Reasons			
Obtain capital for expansion	5%	4%	5%
Reduce costs	6%	8%	2%
Improve financial position	6%	8%	5%
Subtotal	16%	20%	12%
Other Reasons	5%	8%	4%
Total	100%	100%	100%

In brief, 79 percent of all responses were market-oriented and 16 percent financially-oriented. These findings, of course, do not suggest that financial reasons are unimportant, but they may reflect a belief that improving competitive position or increasing market share will result in a stronger financial position.

Larger hospitals in both the involved and interested groups tended to cite market-oriented reasons more often than did smaller hospitals. A higher percentage of smaller than of larger hospital participants tended to be involved and interested in joint ventures for financial reasons. This probably reflects greater access to financial resources among larger hospitals.

PUTTING TOGETHER THE JOINT VENTURE

The experiences of survey participants in evaluating their joint ventures, negotiating the agreement, reaching a go/no-go decision, and establishing investment requirements and the legal form are useful for potential joint ventures. Because many of the questions relate to actual experience, much of the commentary in this and in the next section refers *only* to survey participants who already were involved in a joint venture.

How Do Joint Ventures Get Started?

More than 70 percent of those involved in a joint venture reported that the opportunity arose from the hospital's strategic planning process and that the hospital took the lead in proposing the joint venture. Sixty percent of the time, the CEO, president, or administrator made the proposal.

Moreover, participants carefully evaluated the venture before proceeding. Respondents involved in joint ventures did the following in preparation:

- evaluated the regulatory and reimbursement environment (84 percent)
- reviewed various legal forms of business (84 percent)
- prepared projected financial statements (84 percent)
- addressed accounting issues (83 percent) and tax issues (77 percent)
- reviewed accreditation or licensing requirements (73 percent)
- conducted feasibility studies (68 percent)
- prepared a formal business plan (66 percent)
- conducted market research (62 percent)

These percentages were even higher for multihospital system participants, larger hospitals, and ambulatory care joint venturers.

Legal Form

There were variations in the legal form of business selected among different types of ventures. Options included contracts, partnerships, corporations, and others. Partnerships and contractual arrangements were the most common legal forms of business (35 percent each). Corporations were established in 23 percent of the cases.

There were significant variations based on type of venture and size of hospital. Ambulatory care participants preferred partnerships—probably because of the real estate tax and investment considerations of their physician partners—more than 50 percent of the time. ADS participants used corporate and contractual arrangements equally (39 percent each); the high frequency was again probably due to the investment and tax realities of this type of venture. Small organizations—hospitals with fewer than 50 beds—favored contractual arrangements.

What Is the Composition of the Board of Directors?

For joint venture corporations, a separate board of directors was established in more than 90 percent of the cases. As shown below, there were most often (57 percent) from five to seven board members.

Number of Board Members	Percentage of Respondents
Less than 5	19%
5 to 7	57%
8 to 10	10%
More than 10	14%

Coventurer representation on the board is shown below.

Hospital majority	26%
Coventurer majority	17%
Equal representation	57%

Equal representation is clearly the preferred composition of the board.

What Are the Typical Investment and Financing Commitments?

Total investment was under $1 million for approximately 66 percent of participants and from $1 to $5 million for 26 percent. Only 7 percent reported ventures with an investment in excess of $5 million, although for multihospital systems this percentage increased to 13 percent. Forty-four percent of the ambulatory care facilities cost $1 to $5 million—not surprising given their higher facility, equipment, and construction costs.

The following table illustrates the percentage of debt used to finance participants' joint ventures.

Percentage of Debt	Percentage of Respondents
0%	18%
1–20%	1%
21–49%	7%
50–79%	21%
80–99%	15%
100%	3%
Don't know/no answer	35%

It should be noted that 35 percent of participants declined to answer this question. Among those who answered, the most (39 percent) financed their joint venture with at least 50 percent debt. Eighteen percent did not use any debt to finance the venture—not surprising given the relatively small investments by larger hospitals.

In a related question, approximately 55 percent of the participants reported that the entire equity portion of the investment was paid within the first year. Thirty-four percent required additional contributions in subsequent years.

IMPLEMENTING THE JOINT VENTURE

The steps taken in implementing a joint venture, as well as obstacles encountered and overall experience, are covered in this section. All the questions were answered only by the group of respondents who were involved in a joint venture.

What Was the Typical Start-Up Time?

Start-up time in the majority of cases (78 percent) was less than one year. About 28 percent of participants implemented their joint venture in less than six months and 21 percent in more than one year. Again, although the majority of respondents implemented their joint venture in less than one year, many perceived their biggest problem as the length of time it took to start the venture.

What Is the Degree of Satisfaction with the Joint Venture?

More than two-thirds of survey participants indicated they were "very satisfied" and more than 95 percent indicated they were "very satisfied" or "satisfied" with their joint venture. This may be partially due to the way participants were selected. It may also be partially the results of the apparently extensive evaluation process undertaken by participants in developing their joint venture. Nonetheless, the fairly large number of hospitals that were participating in more than one venture suggests that joint venturing in fact has generally been satisfactory. There were no significant differences by hospital ownership, size, or type of joint venture.

Are Utilization Rates at the Expected Level?

Almost half of the respondents said utilization rates were at the expected level. About 18 percent said they were lower and 22 percent said they were higher. The remaining respondents declined to comment because operations had just recently been started. There were no significant differences by hospital ownership, size, or type of venture.

What Obstacles Were Encountered?

Although start-up time was typically less than one year, the complaint about development and implementation mentioned most often (almost 30 percent) was that putting the venture together took longer than expected. The obstacles included

Disagreements between the boards	13%
Lack of physician support	7%
Lack of understanding of the issues	6%
Higher costs than expected	6%
Legal issues	5%
Lack of management support	4%

More than 15 percent of the respondents involved in at least one joint venture said that there were no obstacles in the negotiation and start-up phases of the venture.

There was no consensus on the greatest day-to-day problem of joint ventures. Approximately 30 percent said there were no problems with their venture. Participants named a variety of concerns, including:

- inability to market services or products
- problems with the reimbursement/monitoring system
- nonutilization of facility or services
- need to increase volume
- difficulty getting the program(s) off the ground
- lack of financial viability
- lack of communication between hospital and doctors

What Is the Degree of Public Awareness and Satisfaction?

In 67 percent of the cases, a new name was selected for the venture. This may partially account for the belief among respondents that the general public was typically not aware of the venture.

Public Awareness	Percentage of Respondents
Highly aware	15%
Somewhat aware	43%
Not at all aware	41%
Don't know/no answer	1%

At the same time, more than 70 percent of the respondents believed their patients were satisfied with the services they were receiving from the venture.

JOINT VENTURE MANAGEMENT CONSIDERATIONS

The following sections discuss some of the tax, operational, and management considerations that should be addressed in developing a joint venture. Methods used in evaluating, planning, and implementing a joint venture will differ markedly from one situation to the next. Yet, as the survey results show, carefully analyzing the planning for the venture will have a significant impact on its success. The effect of these tax issues, regulations, and payment considerations should be discussed in detail with professional advisors such as accountants, health care consultants, attorneys, and investment bankers, among others.

Tax Considerations

The four general categories of tax issues discussed in detail below should be addressed by those planning a joint venture involving a tax-exempt entity: (1) tax treatment of joint ventures; (2) protection of the exempt status of the hospital or other health care organization; (3) avoidance of unrelated business income tax liability; and (4) the effect of the tax-exempt entity leasing rules.*

Tax Treatment of Joint Ventures

Many tax-exempt hospitals raise capital through joint venture transactions. These ventures are usually structured as partnerships for such projects as constructing and managing medical office buildings and operating medical equipment. For federal income tax purposes, partnerships and joint ventures are viewed as an aggregate of individuals or organizations contributing capital or services in a joint business venture. As such, the partnership is not a separate taxpaying entity, but is merely a conduit through which income, deductions, credits, etc., flow to the partners' own tax returns. Thus, the partnership files an annual information return with the IRS showing the results of operations for the year, along with each partner's share of the various items of income, deductions, credits, etc.

The most common joint venture arrangement is a limited partnership, which is the form used in most tax shelters (i.e., mechanisms for providing tax advantages to investors).† At least one general partner manages the underlying assets of the limited partnership. The limited partners are analogous to corporate shareholders in that they invest money in exchange for their limited partnership

---

*Many individual and corporate tax considerations have changed with the passage of the 1986 Tax Reform measure. Thus, joint ventures structured prior to 1985 may have been desirable under former tax principles but are not necessarily appropriate models under current tax law. Detailed tax analysis should be done by the organization's accountants and tax lawyers.—Eds.

†Tax shelter provisions have been changed substantially by the 1986 Tax Reform and are no longer as desirable an investment as under previous tax provisions.—Eds.

interest. As limited partners, they cannot participate in management and the amount they can lose is generally limited to the amount they actually invest or are obligated to invest. This limited liability is one of the main advantages of a limited partnership.

Among the issues that need to be resolved before proceeding with a partnership arrangement are the following:

- Will another type of structure (e.g., a corporation) meet needs better than a partnership?
- How will profits and losses be allocated among partners?
- If a limited partnership format is used, how will the general partner be compensated?
- Are organizational and/or syndication expenses deductible?
- What are the consequences of terminating the partnership?

Tax-Exempt Status

Certain requirements must be satisfied in structuring the joint venture arrangement to ensure that the health care organization does not lose its exempt status.

The IRS had held, in a 1978 private letter ruling, that a tax-exempt organization would jeopardize its exempt status by serving as the general partner of a limited partnership. The IRS rationale was that, by serving as the general partner, the organization would be taking on an obligation to further the private financial interests of the other partners, and this would create a conflict of interest legally incompatible with operating exclusively for charitable purposes.

The IRS has reversed this position and now permits exempt organizations to participate in joint venture arrangements and as general partners in partnership arrangements with taxable entities or private investors. These arrangements are often made through subsidiaries established as a result of a hospital reorganization.

The IRS applies what it calls the "strict scrutiny" test in determining whether a partnership or joint venture jeopardizes exempt status. To obtain IRS approval, the facts and circumstances surrounding the arrangement must indicate that participation in the arrangement furthers the organization's charitable purposes. Also, the terms of the joint venture arrangement must adequately protect the organization's interests and not yield excessive benefits to private interests.

For example, the IRS has issued private letter rulings stating that partnership and joint venture arrangements further exempt purposes when the arrangement is formed to construct or acquire and operate a medical office building, parking structure, and related facilities; a psychiatric hospital; a blood fractionation facility; a C.A.T. scanner; or a nuclear magnetic resonance system. Also, although IRS private letter rulings and general counsel memoranda indicate that the exempt organization's interests must be adequately protected, the IRS has, in certain situations, permitted exempt organizations to provide guarantees or subsidies to partnerships. Examples include a guarantee of lease payments for unleased space, guarantee of bonds issued to finance the partnership, and ground leases for nominal rents.

However, a recent IRS training publication indicates that any of the following factors could jeopardize the health care organization's exempt status because they may indicate private benefit:

- disproportionate allocation of profits or losses
- existence of commercially unreasonable loans by the health care organization to the partnership (e.g., unsecured or below prevailing interest rates)
- sale or lease of land by the health care organization at less than fair market rates
- payment of inadequate compensation to the health care organization for its services as general partner

Further, an organization's exempt status may be jeopardized by payment of incentive management fees based on a percentage of net income or capital to a for-profit general partner by a partnership in which an exempt organization is a general or limited partner. This situation can be avoided if the management agreement is negotiated at arm's length and certain other requirements are satisfied.

Exempt organizations considering a joint venture or partnership arrangement with individuals or taxable entities, either directly or through a taxable subsidiary, should consider requesting an IRS private letter ruling before entering into the arrangement. This is advisable because of the risk associated with entering into a joint venture arrangement (i.e., loss of exempt status). In addition, there currently are no published IRS guidelines to help an exempt organization in these types of arrangements. The factors listed in the preceding paragraphs are taken from IRS private letter rulings, general counsel memoranda, and training materials (which may not be relied upon by taxpayers but do provide insight into IRS policy).

Unrelated Business Income

Income derived by an exempt organization from a partnership or joint venture arrangement will not constitute income from an unrelated trade or business if the venture is engaged in activities substantially related to the organization's exempt purposes. This rule applies to the exempt partner's share of the partnership income, to management and development fees, and to ground rents, interest, and other payments from the partnership to the exempt organization.

An exempt partner, however, will have to treat income (and deductions) from a partnership interest as unrelated business income to the extent the partnership receives income from unrelated debt-financed property or is otherwise engaged in unrelated business activities. Similarly, a portion of management and development fees, ground rents, interest, and other payments from such a partnership may have to be treated as unrelated business income.

Payment Issues

The implication of third party payer rules must be considered in the process of forming and operating a joint venture. Areas of potential concern that should be considered during the joint venture evaluation and planning process are payment implications and Medicare and Medicaid fraud and abuse law.

Although payment is now largely determined on a prospective basis, there remain three common situations where reimbursement rules could significantly influence joint venture decisions. There may be other payment implications for a particular joint venture, and joint venture considerations may change as new changes in payment regulations are enacted.

Funded Depreciation Recapture

Hospitals that wish to use the cash invested in hospital-funded depreciation accounts to partially finance their joint venture should be aware that this may not meet restrictions placed on these assets. The income earned by funded depreciation investments has historically been protected from and offset against interest expense. At the same time, amounts in the accounts can be used *only* to purchase capital assets for the Medicare provider or to pay the provider's long-term debt.

If funded depreciation is used to finance the joint venture, the transaction could be viewed as an improper use of funds and may result in significant prior-year cost adjustments by Medicare. To avoid recapture of funds by the Medicare program, providers investing in a joint venture should not use funded depreciation money. However, in some cases, a loan from the funded depreciation account to the provider could provide necessary start-up funds while affording some protection from reimbursement penalties.

Capital Cost Reimbursement

Generally, current federal income tax rules prohibit investors from claiming investment tax credit on equipment leased to not-for-profit institutions. Some investors have tried to obtain this credit by retaining ownership of the equipment and providing the equipment's service to the institution on a per-use basis. Photo copy machines are one example of this process—the owners charge users on a price-per-copy-made basis and claim tax credit. Such arrangements may or may not meet Medicare capital cost definitions or reasonableness tests. If they do not meet these tests, capital reimbursement will not be provided. Consequently, the potential tax benefits should be weighed against the possible loss of capital reimbursement.

The Medicare program reimburses providers for the costs associated with capital assets located in the provider's facility. For example, if a provider were to install a large mainframe computer to provide data processing services, the capital costs of the equipment would be separately reimbursed by the Medicare program. Other operating costs would have to be covered from the diagnostic related group (DRG) payment. If, however, the provider entered into a joint venture to provide data processing services through an offsite facility, the capital-related costs of that facility would not be directly reimbursed by the Medicare program. The provider would have to pay for services provided by the facility from its DRG payments. It could, therefore, cost the provider more, because the DRG payment would be the only reimbursement received.

Location of Service Issues

Health care joint ventures are often formed to provide a new health care service (such as home care) or to offer an existing service (such as an independent laboratory) in a different way or in a different location. A critical question for such ventures is the organizational form the venture should take for payment purposes.

Medicare and other third party payers often will pay different amounts for similar services provided by different health care organizations. The reason for the difference is that cost limits are often higher for hospital-based services. For example, hospital-based skilled nursing facilities have a higher routine cost limit than free-standing nursing homes. Hospital-based labs are paid more for lab tests than are independent laboratories.

An evaluation of service location issues should include a review of payment alternatives and of the payment levels expected under each.

Medicare and Medicaid Fraud and Abuse Law

Many health care joint ventures organized between hospitals and the physicians on their medical staffs can come under the scrutiny of Medicare's fraud and abuse provisions, as well as those of other insurers.

Essentially, fraud and abuse provisions prohibit payments to individuals in exchange for patient referrals. Any significant transaction between a health care provider and someone in a position to refer a patient to the provider may be examined to determine if it is a valid economic transaction or simply a disguised referral payment. Generally, valid financial arrangements are those in which equal value is received by both sides at a price similar to that charged in the open market. These arrangements should be supported by a contract and by proper documentation showing the contract was faithfully followed.

If a financial arrangement does not appear to benefit both parties or if the amounts paid appear much higher than the market price, the transaction may be improper. The penalties for improper payments can include civil penalties, imprisonment, and loss of payments. A joint venture with a referring physician should be carefully reviewed for propriety and economic reasonableness.

Legal and Regulatory Issues

Joint ventures are affected by a number of legal and regulatory concerns. These include accreditation and licensure, antitrust law, certificate of need and Section 1122, and corporate practice of medicine laws. These issues vary from state to state. A thorough investigation, including advice from experts in state and local regulations, should be done in preparing the initial analysis and the subsequent business plan for a joint venture.

SUMMARY

The results of the survey of 400 chief executives involved or interested in joint ventures indicate that this form of arrangement will continue to be a viable option for health care organizations to develop and expand service capability. The findings indicate that careful analysis and planning for the venture will have a significant impact on its success. A rigorous business plan should be prepared early in the process of formulating the joint venture. The business plan should include definition of goals and objectives, market analysis, service or product definition, criteria for business partners, business strategy, and an implementation plan. In addition, financial, operational, and management considerations should be addressed. Tax issues, regulations, and payment considerations should be evaluated in detail. Professional advice should be solicited from lawyers, accountants, tax specialists, and other technical advisors. Properly planned and thoughtfully implemented, joint ventures can be successful diversification and investment vehicles for all involved. Following is a list of steps that should be taken in developing a joint venture:

- evaluate the regulatory and reimbursement environment
- review legal forms of business
- prepare projected financials
- address accounting issues
- address tax issues
- review accreditation/licensing
- conduct a feasibility study
- develop a formal business plan
- conduct market research
- prepare a prospectus
- prepare a certificate of need

Chapter 10

Human Resource Issues

Arthur A. Sponseller

The premise of this chapter is that creating an integrated continuum of care organization is possible from the human resources point of view, although it presents a number of complex problems. Whether starting a new organization or building up an existing one, the issues of structure, interchangeability, and portability within the system are similar. In all situations there will be tension between the need for new entities to be independent and the benefits of centralized organizational structure. There will also be tension between the tendency to fragment and the advantages of being part of one organization. A durable medical equipment company acquired by a large medical system has its own needs, which can lead to fragmentation in areas such as salary levels and marketing methods; the needs of the entire organization, including the economies of scale inherent in a common financial reporting system or employee benefits package, lead toward uniformity.

The key is to recognize that neither complete fragmentation nor complete uniformity is best, but rather that the goal should be a compromise that enhances overall objectives and allows for individual business decision making where required.

NEW CORPORATE STRUCTURES

Negotiation for a merger, acquisition, affiliation, or joint venture will be more productive if the human resources issues are identified and understood in the beginning. Most companies that grow in such ways do a good job on the financial and tax side of the transaction, but often do not consider the related personnel issues until it is too late. Issues such as union representation status and employment-related litigation can, if identified early, be brought to the negotiating table or included in the implementation strategy. Advance attention in this area can prevent undisclosed personnel issues from turning an apparently astute collaborative venture into a financial nightmare. As expressed in a recent book on hospital reorganization:

The parties to structural and operational changes can reduce the like-lihood of financial liability and operational impediments by inventorying the relevant labor and employee relations considerations and designing appropriate strategies to satisfy their legal obligations. The parties also can capitalize on the opportunities created by structural and operational changes.[1]

When one business acquires another, it is also probably acquiring a set of liabilities based on the previous employer's personnel policies and practices. In order to identify what those liabilities are, the buyer should begin by inventorying the seller's policies, employee handbooks, employment-related contracts, pending lawsuits (if any), and, if possible, supervisory communications or statements (oral or written) about job security and other terms and conditions of employment. The more information the buyer can gather, especially about unwritten codes of conduct and employee attitudes and expectations, the better. The seller, as an employer, has probably committed some employment-related errors, the consequences of which may not come to light until the transaction is completed. Examples include wrongful termination lawsuits, discrimination claims under state and federal discrimination laws, violations of state and federal equal pay laws, and wage hour violations that may result in significant backpay awards.

A common wage hour problem of health care employers is the misclassification of workers as exempt for overtime purposes. Especially in states such as California, where the state definitions of exemption are more strict than at the Federal level, many so-called salaried employees who are not paid overtime would not meet the definition of exemption and would be entitled to backpay for unpaid overtime. Therefore, a buyer should look closely at the seller's pay practices with regard to this issue.

The investigation of the seller should also include all pending lawsuits and agency actions, as well as prior settlements, awards, decrees, consent actions, etc. Finally, the buyer should thoroughly investigate the seller's payment habits and status with regard to mandatory benefits such as unemployment and social security taxes. These items can be a source of significant prior liability and can be negotiated in the financial arrangements of the purchase.

The acquiring or resulting entity should negotiate an acquisition agreement that catalogues pending and threatened litigation. The acquired entity should guarantee (warrant) that the list is complete, should covenant not to make changes in specified terms of employment, and should indemnify (hold harmless) the acquiring entity from liability for the predecessor's conduct. The nature of the problems identified, the resources available to the former employer and its relationship with the acquiring entity might suggest the need to hold back a portion of the purchase price or require bonding or escrow accounts to insure compliance with the covenants, warranties and indemnification agreements.[2]

Employee benefit plans are another area fraught with potentially adverse financial consequences. Employee benefits that are accrued or vested can become the liability of the buyer. Generally accrued benefits can be voluntarily assumed or not, unless the acquired employees are covered by a union contract or other binding contractual arrangement. Vested benefits, however, cannot be disavowed. Examples include retirement or pension benefits, sick time, vacation time, seniority, insurance, and severance pay. Many states have rules on acquisitions and, depending on the type of transaction, may require the buyer to give severance pay to the workers even though there has been no disruption of the employment relationship and the workers are still on the job.[3] In California, for example, employees have a right to be paid all accrued and vested vacation time upon termination but have no right to accrued sick time. One final note about pension plans: buyers should be especially careful of sellers who are members of a multiemployer pension plan. The Multiemployer Pension Plan Amendments Act of 1980 (MEPPA) makes many structural changes constituting partial or total withdrawal acts that trigger substantial financial liability.[4]

When a union is present in any of the parties to a transaction the situation is made even more complex. Under the National Labor Relations Board (NLRB) concept of *successorship*, a buyer can stand in the shoes of the seller and be required to bargain with an existing bargaining representative. The manner of sale or transaction is also significant. In a stock sale, for example, a buyer is automatically a successor. The parties tend to have more flexibility in a sale of assets. However, the facts of each individual situation will be examined to determine successor status. The primary consideration of the NLRB will be the continuity of the employment relationship and the number of employees of the seller employed by the buyer. In addition, the terms of the labor contract may be relevant in spite of the fact that the National Labor Relations Act does not require that a successor assume a contract, just as a union can disavow a contract if it feels it can get a better deal from the successor.

A related but opposite concept is *accretion*. Under this concept, a buyer who has a represented work force and acquires a nonunionized work force or one represented by another union may be faced with an extension of the buyer's bargaining unit to the new employees without regard to the desires of the acquired employees.[5]

Unions can also have a role in decisions involved in making a corporate change. These decisions are divided into two categories: 'decision'—the actual decision to make a change and 'effect'—the decisions made as a result of a change. Generally the employer is not required to bargain about a decision to make a change unless the reason for the change is to reduce labor costs. This can be a complicated question when labor costs are one factor among many that are leading to the decision. On the other hand, employers are generally required to bargain about the effects of a decision to make a change. The union must receive reasonable notice of the change in order to prepare for bargaining, and changes may result in grievances.

One of the major challenges faced when acquiring another business is the merging of two cultures. Management and personnel policies of any organization are central to its operation and culture. One of the first things a new owner wants to do is establish its own policies. Although beyond the scope of this article, how this is done can have significant implications for all the issues discussed herein. Experienced labor counsel should be used to develop a strategy to establish new policies while maximizing the buyer's objectives with regard to any union, minimizing past liability, and preventing future lawsuits and other claims.

COMPENSATION AND BENEFITS

Compensation and benefits planning is one area in which practical issues and problems surface when a health care organization begins development of an expanded and integrated system. As the major cost factor in any labor intensive enterprise, pay levels are extremely important in the pricing of services. Pay affects any health care organization's marketplace competitiveness. This is most dramatic when a hospital is involved. In such a situation, there is a natural desire to maintain pay equity across the system at a level comparable to that of the hospital. This will often price activities such as home health or community clinics out of the market.

All organizations must determine what is the minimum it must pay to recruit and retain the level of qualified personnel needed to ensure a successful operation? This is a strategic marketplace issue, and the question facing the planners of any integrated system is whether or not to make this determination from the perspective of the individual entity within the system or from the perspective of the overall system. The key to how to decide this is the degree to which individual entities must stand on their own ''bottom line.''

The traditional factors that determine an individual's pay are market rates for comparable jobs, the internal value or worth of the job to the organization, and the performance of the individual. These are complicated by the business considerations noted above.

From the human resources perspective the question must be asked, ''How can an organization via its compensation system, facilitate the free flow of staff through an integrated system either to follow a specific patient or to work where the greatest patient care needs exist?'' A system can take three basic approaches to this issue, which are discussed below.

Individual Compensation Programs

With individual compensation programs, each entity within the system would have its own separate wage and salary administration program. Whether wage and salary administration is handled centrally or locally by each entity, the wage structure is individualized for each entity on the basis of competitive market rates and internal equity. As employees move through the system, they earn pay at different rates.

Advantages

This approach matches the ability of each entity to its own ability to pay. Pay rates, rules, and policies may be tailored to the specific issues presented by the operation of each specific entity. This approach also maximizes the specific entity's ability to price its services competitively.

Disadvantages

The most serious disadvantages of this approach are the reaction of employees and the complexity of administration. A variety of pay rates would be possible within a pay period, depending on scheduling within that period. Employees would also receive a separate W-4 form for each entity for which they worked during the tax year. This creates complexity for payroll personnel and for the tax reporting required for each entity.

In addition, there is the natural resistance of employees to such a situation. Most employees, even the most flexible, require more financial stability in their lives than this system would permit. Moreover, most employees find it difficult to accept that their work is "worth more" in some settings than others. One way to overcome this situation is to recruit new employees interested professionally in the concept of following patients through a continuum of care system with the understanding from the beginning of how their pay will be determined. A minimum monthly or annual salary could also be guaranteed if all entities are part of the same parent corporation.

Portable Compensation Package (Traditional)

In this approach a systemwide wage and salary program is developed measuring each job on the basis of traditional job evaluations. For example, in this system no distinction is made among nurses, and the organization decides what a nurse is "worth" and pays at that rate regardless of where the individual employee works within the system.

Advantages

The advantage of this system is its simplicity. Everyone, including the employee, knows what the employee will earn. Both wage and salary administration and payroll are simplified. In addition, scheduling is simplified: Pay ceases to be a concern for the organization, the department, or the employee.

Disadvantages

The primary disadvantage of this approach is the extra cost to the organization of paying for all jobs at the same rate regardless of the setting. Also, because of central payroll administration, there may be a greater possibility that specific wage hour regulations covering a particular setting may be overlooked. Financial success of the organization must be measured based on the finances of the overall system and not of individual entities within the system, which do not have total control over personnel costs. A method of accounting for each individual's hours and charging those hours back to the corporate entity receiving the service must be developed for accounting and financial purposes.

Portable Compensation Packages (Nontraditional)

In this approach an employee's pay remains constant as the employee moves through the system performing different kinds of work, but for a different reason than in the traditional approach. Here the basis of an employee's value to the employer is different. Instead of measuring the worth of the single job performed, the individual's ability to perform more than one job is measured and rewarded. In other words, the employer rewards flexibility and the ability to perform more than one task.

Advantages

Flexibility is the primary benefit. The system will develop a cadre of highly trained employees who can go where the work is. Also, overall costs may be lower as fewer employees are needed. The theory is that money is saved because the organization does not have to pay for specialists who wait around for their skills to be needed. This approach shares other advantages with the traditional approach, such as having a single compensation system and simpler payroll processing.

Disadvantages

The primary disadvantage with this approach is that it is new and will require a certain amount of experimentation to perfect. Currently, jobs are measured based on job content; it will require the development of new tools to measure the skills and abilities of people who perform multiple functions. Because this approach may only be appropriate for some jobs, many jobs, such as those in service and maintenance categories, will continue to be measured and payed in traditional ways.

This approach also shares some common disadvantages with the traditional approach. The complexity of central payroll processing may obscure certain setting-specific regulations. Also, the success of the organization must be measured on how the total organization performs, not just an individual entity.

As an example of this approach, an organization might train R.N.'s to be competent and functional in the areas of med-surg, rehabilitation, and home care so that they could work in all three areas with equal effectiveness and skill. A classification might be built on the concept of a ladder in that as nurses gain certain experiential and educational training, they move upward toward the goal of providing care in all three areas. Then this group of nurses would become a staffing source to be assigned to patients on the basis of need in a given area. Such a system would also permit a specific group of nurses to work with the same patients in different settings, depending on census and on staffing needs. Similar ladders might be developed in other areas of nursing where the grouping of clinical skills for the delivery of patient care is logical and appropriate to the needs of the system.

Another example is the creation of a health delivery system case manager role for a nurse who is proficient in acute outpatient rehabilitation, skilled nursing, and home care settings and who can act as a coordinator of patient care for a specific group of patients regardless of their health care needs within the system at any given time.

Other Compensation Issues

Human resource and other management personnel in health care will need to formulate new sets of compensation skills and programs as they participate in the evolution of new health care systems. In addition to the issues discussed above, the new business reality will require that health care organizations adapt techniques that have been used for years by other industries, such as pay delivery systems that incorporate profit or gain sharing, sales commissions, and other types of bonus and incentive plans. Business development, sales, and financial success will need to be rewarded. Many health care professionals will begin to demand a share of what they produce. As health care organizations recruit skilled specialists from other industries, such as marketing and sales, these personnel will bring with them expectations of incentive-based pay delivery systems. In fact, such arrangements as profit sharing or commissions on new business developed may be the "cost" of recruiting such individuals.

There are special issues for benefits administration as well. Typically, a system will maintain one pension plan for ease of administration, regulatory compliance, and funding. Complicated issues related to pension plan design and administration are beyond the scope of this chapter. Any continuum of care system considering a different approach should consult a qualified benefits and retirement plan attorney.

Another benefits issue for the human resource director to consider is managing the benefit plans of other entities within the system. In a hospital-based system, it is usually a relatively simple matter to add employees of a subsidiary company to the group benefits plan of the hospital. In these situations the human resources department can become a revenue producer by selling services to the subsidiary. Of course, such an arrangement would have to be acceptable to any insurance carrier involved and should fit into the organization's overall strategy regarding its status as a joint employer. Supplying benefit services can be very traumatic, and yet a very powerful tool for a human resource department. Alternatively, an independent subsidiary with the ability to "buy" services from any supplier and with its own financial objectives to meet can present a challenge. A human resources manager may for the first time need to justify the cost and value of his or her services. However, an in-house supplier has the potential to usually provide less expensive and more appropriate services. In such cases, the supplier's reputation within the organization is enhanced.

Another way of managing the compensation issues within a system is the use of intrasystem employee leasing by individual entities. For example, an independent, not-for-profit hospital might lease employees to a not-for-profit subsidiary operating a regional reference laboratory. Under this arrangement, the two corporations contract for staffing services at the reference lab and, as with other employee leasing arrangements, the lab pays the hospital a fee equivalent to the cost of salary and benefits plus administration, while the hospital assumes the legal obligations of hiring the employees, paying them, etc. This situation has several advantages for the subsidiary, which with the payment of a fee equivalent to its total personnel cost, can be staffed without putting in place a human resources system to do so.

Wage/Hour

Health care employers must comply with both state and federal wage/hour regulations. There is significant complexity inherent in health care settings not experienced by other industries; it is caused by providing around-the-clock services—in some cases emergency services—to patients.

A major wage/hour issue sometimes presented within the context of a health care system concerns joint employer status. Any time one employee works for or provides services and/or benefits to two or more entities, the question arises as to whether or not the hours worked by the employee must be aggregated for purposes of determining overtime liability and, in some cases, liability for payment in addition to minimum wages and for record keeping. The consequences of joint employer status are that "all hours worked by the employee during the work week for all the employers considered must be aggregated when determining the number of hours worked for wage/hour purposes. Joint employers are responsible for compliance both as individuals and jointly with all applicable wage/

hour requirements during the entire work week including minimum wage, overtime and record keeping.''[6]

There is one advantage of joint employer status which is that one entity may take full credit for all payments made by other entities considered joint employers. Accordingly, the determination of joint employer status will be made on the basis of all the relevant facts of a case and will be found if the work performed by the employee benefits each of the alleged joint employers or the employee works for each at different times during the week. The employers will be considered joint if there is an arrangement between the employers to share the employee's services, if one employer is acting directly or indirectly in the interest of the other employers in relation to the employee, or if each of the employers is under common control. It would be extremely difficult and ill-advised for a health care system either to employ a nurse in a rehabilitation unit and in a home care setting within a designated pay period, or alternatively to employ that nurse in one entity but schedule him or her to work in two entities within a pay period, and not aggregate hours of work for purposes of determining minimum wage and overtime.

A simple and effective way to avoid the problems of joint employer status is to ensure that each individual employee is an employee of only one entity within a system and is not allowed to be employed by different subsidiaries, ventures, or other entities. Of course, employees assigned by one entity to work in another will have their hours aggregated automatically for purposes of determining overtime and minimum wage when they are allowed to work for only one entity within the system. Another way of avoiding problems is to ensure that employees, when they move through the system on other than a scheduling assignment that would be considered temporary, have a formal transfer from one employer to the next or from one employing entity to the next.

Scheduling

Scheduling is one of the major activities in any health care business due to the labor intensive nature of providing health care over a 24-hour period. Scheduling within one entity, such as a hospital or a home care agency, is itself a significant task, much less scheduling for more than one entity, the prospect of which sends chills down the spines of staffing and scheduling coordinators everywhere. It redounds to the credit of these individuals that for years they have maintained scheduling systems without the aid of computerization. And indeed the computer is just finding its way into the scheduling systems and practices of health care.

Of primary concern, in addition to the needs of the employer, are the skills and preferences of the employees. Sharing and spreading of the staff will be successful within a system only if the personnel have skills appropriate for the positions. Health care professionals are acutely aware of their professional, legal, and ethical responsibilities to their patients. They will object to scheduling and staffing assignments that they believe are not consistent with their skills and abilities. In addition, health care professionals, like individuals in other walks of life, prefer doing certain kinds of work and may object to the hours or type of work in a given setting.

The employment system of organization plays a crucial role in the staffing and scheduling. To date, most health care systems have adopted an employment system allowing transfers within the health care system. Scheduling and staffing are done by each entity within that system. This requires making the job vacancies within the system known to employees and providing mechanisms that allow individuals to submit bids or applications for positions in different parts of the system.

Such an open transfer system is not required, and each individual entity within the system can recruit and staff individually. However, there are several advantages to maintaining a systemwide and open transfer system. First, it allows the human resources department to control and audit the selection systems within an organization and thereby helps management minimize the opportunities for mistakes that could lead to unintentional but expensive discrimination and other employment-related lawsuits. In addition, it allows an organization to restrain managers of one entity from raiding good employees of other entities.

No organization, department, or work unit likes to lose a good employee. But better they should be lost to another unit within the system than to the outside. An open system allows an organization to regulate the process of selection so that all parties are aware a transfer of an employee is possible and so that adequate time is provided to the department losing a good employee to recruit a replacement.

Other staffing and scheduling issues that are going to become more important to the future of health care involve job enrichment and job sharing. In these programs, individuals are trained to do more than one job within the system and may even be encouraged to share a given set of responsibilities with another employee. The purpose, of course, is to promote staffing flexibility within the system in order to match staffing (including both the skills and preferences of employees) with the needs of patients for any given day, week, or month. But whenever the issue arises of scheduling employees in more than one entity, subsidiary, joint venture, etc., within a health care system or of job sharing within such a system, employers are faced with the question of joint employer status, which may have serious consequences. Therefore, it is important that each health care system examine its potential liabilities and the consequences of joint employer status and strategies accordingly.

Joint Employer Status

As health care develops new corporate and legal relationships within systems (such as parent-subsidiaries, affiliates, and joint ventures) and engages in practices such as borrowing, loaning, or leasing employees to otherwise independent companies, increasing caution must be exercised toward the consequences of joint employer status. The finding of joint employer status can cause adverse consequences in the area of joint liability for labor law violations and of overtime liability for work performed for two or more entities, as well as for the expansion of bargaining units and for union contracts. This is an area where the pros and cons should be evaluated and a policy decision established and then periodically reviewed to ensure that policy matches reality.

For example, under the National Labor Relations Act the NLRB has long held that if two or more business entities are sufficiently integrated and exert significant control over the same employees, each entity will be treated as a joint employer for purposes of applying federal laws. The joint employer relationship arises in several contacts and can have devastating effects on employers. First, joint employers may be held jointly liable for unfair labor practices under the Act, even though only one of the employers may have played an active role in the illegal conduct. Second, a nonunion business entity found to be a joint employer with a union company may be obligated to apply the terms of that company's labor contract to its employees and bargain with the union. Finally, a joint employer might not be entitled to the protections of the secondary boycott provisions of the Act, which generally prohibit a union from picketing an employer not directly involved in a labor dispute.[7]

Another area of concern is employment discrimination, for an employee of a single employer may seek to include in a suit a parent or other related organization. Generally, this would occur when the employee names both the subsidiary and the parent corporation as defendants, seeking to hold both jointly liable. There may be many financial and legal reasons why including the parent corporation enhances the plaintiff's case. In separate organizations where an employee is on loan (e.g., scheduled to work for a separate employer for a period of time), the loaning employer can also be named in a lawsuit—for the same reasons as a parent corporation would be—to enhance the plaintiff's case. The plaintiff also will name a parent or other affiliated corporation where the immediate employing subsidiary does not have the requisite number of employees (15) to qualify for coverage under title VII. Finally, a joint employer status can be an issue under the Fair Labor Standards Act and state wage/hour law, as explained in the section ''Wage/Hour'' above.

Corporate Culture

One of the primary challenges facing chief executives developing a health care system is the managing of change. Developing a health care system involves consolidating providers and introducing new types of professionals, which creates tension and conflict and thus increases the need for conflict resolution and communication skills. It makes the development and implementation of personnel policy more complex. Moreover, it raises questions about management development and training. Enhancing and maintaining staff morale also become issues.

One of the most interesting phenomena in the development of health care is the rise of new types of professionals, new health care needs, and new relationships faced by traditional professionals. For example, in joint ventures, hospitals and physicians become, technically at least, consolidated providers, and this may result in the spreading of the traditional but heretofore rare phenomenon of the physician as manager. Physicians who are excellent clinically may not be prepared to act as managers in the modern complex world of employee regulation and employee rights. In addition, health care is employing for the first time people in sales, marketing, and other entrepreneurial activities.

Sources of conflict for traditional health care managers are almost unlimited in today's health care system. Not only do they face competition from new individuals (such as sales and marketing staff, whose skills they cannot match), but the development of a system itself may put managers in decision-making roles fraught with ethical and legal conflicts. One essential need, then, in management will be to develop conflict resolution skills and programs designed to help managers understand and deal with the host of new conflicts. For example, when a health care system develops an HMO, it will encourage its own employees to join the HMO while simultaneously the hospital entity in the system, as a provider, will be negotiating with the HMO for services and prices.

In addition to management development needs, these types of potential conflict increase the need for communication. Too often a narrow view is taken of communication and the focus is only on managers. Although it is important that managers know when change is occurring, so that they can both communicate the change to their subordinates and also manage the change, they also need to know where the organization is "coming from." During the development of a health care system, communication about organizational philosophy and direction is essential. What are the strategic and other business objectives of the organization? What is the organization's philosophy and how does it apply in a given situation?

These are communication issues that need to be addressed not just once but continually throughout the building of a system—almost as part of every management communication effort. Managers throughout the system are going to be making decisions that will create conflicts for other managers within the system; therefore, all managers, all decisionmakers, need to know how their decisions fit within the overall scheme of the organization. The fact is that employees and managers will find themselves working in new and cooperative relationships with each other (not necessarily with their consent), and turf issues and misunderstood priorities will limit effectiveness.

Conflict resolution needs are great at the staff level as well. Corporate culture and employee communication are created and facilitated in three ways: first, through an organization's policies and handbooks; second, through how decisions, policies, and rules are carried out, especially by managers; finally, through the examples set by managers as they carry out their responsibilities within the organization.

Communication efforts in these three areas are imperative if changes necessary to create a health care system are going to be made in ways that enhance the organization's values, provide a framework for conflict resolution, limit unnecessary ambiguity, and keep employees from looking to outside third parties for protection. For example, personnel policies and handbooks should be kept up-to-date and revised as needed. Managers should be given sufficient training about changes in policy and application before those changes occur so that they are able to carry out new policies effectively. And finally, the organization needs to have conflict resolution procedures for employees who disagree with the way policies that affect them are being applied by their managers.

The development of a health care system also provides hospitals and other health care employers with some things that they have not had in previous years, namely, more opportunities for management development, career paths, and succession planning for managers. A recurring problem that top management will face is the decision whether to select appropriate individuals from the outside for a new business venture or to develop internal talent to handle it.

CASE EXAMPLE

In 1985, Community Hospital was feeling pressured to discharge patients quickly, and at the same time it was facing declining census and loss of revenues. The hospital decided to purchase American Home Care, a for-profit home health agency. In reviewing the financial statements, American seemed to operate according to Medicare regulations, and it made a small profit as allowable return on equity. More importantly, American had the potential to generate additional revenues for Community Hospital's for-profit subsidiary through new lines of business in durable medical equipment, high-technology home therapy, and a private home care business. Furthermore, the hospital expected to offer attractive continuity of care to patients and additional work to its underutilized clinical staff, who would follow patients from the hospital into the home. The legal, financial, and accounting implications of the purchase were reviewed by the appropriate administrators and advisors of the hospital. The presidents of the two companies came to agreement quickly, board approval was given, and the purchase completed.

As Community Hospital began to take over the business, human relations problems emerged. It was quickly discovered that none of the employees of either organization had been involved in the discussions about merging. The discharge planners of the hospital usually referred home care patients to the Visiting Nurses Association (VNA). After many years of interacting with the

VNA and developing personal familiarity with the staff, the discharge planners were not enthusiastic about changing to American. They felt that quality of care might suffer.

When the hospital informed the nursing staff that those who were on the list for potential lay-off or decreased hours could sign up for home care training, the majority of the nurses rejected the offer. The inpatient nurses informed the vice-president of nursing care in no uncertain terms that they elected the setting because they preferred to work at a single location, liked the excitement of high-technology care, and enjoyed having the support of other staff immediately available. The nurses of the hospice unit, who had been seeing patients in their homes on their own time—as friends rather than professionals—were somewhat pleased that they could now continue their visits, but receive pay and be covered by the hospital's liability insurance. However, they rebelled at the idea that their patients would be charged by the home care program for these visits. The hospital staff also resented the fact that the home care staff, although now a part of the hospital's organization, came to work at 8:30 or 9:00 A.M. instead of promptly at 8:00 A.M., wore whatever they wanted instead of uniforms, and set their own schedules.

The employees of the home health agency were as concerned and resentful as the staff of the hospital. They had not been aware that the president was negotiating the sale of the agency. When they found out, they feared that the hospital would impose major changes. Most considered resigning on the spot; many started sending out their resumes and signing up with temporary agencies—just in case things didn't work out. The staff were annoyed when the senior administrators from the hospital informed them that they would have to follow a dress code; they were furious when they learned that the hospital's allowable payment for mileage was 20 cents per mile instead of the 22 cents they had been receiving.

In attempting to reconcile their human relations problems, Community Hospital and American Home Care realized that they would have to revise the employee orientation of both groups (including by accurately describing relationships, by explaining internal referral procedures, etc.), revise and standardize personnel policies, and rewrite and reprint the employee handbooks. Although legally the hospital and home health agency could have maintained distinct operating policies, for achieving staff satisfaction it was imperative to be consistent.

In addition to precise changes in policies, the two organizations realized that they needed to make a conscious effort to educate and to improve relationships between the two staffs. A joint employee relations committee was formed. An afternoon reception was held from 2:00–4:00 P.M. Although it reached only two of the three nursing shifts and many home care staff found it difficult to get in from the field, at least some staff had a chance to meet. Moreover, the publicity provided a good basis for starting to create good will. The hospital's monthly newsletter featured a story on a hospital nurse and a home health nurse who had shared the care of one of the hospital's best-known patients. The position of *liaison nurse* was created, and home health nurses rotated at attending daily rounds of the nursing floors likely to refer the most patients. The home health nurses were invited to tour the hospital and the hospital nurses to tour the home health agency. A joint education program was arranged, with continuing education credits available. The joint employee relations committee planned and conducted social and professional programs for an entire year that were designed specifically to attract members of both staffs.

Wage and salary levels, as well as fringe benefits, also had to be standardized. The fringe benefit programs were different. For example, at American the staff had ten holidays per year, including their birthday. At the hospital, staff received eight recognized holidays per year, plus two "floating" holidays. But permission to take a floating holiday had to be arranged with a supervisor, and acceptance depended upon the level of activity, other staff on vacation, etc. Thus, the home health staff found that predictable holidays were not automatic.

Also, the home health agency gave salary increases according to each employee's anniversary date; the hospital gave them to everyone at the start of the new fiscal year. The hospital gave automatic cost of living increases and had recently installed a system of bonuses determined by performance. The home health agency had used routine, but not very strict, performance evaluation criteria and had given raises across the board, with steps for seniority.

Perhaps the biggest issue was job classification and wage parity. The pay scales for nursing staff, therapists, and administrators were quite different for the hospital and home health agency. Moreover, determining appropriate similarities and differences proved to be difficult. The hospital, as expected, had the greatest number of employees in each category and had access to industry standards. The home health field, however, had less sophisticated nationwide salary scales and job classification systems. Some of the job categories in home health, such as a homemaker, did not even exist in the hospital. The hospital had a human relations department responsible for handling such matters, but none of the staff was familiar with home health. Thus, the home health agency administrators spent a great deal of time educating the staff of the human relations department. In the end, constructing an appropriate pay scale to acknowledge the similarities and differences among home care staff required six months of effort by the human relations department of the hospital.

When the private home care service was started, yet additional wage and salary scales had to be constructed. Administering personnel activities and keeping records also proved to be more complicated than initially anticipated. One of the advantages for the home health agency in joining with the hospital was the streamlining of administrative functions, which had become unwieldy for the home health agency as it had outgrown the efficiency of a paper system.

In order to take advantage of the hospital's computerized personnel system, the home health agency had to convert the content and format of its timecards, travel reports, vacation and time-off reports, and task records. Even the pay period had to be adjusted. The accounting staff of the hospital had to educate the clerical and clinical staff of the home health agency about how to prepare the required records accurately. The staff of the home health agency had to work with accounting, human resources, and information systems staff to incorporate home health measures into the hospital-oriented systems. In the short-term, separate systems were maintained. However, both the hospital and the home health agency recognized that, for the long-run, total integration would be necessary to streamline and achieve cost efficiencies and quality in the reporting for all systems.

Two major problems, each of which had significant legal and financial implications, were discovered after the sale had been completed. First, a discrimination suit had been brought against the home health agency by a former employee. Although at the time of the sale the president had won, the employee subsequently appealed. The hospital was then responsible for the outcome of this case. Second, the home health agency pension program had been started prior to the Employee Retirement Income Security Act (ERISA). The hospital's pension program had also been started prior to ERISA, and had very different terms. Combining the two pension funds turned out to be difficult.

A final problem was employee performance. The hospital had purchased the home health agency in one of its for-profit subsidiaries with an agreement not to terminate any of the employees, including the senior management team, for a minimum of one year. Shortly after the purchase, the president of the for-profit subsidiary realized the senior management team were going to be a problem, for it became apparent their supervisory skills, general knowledge of the health care field, and orientation to productivity were not consistent with the standards of the for-profit operation. Yet the president was unable to take any action for fear of legal recourse. After waiting a year, during which time leadership was weak and even detrimental, all senior managers were let go. The cost to the organization of carrying these high salaries for a year, plus the payment of many years of accrued vacation and benefits, was great, not to mention the cost of a year of ineffectual operation. Had the hospital known, it would have negotiated different terms and financial conditions during the purchase negotiations.

Eventually, all of the personnel problems were resolved. However, the integration would have been much easier for the staffs (managers and clinicians) of both organizations had the human relations aspects been considered in advance. In addition, the collaborative effort would have had a more successful business performance had the subjective and objective concerns of staff been resolved early on.

In summary, it is strongly recommended that health care organizations considering merger, joint venture, purchase, or other forms of collaboration, examine the human relations aspects well in advance of establishing final formal relationships.

NOTES

1. Stephen Erf and Julie Bodel, *Hospital Restructuring: Employment Law Pitfalls* (Chicago, Ill.: Plumbus Press, Inc., and American College of Hospital Administrators), 8.
2. Ibid., 12.
3. Ibid., 11.
4. Ibid., 26.
5. Ibid., 21.
6. Richard J. Simmons and Frank H. Smith, *Wage and Hour Manual for California Employees*, 2nd ed. (Van Nuys, Calif.: Castle Publications, Ltd.), 89.
7. Erf and Bodel, *Hospital Restructuring*, 82.

Chapter 11

Marketing the Continuum of Care

William C. McMorran, MDiv

Marketing is a critical element within a continuum of care. The key element of any marketing effort is the ability of the organization to understand the concept thoroughly and then translate it into a clear message. Ideally, this clear message will make the concept appropriate to several diverse audiences, who will then utilize the service. All of this is easier said than done, because a continuum of care is something with which most people are not familiar.

Professionals continue to wrestle with the concept and definition of a continuum of care. Consumers, already confused by a rapidly changing health care marketplace, are often lost at the outset. The complexity of services that are being considered as part of the specific continuum further increases the difficulty in communicating precisely what the agency or institution is offering.

In developing a marketing plan for the continuum of care, there are several basic issues that must be considered. Who is the audience? Will the marketing reach them as ''brokers'' or consumers? Will the services be presented as a comprehensive package (bundled) or as a series of packages that users can pick and choose from (unbundled)? Obviously, marketing is closely related to planning. How the organization deals with the marketing and planning process of the continuum is a critical element in the long-term success of the organization.

An organization that commits itself to developing a continuum of care must deal with unfamiliarity, uncertainty, complexity, and change. It will have to move steadily and resolutely forward, providing education and an ongoing flow of information to increase understanding of the continuum while at the same time building internal and external confidence through reliable performance and honest communication.

The following chapter deals with these issues in more depth and subsequently illustrates how a continuum of care marketing plan might be developed in spite of the difficulties.

A BASIC MARKETING APPROACH

A marketing plan for a continuum of care does not, like Athena, spring forward instantly from Zeus. Rather, marketing must begin when the organization determines that it will develop a continuum of care. The basic questions that are integral to any marketing effort will influence the eventual shape of the overall continuum effort.

The elements in successfully marketing a continuum of care rely on the traditional marketing steps, which include the following:

- setting goals
- determining target markets
- defining product(s) and price and then exploring potential market niches
- preparing a marketing plan and outlining the required resources
- defining the marketing source of reference, including
  —marketing tools
  —marketing techniques
  —internal markets
  —external markets
- implementing the plan
- evaluating and revising services and marketing as necessary

SETTING GOALS AND MEASURABLE OBJECTIVES

An effective marketing effort depends upon having an initial goal for the program clearly specified and agreed upon. The range of goals and objectives often giving impetus to a continuum is discussed in Chapter 5.

The goal of the program to be marketed must be consistent with the organization's overall focus and definition. Otherwise the disparity between the program and the organization will undercut the impact and success of the marketing effort. This can only harm the overall organization.

TARGETING THE MARKET

Those who need to understand the concept for a continuum of care include the internal staff, the leadership and senior administration, and the constituent population. Today's health care and social service agencies are increasingly market-driven. In earlier times, physicians were the primary brokers of health care services, while families and friends made referrals to social service agencies. This is in contrast to today's market, where the current environment is highly competitive and the target markets are increasingly diverse and complex.

Organizations are recognizing that to attain and maintain the desired market share, their services and style of operation must be responsive to the consumer. This is critical for a market-driven industry. Thus, one of the organization's goals, applicable to its overall mission and to the continuum in particular, might be to increase its sensitivity and responsiveness to its market.

A second factor that prompts health care and social service agencies to give more attention to marketing is the rapidly changing environment. Heightened competition, changing financing requirements, expansion and diversification, tightened regulations—all of these force service providers to be highly attuned and responsive to their environment. Marketing includes analysis of and responsiveness to the environment as well as particular market audiences.

The spectrum of services contained in a full continuum of care exceeds the capability of almost all organizations. Hence, collaboration with other providers in the community is necessary in order to assure clients access to the full range of health care and social services. An awareness of other community service providers, both potential collaborators and competitors, is essential in achieving a comprehensive service program. Thus, such awareness must be incorporated into the initial market analysis.

The overall goal of an organization in expanding into a continuum of care may simply be stated: to provide high-quality, financially viable services that are responsive to consumer demand, the community, and the changing environment. This goal may be relatively new for many service providers, as it requires an emphasis on marketing that has been previously absent.

Whatever the goals, they must be clearly articulated and include measurable objectives. How an organization formulates and evaluates the results of its marketing campaign will depend on the specific objectives to be accomplished and the ways in which success is to be measured. A continuum of care defined its goal as follows: to be a creative, responsive, and supportive service organization providing a broader range of services than the more focused agencies in the community.

The starting point of a marketing effort is to define the purpose of the organization in a simple statement, which can then be used as a basis for marketing to several diverse target groups. Once the goals of the organization are defined, the goals and objectives of the marketing program should follow. These, too, need to be precisely stated.

CASE EXAMPLE

Imagine an agency funded in part from public donations and in part from fees. It is committed to acting as a community focal point for older adult services that are designed to help older persons avoid or postpone nursing home utilization. There are several diverse service providers in its service area, but none provide the level of case management that this agency does.

The starting point of the actual marketing plan begins by developing the primary goal and the objectives. The goal of the organization through its marketing objective is to firmly establish the continuum of care in the community as a creative, responsive, and supportive service organization, one that enhances the work of other, more focused service agencies.

The specific objectives of the model project are as follows:

1. to increase utilization of the continuum of care by older adults
2. to maximize consumer utilization while monitoring staff workloads for effective service delivery
3. to expand agency contacts in the community, particularly in previously underserved sections of the target community
4. to enhance the role of the advisory council (a representative group of community leaders and clients)
5. to establish a viable base for the continuum of care's ongoing outreach activities through community participation
6. to establish a structure for determining consumer satisfaction and feedback

These objectives represent fundamental issues that can be adapted to any marketing plan. Once basic objectives are in place, usually after thorough consideration and planning with project managers, the marketing work begins.

There are several different audiences the continuum of care must address in establishing a clearly defined program concept. Based on their proximity to and awareness of the continuum of care, they are the following:

- the continuum's internal staff
- the leadership and staff of the parent organization
- the continuum's advisory council
- community service agencies (providers of services)
- community social workers, such as case managers or discharge planners (managers of care)
- existing clients
- community residents and potential clients

Each of these groups must come to understand the continuum of care in its own terms, but in a way that is consistent with all of the other groups. Establishing this commonality is a goal of the marketing plan. It also is the foundation for future success in outreach and for subsequent service growth with respect to the group in question (or any other).

The first step in addressing the above audiences is to begin outreach to key broker groups one at a time, but as quickly as possible. The ranking of these groups in order of approach may vary depending upon several planning decisions. In the case of the continuum of care, it might reach them progressively as follows:

1. physicians
2. hospitals
3. community service agencies
4. city, county, and state employees in aging and disabled services
5. direct consumers
6. adults who have older parents
7. prepaid health plans

This order is based on the strength of existing ties and the potential for each group to assist the continuum in achieving its marketing goals.

In approaching these audiences, operational questions that need to be asked at the outset include the following:

- What are the needs in the community?
  —Demographics: Is there an audience?
  —Competition: Is anyone else doing it and how well?
  —Payment mechanisms: Is it worth it?
  —Decisionmakers: Who must be reached to increase use of the service?
- What are the operational issues?
  —Internal staff understanding: Do we know what the product is?
  —Resources for promotion and outreach: How much money and time? What staff skills are needed? How can we educate everyone about the product in a nonthreatening way?
  —What do we want to accomplish?
  —How will we know if we are successful?
- How should the product be designed?
  —As a package of services (bundled) or a series of single product items (unbundled)?
  —As a product or a service?
  —For one-time use or for an ongoing series of uses?

In confronting these basic management issues, the marketing plan can begin to take shape. The following market product definition outlines how a community service provider of case management services might develop an outreach effort.

PRODUCT DEFINITION

Plan Overview

In preparing a market plan, it is important to conceptualize the overall approach, one that crystallizes the planning effort and suggests a range of activities that can fulfill the stated goals and objectives. The beginning is important, for it shapes subsequent steps. The following overview represents the approach used by the model community case management agency considered in the previous section.

The proposed marketing plan takes an evolutionary approach that is designed to establish a strong and growing community base for the continuum of care, helping it to establish a strong market share, which is the primary goal. It is a progressive plan and builds steadily, designed not only to achieve the immediate objectives but to assure a steady series of positive results over the duration of the continuum of care program.

As a starting point, it is necessary to define the purpose of the continuum of care in a simple statement, which can then be used as a basis for outreach to several diverse target brokerage groups that have been already identified. The effort spent in defining and applying the continuum of care concept will also be of benefit for more general outreach activities among the several diverse audiences that the continuum must address. However, these are of secondary importance, as they only strengthen the continuum's primary marketing. If key decisionmakers are aware of the continuum's services and make referrals, there will be more than ample demand, while at the same time staff screening will be minimized because of the quality of those referrals.

Prior to exploring the specific approaches to each of the above brokerage groups and outlining how each of the objectives will be achieved, it is necessary to consider the several audiences to be addressed, the resources to be developed, and the marketing framework. In doing this, it is important to recognize that a continuum of care is not a simple product. In any market analysis, consideration must be given to exploring what impact the concept of the continuum might have on the definition of the theme, or to what extent a single theme should be emphasized. There may need to be some experimentation. Also, the use of focus groups may be more advantageous than broader-based surveys, such as those involving interviews or mail responses.

Timeframe, Budget, and Resources

The final steps in implementing a successful marketing plan are the preparations of the formal budget and the timeframe. Both should be reasonable reflections of the actual plan. Nothing is more detrimental than to establish grandiose plans without sufficient budget or time to carry those plans forward.

There are three key elements in considering the budget. They are (1) money, (2) staff, and (3) leadership. The financial budget is only one part of the whole. Once the plan begins to take shape, basic questions concerning staff, leadership, time, and capability become budget issues as well. Careful consideration in each of these areas is necessary to build a workable plan in a reasonable timeframe.

PLANNING CONSIDERATIONS

Required Resources

In order to accomplish the proposed marketing effort successfully, there are basic resources that must be established. The following discussion outlines these resources.

Marketing Techniques (Internal)

There are several internal questions that must be addressed in orienting staff and establishing an operating base. They include the following:

- What will the concept and program be named?
- Where will the program be located within the structure of the organization?
- Will an advisory committee be established to lend authority, credibility, and technical insights?
- How will the concept be introduced to staff?
- Should the concept be presented to the board, and if so, how?
- Are ongoing educational efforts required internally?

The review of these issues will always have territorial, budgetary, and political overtones. It is important to define the product clearly for everyone so that they can see that the plan is not a threat to them. They need to perceive the project as beneficial to their efforts and not simply as something that will add to their workload or detract from their patient load, staff, or budget.

Market Framework

The market framework is a result of the internal market effort. It is essentially the unfolding of the marketing effort based upon its goals and objectives. It entails

- initially defining a common message among the several target audiences
- establishing a strong relationship with the several brokers who act on behalf of potential clients (to support this effort requires personal contact and education or briefing sessions backed up by useful resources)
- building momentum and support as community recognition increases and expanding the focus of outreach efforts to additional target audiences
- monitoring the effectiveness of the marketing plan and levels of service and adjusting the implementation of outreach efforts accordingly in order to have a strong base for the future

Like the marketing plan itself, the marketing framework is progressive.

Marketing Techniques (External)

Once movement is underway, basic methods of outreach must be examined. The following discusses several basic options.

1. *Promotional Brochure.* A basic brochure clearly delineates the purpose of the project, defines the service area, and encourages individual follow-up through a simple, direct response mechanism. It might include a postage-paid card and/ or a telephone number.

The purpose of this brochure is twofold. In marketing the continuum to brokers, it is necessary for them to have something they understand to hand out to the individuals they are referring. In the absence of such a handout, or if it is too complex to be readily understood, the brokers will be far less likely to make referrals. Similarly, the brochure can partly define the corporate concept of the continuum, helping all of the internal and external audiences to share a common perception of the program.

The brochure is also crucial for reaching the general public. A secondary product of the overall marketing effort will be heightened visibility. This increases requests for information. The availability of a well-designed brochure and a prompt response further enhances a continuum's public credibility.

2. *Targeted Informational Bulletins.* In reaching the several diverse audiences, particularly the key broker groups, a single-page bulletin on timely issues may often prove effective. By segmenting the market, a project can get optimal return for minimal time and cost. In developing the bulletin, design a common masthead and use particular colors of paper for specific target groups in order to keep each separate for analysis of which target groups were more responsive to the bulletin.

Initially, a regular mailing should be made to community service providers updating them on critical issues to help them work more efficiently. The bulletin can include agency-specific information as well as serve as a community "bulletin board" for other related services.

Over time, specialized bulletins can be developed for families, other health care groups, membership, etc. In the meantime, back issues of bulletins can be used as informational handouts for other professionals to illustrate the agency's community involvement and services.

3. *General Newsletter.* A general newsletter can be considered. Newsletters are useful for fund raising, general visibility, and maintenance of an organization's membership base. The effectiveness of a newsletter is often in direct proportion to the time spent writing and designing it. If the agency seeks to build a provider network, must compete with a multitude of other community groups for the elderly, and does not have a formal membership, then development of a newsletter would not be an effective marketing mechanism. Bulletins provide a much better focus and are more likely to be read by key community decision-makers or brokers.

4. *Introductory and Technical Columns.* In order to explore the concept further and increase community awareness at an early stage, brief introductory columns on the project in the organization's newsletter and other publications are effective. More important, presentations to area professional organizations and information pieces in appropriate journals allow a preview of public response. This in turn allows time to fine-tune the organization's image before developing a large-scale campaign.

5. *Newspaper Coverage.* The organized development of consistent human interest stories sent not only to major newspapers but to local weeklies and shoppers' specials creates crucial local awareness. This is further enhanced by ensuring that regular information is given to all community calendar sections and "What's Going On" columns in the appropriate publications.

Much is made of print advertising. Wars have literally erupted in the pages of newspapers as institutions engage in reactive advertising, seeking to outdo each other through the use of large advertising budgets. This is not effective use of resources over the long term. Paid advertising is best used sparingly, mainly to announce special events or major product introductions.

6. *Radio and Television.* Public service announcements are occasionally effective. The difficulties in promoting a continuum are further magnified in trying to make it understandable in thirty seconds. A total media campaign can be very expensive and for minimal return. This is especially true if many of the people who see the campaign live outside of the target service area.

7. *People.* The initial and enduring strength of any continuum is its leadership and staff participants. This is true for marketing at its beginning and its conclusion. There will be a growing nucleus of people who understand and support the continuum, which is critical in any evolutionary marketing effort. If a service is to succeed, people must understand the program's services, support its goals and objectives, and then tell others about its benefits.

In most successful service programs, a minimum of one-third of the referrals are by word-of-mouth. The development of a strong word-of-mouth campaign is the underlying key to the success of a continuum of care. The resources available to an organization through its supporters constitute a vast, untapped potential. The issue is whether the concept of the continuum can be defined, packaged, and implemented well enough to unleash that potential.

In developing this resource, there is an established progression, which is based on each of the several audiences that the agency must address. Each of these audiences can become major supporters of the program. Each of them requires a different approach. But when they understand the program and carry forward its concept, many cross-links among the several groups will evolve.

Such synergism does not happen spontaneously. It must evolve through hard work and ongoing outreach. Still, potential for the development of active support must exist if the continuum is to be effective.

THE MARKETING GOAL AND OBJECTIVES

In applying all of this to the model agency under consideration, the following marketing approach might be developed.

Goal

The goal of this marketing effort is to firmly establish the continuum of care program in the community as a creative, responsive and supportive service organization, one that enhances the work of other, more focused service agencies. Central to this goal is the overall effectiveness of the continuum of care effort itself. If the program is not creative, responsive, or supportive, the marketing program will not be effective. Thus, it is important to recognize at the outset that the creative and effective implementation of the continuum program is the critical element in a successful marketing campaign. Before substantial outreach occurs, the continuum program must be poised to fulfill what it claims to make available.

Objectives

1. *Increase utilization of the continuum of care by older adults.* In measuring a program's effectiveness, a key determinant is the number of persons assisted. The continuum seeks to expand its client base among specific population groups as required by its board. The marketing plan will meet this objective by (a) establishing a common perception of the program among diverse audiences, and (b) directing specific, personalized outreach efforts to the key brokers who make decisions on behalf of, or provide direction to, potential clients. The specificity of the latter strategy anticipates that some populations are easier to reach than others and that there may be subsequent changes in policies or target audiences. The continuum will have the ability to modify its outreach as appropriate.

2. *Maximize consumer utilization while monitoring staff workloads for effective service delivery.* A simple outreach program (e.g., an advertisement in the major area newspapers or a television public service announcement, if it was ever used), might result in countless follow-up calls. However, the vast majority of those calls would not produce appropriate clients. Moreover, a great deal of staff time would be wasted in answering calls and determining possible eligibility. This would harm the continuum program in several ways:

- Respondents would have difficulty getting through in the first place.
- Telephones and staff would be tied up fielding calls and thus unable to carry forward ongoing tasks.

- The majority of those who did get through would be disappointed or, worse, frustrated.
- Other community groups would see or hear of the ad and make inaccurate assumptions about the continuum.
- The continuum's image as a caring and responsive group would be damaged.

These circumstances are to be avoided at all costs! Thus, the proposed mar-‾ keting plan allows for a more specific and orderly implementation effort. By reaching the brokers, the continuum can use their expertise in screening potential clients. A specialized screening instrument, modifying the existing material, is to be developed. The target brokers can also be used to monitor referrals and provide back-up support, thereby optimizing staff efficiency.

3. *Expand agency contacts in the community, particularly in the newer service locations.* Working with community service agencies is a complex problem. Each of them is in competition for funding, clients, visibility and recognition. Nonetheless, they are committed to the well-being of their client populations and generally are able to overcome parochial differences if their clients can benefit. Each agency staff's initial perception of another organization's ability often colors their relationship for years. Thus, the continuum must work quickly to establish good relationships in the communities it serves—by delivering what it promises.

There are several ways to accomplish this, including the following:

- affiliation with respected centralized institutions such as the local area agency on aging
- outreach through individuals who are already held in esteem
- careful evaluation of each agency's needs and interests and a subsequent contact to reinforce how the continuum can assist it in its work
- quality service, including a quick response and ongoing communication and follow-up whenever an actual referral is made

These strategies should be incorporated in the proposed plan. In trying to develop a consistent message across several diverse audiences, positive word-of-mouth outreach will greatly enhance acceptance by local agencies. Further, effective coordination with the continuum's advisory council will facilitate acceptance.

4. *Enhance the role of the advisory council.* Advisory councils often merely rubber-stamp funding or policy guidelines set elsewhere. Allowing this is a disservice to the council participants and to the project itself. The continuum advisory council is an important resource for honing the program structure, guidelines, and services. It is also a critical link to several diverse audiences and can help validate and make understandable the continuum's mission and operations. The role of the advisory committee can be enhanced to include

- review and discussion of the marketing concept
- refinement of concrete actions and priorities
- interpretation of the continuum to the community
- implementation as appropriate
- feedback and analysis of impact and success
- adjustments as appropriate

The first step in this process is a special briefing and discussion of the planned changes with the advisory council.

5. *Establish a viable base for the continuum's ongoing outreach activities through community participation.* One measure of a continuum's success is its ability to provide timely and specific services to clients in order for them no longer to require its support services. This necessitates an ongoing marketing effort that is integrated into routine operations. The initial marketing effort must develop the necessary community participation base in such a way that it can be smoothly integrated into overall future operations. The outreach activities to the brokers, the continuum of outreach, and the involvement of continuum staff and participants will be the key to developing and maintaining this base.

6. *Establish a structure for determining consumer satisfaction and feedback.* While there are several evaluative criteria available to quantify the effectiveness of a continuum, it is also necessary to monitor its qualitative aspects as well. Client satisfaction, broker confidence, and the overall perception of the program must be evaluated. To accomplish this requires formal survey work and an operating grievance procedure in which complaints are monitored and analyzed.

More important though, monitoring consumer satisfaction requires the continuum's staff to maintain a steady, direct, ongoing relationship with the several publics that use it. This provides an early-warning system that allows staff not only to anticipate any issues that might arise, but to maintain the relationship, to strengthen the continuum's reputation, and in effect to further extend its visibility and effectiveness.

Follow-up is also a way of capturing the market for future use. Even though clients may resolve their needs, future problems may prompt them once again to seek assistance. If the continuum retains contact, even with a device as simple as a birthday card or semiannual telephone call, the client is likely to use the continuum once again when a need occurs.

OPERATIONAL PLANS

A major activity to be undertaken is the development of the basic brochure. This includes finalization of the thematic approach, writing copy, layout and design, and printing. While the design of the brochure will be influenced by existing materials, feedback from meetings with key broker groups will also affect the final product.

Once brochure activities are underway, the bulletin format can be determined. This includes designing the masthead and developing a routine production schedule. From the outset of public contact, specialized mailing lists of the key broker groups should be developed. This is important to ensure that there is a specific audience for each bulletin and that copy is relevant to the group's needs.

Production of the bulletins will be straightforward once the masthead and format are determined, for each bulletin only involves having a single sheet typed and copied. The initial circulation of these bulletins will not exceed two hundred copies. Any more would defeat the personalized target approach that is necessary. Most production costs will be part of normal overhead. Further, content should be solicited from project staff. It not only keeps them involved but assures that the contents will be relevant to operations.

A Model Approach

To indicate how an operational plan will work specifically for a continuum of care, consider the steps in approaching hospital social service workers or discharge planners.

A meeting with these individuals at one hospital already familiar with the continuum will be held quickly. At that meeting the work of the continuum will be described, questions will be answered, and a revised screening format will be introduced. (This format will assist the staff in making appropriate referrals.) At the same time, a list of target hospitals will be developed for further follow-up and meetings. Priority will be given to the newer service areas. Finally, contact will be made and meetings held. All of the meeting participants will be added to the hospital broker list.

A similar pattern will be carried forward in developing each of the identified broker groups. Each of the groups will be progressively larger and less centralized, except for the final target. This is why the plan is progressive. Bringing each group on board positions the continuum to take the next step, using the experience it is acquiring to become more efficient while at the same time increasing the number of supporters using the program.

In working with each group, the continuum's staff will draw in key people to help establish contact and build rapport. Moreover, as the nucleus builds, there is increasing potential for secondary outreach activities involving public media. For example, an article on how participating hospitals have a unique service to offer patients is more likely to be used than an article purely on the continuum. Not only does it include major institutions, but the continuum can engage the skills of hospital PR staff in getting the article written and printed.

SUMMARY

As the above suggests, there are several common elements to all successful marketing plans. The example concerned a community agency's efforts to develop market penetration using a limited budget. The same marketing plan can be adapted to a major health provider's national campaign. Basically all that changes is the budget for advertising and promotion, although of course the level of staffing necessary to carry the campaign forward simultaneously at several levels must be substantially increased. Nothing can replace the need for

- careful evaluation and planning at the outset
- a clearly defined statement of what the organization is attempting to do
- a basic informational piece that can be used by diverse audiences
- a commitment on the part of the service provider to provide personalized, quality service

These are the keys to success in marketing any continuum of care.

REFERENCES

American College of Healthcare Executives. *Healthcare Executive* 1, no. 1 (November–December 1985).

Cooper, Phillip D., and Robinson, Larry M. *Health Care Marketing Management: A Case Approach.* Rockville, Md.: Aspen Publishers, 1982.

Kotler, Philip. *Marketing for Nonprofit Organizations.* Englewood Cliffs, N.J.: Prentice-Hall, 1975.

MacStravic, Robin E. *Marketing Health Care.* Rockville, Md.: Aspen Publishers, 1977.

Uchi, Theresa I., and Studin, Ira. "Marketing In Business And Health Care Organizations." Center for Health Management Research Working Paper Series, no. 4. 1982.

Winston, William J., ed. *Marketing Long-Term and Senior Care Services.* New York: The Haworth Press, 1984.

Part III
Integrating Mechanisms

Without integration and coordination, the continuum of care is merely a series of fragmented services collected under an organizational umbrella. In addition to the coordinated structure described in Part II, management information systems, care management, and integrated financing systems are essential. At the present time, these systems are still quite new. Few good examples exist, let alone organizations that have all of them in place and fully refined.

The chapters in this part describe the ideal and the issues that must be confronted in getting there. It should be noted that the evolution of the systems is not always synchronized, and thus the development itself may pose its own set of (temporary) problems. The benefits of efficient management systems are mainly assumed, although supported by a small amount of empirical evidence. Once the systems are installed and operating, concrete research is needed to test the effects of the continuum of care on quality, financial performance, and consumer satisfaction.

Chapter 12

Financing and Delivery of Long-Term Care Services for the Elderly

Carol O'Shaughnessy, MA
Richard Price, MA

At least 80 federal programs assist persons with long-term care problems, either directly or indirectly through cash assistance, in-kind transfers, or the provision of goods and services. Among these 80 programs, 5 are generally considered to be the major programs of federal support for long-term care: Medicaid, Medicare, the Social Services Block Grant (SSBG) program, the Older Americans Act program, and the Supplemental Security Income program. No one program, however, has been designed to support the full range of long-term care services on a systematic basis.

For example, the Medicare program is intended to address the acute medical care needs of the aged and disabled. To the extent that it provides coverage for certain long-term care services, it does so with the intent of reducing the need for more intensive and expensive acute care services. The program was not designed to respond specifically to the chronic care needs of the elderly, for instance, those with Alzheimer's disease, over a sustained period of time.

The Medicaid program on the other hand, does support long-term services, principally nursing home care, but only for certain low-income people or for persons who have depleted their income and assets. Many persons become eligible for Medicaid's nursing home benefits only after they have depleted their income and assets on sizable out-of-pocket expenditures for long-term care.

The SSBG program, in contrast, is generally limited to the provision of community-based social services selected and defined by the state. This program may cover medical care only when it is integral, but subordinate, to the provision of a social service. Funding under Title III of the Older Americans Act is used for the development of a service delivery system for older persons that focuses on social and nutritional services. The Supplemental Security Income program provides cash assistance to needy aged, blind, and disabled individuals.

This chapter was adapted from "Financing and Delivery of Long-Term Care Services for the Elderly" by Carol O'Shaughnessy, Richard Price, and Jeanne Griffith, Congressional Research Service, Library of Congress Publication No. 85-1033 EPW, October 17, 1985.

In addition, varying eligibility requirements, service benefits, service definitions, and reimbursement policies among these five major federal programs supporting long-term care have resulted in a fragmented and uncoordinated long-term care policy at the federal level. This lack of coordination among federal programs has also presented major implementation challenges to the states, especially where certain of these programs delegate administrative responsibility to state governments.

Table 12-1 summarizes some of the major differences among federal programs that support institutional and community-based care.

PUBLIC SECTOR PROGRAMS FOR FINANCING AND DELIVERY OF LONG-TERM CARE SERVICES

Implicit in any discussion of long-term care policy is the fact that large amounts of public dollars currently finance long-term care services and that even greater amounts will be spent in the future as the elderly population, especially the very old, increases. Aggregated data on spending for all nursing home and noninstitutional long-term care services under the complete array of federal, state, and local programs are not easily available. At least 80 federal programs assist persons with long-term care problems, either directly or indirectly through cash assistance, in-kind transfers, or the provision of goods and services. In addition, differences in definitions of services to be included in long-term care and inconsistent reporting across programs make aggregation of expenditure data very difficult.

However, it is generally agreed that most of the public sector's expenditures for long-term care services are for nursing home or other institutional care. In 1983, nearly $29 billion was spent nationally for nursing home care, accounting for 8.5 percent of total personal health care expenditures. Almost 50 percent ($14 billion) of nursing home expenditures was financed by federal, state, and local governments.

By far the largest portion of public expenditures for nursing home care is financed by the Medicaid program for the poor and medically indigent. In 1983, federal, state, and local Medicaid expenditures for nursing home care amounted to $12.4 billion. This represented 43 percent of total national spending on nursing home care and 89 percent of public spending for nursing home care in 1983. Medicaid's expenditures for nursing home care also represented a significant portion of total Medicaid spending. In 1983, Medicaid nursing home expenditures amounted to about 43 percent of total Medicaid spending for all health services covered under the program. In addition, an analysis of Medicaid expenditures found that 27 states spent 50 percent or more of their Medicaid budgets on nursing home care in 1982.[1]

In contrast, the Medicare program for the aged and disabled accounts for only a small portion of the Nation's expenditures for nursing home care. Medicare's expenditures amounted to $500 million and represented less than 2 percent of national spending and 3.6 percent of public spending for nursing home care in 1983.

Expenditures for noninstitutional community-based services are relatively small compared to spending for nursing home services. Whereas nursing home care accounted for about 43 percent of total Medicaid expenditures for health care services in 1983, home health care accounted for only 1.8 percent of total Medicaid spending in that year and amounted to approximately $600 million. In only 11 states did home health benefits constitute more than one percent of total Medicaid expenditures. One state (New York) alone accounted for nearly 80 percent of total Medicaid home health expenditures.

Medicare's expenditures for home health benefits are also a small proportion of total expenditures. In 1983, they amounted to $1.5 billion, or 2.7 percent of total program expenditures.

It should be noted that while its share remains small, home health care has become one of the fastest growing components of both the Medicare and Medicaid budgets. Between 1974 and 1983, home health care expenditures under Medicare increased from $119 million to $1.5 billion. This represented a 32.5 percent annual compound rate of growth. Medicaid expenditures for home health also increased rapidly—from $31 million in 1974 to $600 million in 1983, a 39 percent annual compound rate of growth.

While the Medicaid program is the predominant federal program supporting long-term care services, a variety of social service programs provide community-based services that may prevent or delay institutionalization. Chief among these are the SSBG program and the Older Americans Act program. While their total resources are small in comparison with total Medicaid expenditures devoted to long-term care, in many communities they are an important source of service to the frail elderly or fill gaps in services not met by either the Medicare or Medicaid programs.

Virtually all states provide a number of home and community-based long-term care services for diverse client groups, including children, the disabled, and the elderly, through the SSBG program under Title XX of the Social Security Act. These may include homemaker, home health aide, chore, and adult day care services. In some recent years expenditures for homemaker services alone have represented the second or third largest service expenditure category under the program. In addition, the increase in homemaker service expenditures from 1979 to 1980 (from $391.6 million to $410.9 million) was attributed to expanded use of funds for the elderly. For FY 1980 the average number of persons receiving this service was over 275,000 per quarter. Because federal reporting requirements for services supported by the program have been eliminated, more recent national data on total expenditures and persons served are unavailable.

Home care, including homemaker, chore, and personal care services, is one of the major service categories under Title III of the Older Americans Act. For

Table 12-1 Major Federal Programs Supporting Long-Term Care Services

Program	Services Covered	Eligibility	Administering Agency	
			Federal	State
Medicaid/Title XIX of the Social Security Act	Skilled nursing facility;[a] intermediate care facility;[b] home health;[c] adult day care[b]	Aged, blind, disabled persons receiving cash assistance under SSI; others receiving cash assistance under AFDC; at state option, persons whose income exceeds standards for cash assistance under SSI/AFDC (i.e., the "medically needy")	Health Care Financing Administration/HHS	State Medicaid agency
	2176 "waiver" services (e.g., case management, homemaker, personal care, adult day care, rehabilitation, respite, and other services at state option)[d]	Aged, blind, disabled, or mentally ill Medicaid eligibles (including children) living in the community who would require nursing home level care; at state option, persons living in the community with higher income than normally allowed under a state Medicaid plan		In some cases the 2176 "waiver" program to be administered by another agency (e.g., state agency on aging)
Medicare/Title XVIII of the Social Security Act	100 days of skilled nursing facility care; home health; hospice	Generally those with Social Security status; persons 65 years and over; persons under 65 years entitled to federal disability benefits; certain persons with end-stage renal disease	Health Care Financing Administration/HHS	N/A

Program	Services	Eligibility	Federal administering agency	State administering agency
Social Services Block Grant/Title XX of the Social Security Act	Various social services as defined by the state, including homemaker, home health aide, personal care, home-delivered meals	No federal requirements; states may require means tests	Office of Human Development Services/HHS	State social services/human resources agency; in some cases other state agencies may administer a portion of Title XX funds for certain groups (e.g., state agency on aging)
Older Americans Act/Title III	Variety of social services as determined by state and area agencies on aging, with priority on in-home services; also, case management, day care, and protective services; separate appropriation for home-delivered meals	Persons 60 years and over; no means tests, but services are to be targeted to those with social or economic need	Administration on Aging/Office of Human Development Services/HHS	State agency on aging
Supplemental Security Income/Title XVI of the Social Security Act	Federal income support; maximum federal payment for persons with no income is $325 per individual and $488 per couple in 1985; supplemental payment for nonmedical housing and/or in-home services, as determined by the state	Aged, blind, disabled persons who meet federally established income and resources requirements; states may make payments to other state-defined eligibility groups	Social Security Administration/HHS	State supplemental payment program may be state or federally administered

[a] Required for individuals over age 21.
[b] At option of state.
[c] Required for individuals entitled to skilled nursing home care.
[d] May be offered under a waiver of Medicaid state plan requirements if requested by the state and approved by HHS. May include waiver of Medicaid eligibility requirements and stipulation that services be offered on a statewide basis.

FY 1984, it was estimated that the program would support over two million home care visits to the elderly. The Older Americans Act also authorizes a home-delivered meals program, with $62 million appropriated for FY 1984. An estimated 67 million home-delivered meals were served under the auspices of the program during FY 1984.

Major Federal Programs and Activities Supporting Long-Term Care Services

As noted above, at least 80 federal programs assist persons with long-term care problems, either directly or indirectly through cash assistance, in-kind transfers, or provision of goods and services. These programs often respond in a manner that is problem specific, categorical in nature, or targeted at specific client groups. For example, certain programs provide health services while excluding social services; others are oriented toward the elderly to the exclusion of the younger disabled. Some programs carry income eligibility requirements, others do not.

This section describes selected federal programs—Medicaid, Medicare, and the SSBG, Older Americans Act, and Supplemental Security Income (SSI) programs—that address the health and social services needs of the elderly population. Taken together, these programs constitute the major focus of federal financial support presently available for both community-based and the institutional long-term services. The differing characteristics of these programs reflect what some observers point to as the uncoordinated nature of federal support for long-term care services.

Not discussed here are a host of other federal programs dealing with such components of the long-term care spectrum as housing, transportation, and tax policy, as well as services provided through the Veterans Administration (VA). It should be noted, however, that numerous long-term care benefits are offered to veterans through the VA, including nursing home care, domiciliary care, treatment in outpatient clinics, and adult day health services, as well as cash payments for aid and attendance for certain severely disabled veterans. Services are offered directly by the VA and are also provided on a contract basis in non-VA hospitals and community nursing homes, and on a grant basis in state veterans home facilities. Issues surrounding the financing and delivery of long-term care services to the veteran population are of increasing concern to the VA because of the growing number of older veterans. By the year 2000, approximately two out of every three males aged 65 or older will be veterans, and the VA is predicting dramatic increases in the need for and utilization of various long-term care services by the veteran population.

The discussion immediately below summarizes some of the major differences of the Medicaid, Medicare, SSBG, Older Americans Act, and SSI programs in their approach to health and social services in general and long-term care in specific. This discussion is followed by a more detailed description of each of these programs.

Program Goals. Medicaid is the major federal program financing health care services for certain low income persons. While it provides health care benefits and, to a limited degree, medically related social services to certain eligible persons with chronic care needs, it is not designed to support the full array of long-term care services on a systematic basis. Its principal form of support for long-term care services is for nursing home care.

Medicare, on the other hand, is a nationwide health insurance program for the aged and disabled and is intended primarily to address acute medical care needs. To the extent that it provides coverage for certain long-term care services, it does so with the intent of reducing the need for more intensive and expensive acute care services; the program was not designed to respond specifically to chronic care needs of the elderly over a sustained period of time.

The SSBG program is designed to assist families and individuals in maintaining self-sufficiency and independence. However, the program is generally limited to the provision of community-based social services selected and defined by each state, and it does not support institutional care.

The Older Americans Act is intended to foster the development of a broadly defined, comprehensive, and coordinated aging service system. However, it is limited in its ability to have a significant impact on long-term care due to its small resources as compared to other programs.

The SSI program's purpose is to provide an income floor for needy aged, blind, and disabled individuals; it provides cash payments but not services.

Administrative Authority and Financing Mechanisms. The Medicare program is administered and financed at the federal level with uniform national standards. The Medicaid, SSBG, and Older Americans Act programs are shared federal-state programs with states responsible for implementation of federal legislation and regulations. The SSI program is administered at the federal level, but allows states to augment the federal SSI payment and this portion of the program may be federally or state administered.

The Medicaid and Older Americans Act programs carry specific requirements for states to match federal funds, whereas the SSBG program does not. By virtue of their statutory obligations to beneficiaries, Medicare, Medicaid, and SSI represent uncontrollable expenditures in the federal budget. In contrast, the total funding available for programs under the Older Americans Act is subject to an annual limit imposed through the appropriations process. Although the SSBG program is considered an entitlement program to states, it carries a statutorily imposed federal expenditure ceiling.

Service Benefits, Definitions, and Standards. As a general rule, Medicare and Medicaid provide reimbursement primarily for medical and health care services. However, in certain instances Medicaid reimbursement is available for social service components of health care services (e.g., under state options for personal care or adult day care services and under home and community-based waiver provisions).

The SSBG program provides reimbursement for social services only, but will provide coverage for medical care when such care is "integral but subordinate" to the provision of a social service. Funding under Title III of the Older Americans Act is to be used for the development of a service delivery system for older persons, focusing on supportive and nutritional services. Recipients of SSI receive a cash payment that is federally determined but states may decide how much and for what purpose to supplement the federal payment.

Definitions for similar or complementary services vary among programs and sometimes among programs within a single state. Certain service definitions are established at the state level or at the local level by individual service providers. Similarly, standards for services may be established upon legislative specifications.

Eligibility. Entitlement for Medicare is generally based on Social Security status. Eligibility for Medicaid is linked to actual or potential receipt of cash assistance under the federally assisted Aid to Families with Dependent Children (AFDC) program and the SSI program for the aged, blind, and disabled. The SSBG program does not require that applicants or recipients meet income eligibility guidelines, although states may set standards. The Older Americans Act program prohibits income testing for services; however, funds under the program must be directed toward those with the greatest social or economic need. Eligibility for the federal payment portion of SSI is based on federally established income and asset rules.

Medicaid: Title XIX of the Social Security Act

The Medicaid program is a federal-state matching program providing medical assistance for certain low-income persons. Each state administers its own program and, subject to federal guidelines, determines eligibility and scope of benefits. In general, each state also determines the payment rate for services provided to Medicaid recipients. The federal government's share of medical expenses is tied to a formula based upon the per capita income of the state. As a minimum, the federal government will pay 50 percent of the costs of medical care; this amount ranges up to 78 percent in the lower-per-capita-income states.

The states vary greatly with regard to services they include in their plans and groups eligible to receive these services. For example, major long-term care services provided under Medicaid include intermediate care facility services, skilled nursing facility services, and home health services. Other Medicaid services sometimes associated with the needs of long-term care patients include private nursing services, clinic services, physical therapy and related services, inpatient care for patients 65 or older in institutions for mental diseases or tuberculosis, inpatient psychiatric services for individuals under 21, personal care services at home, and adult day health services. However, not all states cover these services equally. In addition, states may cover certain other home and community-based services under special waiver programs reviewed and approved by the Secretary of Health and Human Services.

Medicaid law requires that states cover under their programs the *categorically needy*, i.e., all persons receiving assistance under the AFDC program and most persons receiving assistance under the SSI program. States may also cover additional persons as categorically needy. These might include persons who would be eligible for cash assistance, except that they are residents in medical institutions, such as skilled nursing or intermediate care facilities.

In addition to the categorically needy, states may at their option cover the *medically needy*, i.e., persons whose income and resources are large enough to cover daily living expenses (according to income levels set by the state) but not large enough to pay for medical care. If the income and resources of a medically needy individual are above a state-prescribed level, the individual must first incur a certain amount of medical expense that lowers the income to the medically needy level (the so-called spenddown requirement). Thirty-four states and jurisdictions cover the medically needy. As a result of state variations such as these, persons with identical circumstances may be eligible to receive Medicaid benefits in one state but not in another; even individuals in the same state with similar incomes may not be equally eligible for benefits due to welfare rules.

Observers have noted that Medicaid's eligibility policies and benefit structure have actually created financial incentives to use nursing homes rather than community services. In general, Medicaid support to the chronically impaired elderly living in the community has usually been quite limited. In addition, certain elderly poor who are ineligible for Medicaid while living in the community may become eligible once they enter a nursing home because the state has a higher income eligibility standard for nursing home residents. Others become eligible for Medicaid once they deplete their resources after entering the nursing home as privately paying patients. The 1983 GAO report "Medicaid and Nursing Home Care" noted studies showing that one-quarter to two-thirds of Medicaid patients in nursing homes initially entered as private paying patients and subsequently converted to Medicaid.[2] Another analysis completed for the House Select Committee on Aging found that in Massachusetts 63 percent of elderly persons over 65 living alone in the community would deplete their assets after only 13 weeks in a nursing home, and for married couples over 65, 37 percent would do so within 13 weeks, if one spouse required nursing home care.[3]

In order to allow states to broaden coverage for a range of community-based services and to receive federal reimbursement for these services, Congress in

1981 enacted new authority for the Department of Health and Human Services (HHS) to waive certain of Medicaid's requirements. Specifically, section 2176 of the Omnibus Budget Reconciliation Act of 1981 (P.L. 97-35) authorizes the Secretary of HHS to approve "2176 waivers" for a variety of home and community-based services for individuals who, without such services, would require the level of care provided in a skilled nursing facility or intermediate care facility. Under the 2176 authority, the Health Care Financing Administration (HCFA), the HHS agency that administers the Medicaid program, is allowed to waive two specific Medicaid requirements: (1) a requirement that Medicaid services be available throughout a state, and (2) a requirement that covered services be equal in amount, duration, and scope among certain Medicaid recipients. By allowing the Secretary to waive these requirements, states are given the flexibility to offer selected 2176 home and community-based services in only a portion of the state rather than in all geographic jurisdictions, as would be required absent the waiver, and also to offer selected services to certain state-defined individuals eligible for Medicaid assistance (including the aged, blind, disabled, mentally retarded, and mentally ill) rather than to offer such services to all persons in particular groups. In addition, states have been able to extend to waiver participants the more liberal Medicaid income eligibility rules that may be applied to persons in institutions.

The expanded services that states may offer under an approved waiver include medical and medical-related services as well as social services. Prior to the implementation of the 2176 waiver program, Medicaid services available to chronically ill or disabled individuals living in the community were generally restricted to medical and medical-related services. The waiver authority acknowledges that a wide variety of services may be needed in order to prevent or postpone institutionalization. For this reason, services traditionally considered to be social services are covered in the waiver authority. These include case management (commonly understood to be a system in which responsibility for locating, coordinating, and monitoring a group of services rests with a designated person or organization), homemaker and chore services, adult day health, and respite care.

The additional flexibility Congress authorized under the waiver as to services, eligibility, and geographic areas to be covered was qualified by a concern about the costs of home and community-based care to be provided under the amendment. Therefore, the law included a requirement that states demonstrate that the costs of services for individuals receiving home and community-based services not exceed the cost to Medicaid of care in institutions.

As of June 30, 1985, HCFA had approved 107 waivers in 46 states. For more information about the 2176 waiver program, see the Congressional Research Service white paper *Medicaid 2176 Waivers for Home and Community-Based Care*, 85-817 EPW.

Medicare: Title XVIII of the Social Security Act

Medicare is a federal health insurance program with a uniform eligibility and benefit structure throughout the United States. The program covers most individuals entitled to Social Security benefits, persons under 65 entitled to federal disability benefits, and certain individuals with end-stage renal disease. Coverage is available to persons without regard to their income or assets.

Medicare is generally not regarded as a program intended to provide support for long-term care. Its coverage is focused primarily on acute care, particularly hospital and surgical care and accompanying periods of recovery. For example, Medicare covers up to 100 days of skilled nursing facility services following a hospital stay of at least three consecutive days. The benefit is further limited in that the patient must be in need of skilled nursing care on a daily basis for treatment related to a condition for which he or she was hospitalized. The skilled nursing facility benefit is subject to a daily patient copayment after the 20th day of care. The program pays for neither intermediate care facility services nor custodial care in a nursing home.

Medicare does pay for some community-based long-term care services, primarily home health services. Home health services covered under Medicare include the following:

- part-time or intermittent nursing care provided by, or under the supervision of, a registered professional nurse
- physical, occupational, or speech therapy
- medical social services provided under the direction of a physician
- medical supplies and equipment (other than drugs and medicines)
- medical services provided by an intern or resident enrolled in a teaching program in a hospital affiliated or under contract with a home health agency
- part-time or intermittent services provided by a home health aide, as permitted by regulations

To qualify for home health services, the Medicare beneficiary must be confined to his or her home and under the care of a physician. In addition, the person must be in need of part-time or intermittent skilled nursing care or physical or speech therapy. Services must be provided by a home health agency certified to participate under Medicare and according to a plan of treatment prescribed and reviewed by a physician. There is no statutory limit on the number of home health visits covered under Medicare. Nor is the patient subject to any cost-sharing (e.g., deductibles or coinsurance) for covered home health services.

In addition to these skilled nursing facility and home health care benefits, Medicare covers a range of long-term care services, especially home care services, for terminally ill beneficiaries. These services, authorized in 1982 and referred to as Medicare's hospice benefit, are available to beneficiaries with a life expectancy of six months or less. Hospice care benefits include nursing care, therapy services, medical social services, home health aide services, physician services, counseling, and short-term inpatient care. For FY 1985, HCFA estimates that Medicare expenditures for hospice care will amount to $15 million.

Social Services Block Grant Program: Title XX of the Social
  Security Act

Title XX of the Social Security Act authorizes a block grant to states for a wide range of social services to diverse population groups, including the aged, disabled, and children. States are allowed considerable discretion in their support of social services as long as the services are structured to meet the following goals of the program: achieving or maintaining economic self-support and self-sufficiency; preventing or remedying neglect, abuse, or exploitation; preventing or reducing inappropriate institutional care by providing for community-based care; and securing referral or admission for institutional care when other forms of care are not appropriate or providing certain services to individuals in institutions (excluding room and board). The SSBG program provides reimbursement for social services only, but will provide coverage for medical care when such care is "integral but subordinate" to the provision of a social service.

A state receives allotments of SSBG funds on the basis of the state's population, within a federal expenditure ceiling. There are no requirements for use of Title XX funds—states are provided relative freedom to spend federal social service block grant funds on state-identified service needs. Legislation in the 98th Congress permanently increased the expenditure ceiling to $2.7 billion, effective in FY 1984; in FY 1985 the appropriation level was $2.7 billion.

The Title XX program was significantly changed by provisions of P.L. 97-35, the Omnibus Reconciliation Act of 1981, effective in FY 1982. Through FY 1981, the program contained certain limited requirements regarding the population to be served and the kinds of services to be provided to families and individuals. Under provisions of P.L. 97-35, states have been given much more discretion in determining the service population and services to be offered. The law eliminated requirements that states expend a portion of funds for welfare recipients, that services be limited to families with incomes below 115 percent of the state median income, and that fees be charged to persons with specified income levels. While previous state planning requirements were lessened, the law continues to require states to develop and make public a report on how funds are to be used prior to the state plan period, including information on the types of activities to be funded and the characteristics of individuals to be served.

The 1981 law also eliminated state reporting requirements; therefore, only very limited data are available as to the extent to which Title XX supports long-term care services. According to HHS analysis of the states' FY 1985 pre-expenditure reports under Title XX (which report on the states' intended use of funds), home care services, which may include homemaker, chore, and home management services, were to be provided to adults and children by virtually all states; adult day care was to be provided by 26 states and adult foster care by 16 states.

According to data compiled by the American Public Welfare Association on a limited number of states, in 1983 home-based services were provided to 11 percent of all Title XX recipients, or about 307,000 persons of all ages. Home-based services accounted for about 14 percent of total expenditures, or $555 million (out of a total estimated amount of federal and state funds of $4 billion).[4] It should be noted that these data are for all Title XX recipients; national data specific to the elderly and disabled population and by service are unavailable.

Although the SSBG program is the major social service program supported by the federal government, its ability to significantly assist the long-term care population is relatively limited. Because it provides a variety of social services to a diverse population, the program has competing demands. Community care programs such as those supported by Title XX are minimal when compared to programs that support institutional care. For example, federal funds available for all Title XX activities in 1983 ($2.7 billion) were approximately one-third the total federal nursing home expenditures in that year ($8.1 billion).

The Older Americans Act

The Older Americans Act carries a broad mandate to improve the lives of older persons in the areas of income, emotional and physical well-being, housing, employment, social services, and civic, cultural, and recreational opportunities.

The purpose of Title II of the Act, which authorizes formula grants to states for services to older persons, is to foster the development of a comprehensive and coordinated service system for older persons in order to (a) secure and maintain maximum independence and dignity in a home environment for older persons capable of self-care, (b) remove individual and social barriers to economic and personal independence for older persons, and (c) provide a continuum of care for the vulnerable elderly. Under Title III, grants are made to state agencies on aging, which in turn award funds to 664 area agencies on aging to plan, coordinate, and advocate for a comprehensive service system for older persons.

Title III aids a wide range of supportive services, as well as congregate and home-delivered nutrition services. Certain supportive services have been given priority by Congress, including in-home services (such as homemaker and home health aide), visiting and telephone reassurance, and chore services. Each area agency is required to spend a portion of its supportive services allotment on these services. Other community-based long-term care services that may be provided under Title III include care management, assessment, adult day care, and respite care. Services under the Title III program are to be provided to older persons without regard to income, although concentrated on those with the greatest social or economic need. Older persons are to be given the opportunity to contribute to the cost of services, but failure to do so cannot be a basis for denial of service.

Unlike the Title XX program, in which states receive a block of funds for unspecified social services, Congress makes separate appropriations of Title III funds for supportive services, for congregate nutrition services (which provide older persons with meals and other services in a group setting), and for home-delivered nutrition services. A state receives an allotment of these funds according to the number of older persons in the state as compared to all states. The law gives states and area agencies flexibility to define the supportive services to be provided and to transfer funds among the three service categories. Total FY 1985 appropriations for Title III were $669 million, with 50 percent ($336 million) for congregate nutrition services and 40 percent ($265 million) for supportive services. Only about 10 percent ($68 million) of the federal appropriation is devoted to home-delivered nutrition services.[5]

In-home services clearly represent an expenditure priority for the Title III program. According to the National Data Base on Aging, in 1984 about one-quarter of the funds controlled by area agencies (including Older Americans Act funds as well as other funds) was directed at in-home services. While a substantial portion of these funds was spent on the home-delivered meals component, which receives a separate appropriation under the Act, almost an equal proportion of the total spent on in-home services was devoted to housekeeping, personal care, and chore services.[6]

The potential for the Older Americans Act to have a significant impact on the long-term care system is limited because of the program's relatively small resources as compared to other programs. However, many state and area agencies have made strides to improve long-term care services through coordination activities with health and other social service agencies and through the development of a social service infrastructure for the elderly at the local level. Some state agencies on aging have also acted as catalysts to reorganize community-based health and social services systems at the state and local levels so as to serve the long-term care population more effectively. For example, state agencies have developed care management and assessment systems through area agencies on aging and have supported services otherwise unavailable to the frail population. In other cases, state agencies on aging have been given responsibility for the administration of the section 2176 home and community-based waiver program under Medicaid.

Although the amount of funding that Title III devotes to home care services is a small fraction of the amount spent for home health services under Medicare and Medicaid, the Title III program has the flexibility to fill gaps in services for persons otherwise unserved. Since Older Americans Act services may be provided without the restrictions required under Medicare and without certain income tests specified by Medicaid, in some cases Title III funds may be used to serve persons whose Medicare and Medicaid benefits have been exhausted or who are ineligible for Medicaid.

Although the home-delivered nutrition program receives less federal funding than the congregate nutrition program, in recent years states have increasingly shifted funds from the congregate program to the home-delivered and supportive services components. In FY 1984 states shifted over $41 million from the $321 million appropriated for the congregate program to the other service components. Reasons cited for this trend include the increasing age of the older population and the increased demand for home-based services by a more frail and older population. A recent evaluation of the Older Americans Act nutrition program performed for the Administration on Aging has shown that recipients of home-delivered nutrition services tend to be older, poorer, and in worse health than congregate nutrition participants.

Another long-term care activity required under Title III is the operation of a statewide long-term care ombudsman program. This authority requires state agencies to conduct the following activities: (a) investigate and resolve complaints relating to the health, safety, welfare, and rights of institutionalized persons; (b) monitor federal, state and local laws, regulations, and policies with respect to long-term care facilities; (c) provide information to public agencies regarding problems of older persons in long-term care facilities; and (d) establish procedures for providing access to facilities' and patients' records (with protection of the confidentiality of such records). Ombudsman activities are to take place not only with respect to policies and practices of nursing homes, but also with respect to activities in boarding homes. State agencies responsible for the ombudsman program have created sub-state programs to carry out these activities; in 1984 there were about 400 sub-state ombudsman programs. In FY 1983, about $12.1 million was expended for ombudsman activities under the Older Americans Act ($8.9 million in federal funds and $3.2 million in state and local funds).[7]

Supplemental Security Income Program: Title XVI of the Social Security Act

The Supplemental Security Income (SSI) program is a federally administered income assistance program authorized by Title XVI of the Social Security Act. Enacted by the 1972 Social Security Amendments and implemented in 1974, it replaced previous programs of state income assistance for the aged, blind and disabled. The SSI program provides a minimum income level for aged, blind, and disabled persons whose countable income does not exceed the federal maximum monthly SSI benefit. In 1985 the monthly federal SSI benefit was $325 for an individual and $488 for a couple with no other income. SSI payments are made to individuals under uniform, nationwide rules with respect to income and assets, and definitions of blindness and disability.

The SSI program allows states to supplement the federal SSI payment through optional supplemental payments to individuals. All but eight states and jurisdictions provide some form of optional state payments. (These are Arkansas, Georgia, Kansas, Mississippi, the Northern Mariana Islands, Tennessee, Texas, and West Virginia.) Each state determines whether it will make a supplemental payment, to whom, and in what amount. These state supplemental payments, also paid on a regular monthly basis, are intended to supplement the basic federal SSI payment for food, shelter, clothing, utilities, and other necessities. Some states provide optional state supplemental payments to all persons qualifying for SSI benefits, while others may limit payments to certain state-defined SSI recipients, or may extend payments to persons who would be eligible for SSI except for excess income.

Because the federal SSI payment may be insufficient to cover an individual's service needs beyond room and board, such as nonmedical supervision or other group living arrangements or personal care services, a significant number of states provide supplemental payments to support selected community-based long-term care services. These services often include supervision of daily living or other protective housing services for the mentally retarded, chronically mentally ill, or the frail or confused elderly.

An analysis of optional state supplemental programs up to January 1985 showed that 35 states support a diverse range of community-based long-term care services through their optional state supplementation programs.[8] Payments are made to individuals to support their residence in a variety of housing arrangements, such as adult foster care homes, domiciliary care homes, congregate care facilities, adult residential care homes, and shared homes for adults. In addition to providing payments for specialized housing arrangements, some states also provide supplemental payments to pay for personal care, home health, and other home care services for eligible individuals.

Federal Research and Demonstration Initiatives

Over the last decade the federal government has supported a wide range of research and demonstration activities designed to test new ways of providing and coordinating long-term care services as well as to achieve cost savings in the provision of care. Federally funded demonstrations have been sponsored principally by HHS, including by HCFA and by the Administration on Aging (AOA), both of which are within HHS. In some cases, HCFA has waived Medicare or Medicaid service or eligibility requirements so that a fuller range of services may be provided to persons who would not ordinarily benefit under the existing programs.

Research and demonstration projects have ranged from those in which systemwide changes have been made in the provision of community services to those in which the existing service system has been modified by the addition of previously unavailable services. The organization, administration, auspices, funding source, and service packages have differed across demonstration projects; however, certain common features exist. Many projects were geared toward the development of procedures to provide assessment, case management, and follow-up of clients with long-term care needs in order to assure care in the least restrictive setting. Multidisciplinary teams (generally composed of medical, health, and social service professionals) were established to accomplish this objective. Most projects aimed to provide or make accessible a range of health and health-related social services for specified client groups (e.g., homemaker, home health, chore, home-delivered meals, adult day care, and transportation services).

Most of these projects have terminated as federal demonstrations, but most have been viewed as precursors to HHS's National Long-Term Care Channeling Demonstration program, funded for the first time during FY 1980. A more recent research and demonstration initiative is the Social/Health Maintenance Organizations (S/HMO) project.

National Long-Term Care Channeling Demonstration

In 1980, three units within HHS (HCFA, AOA, and the Office of the Assistant Secretary for Planning and Evaluation) initiated the National Long-Term Care Channeling Demonstration. This project was designed to test whether a carefully managed approach to the provision of community-based long-term care services to a frail elderly population living outside institutions could help control overall long-term care costs while maintaining or improving the well-being of the clients.

The term *channeling* refers to organizational structures and systems that co-ordinate available long-term care resources and manage them effectively on behalf of clients. Channeling was expected to achieve its effects principally by substituting less costly community or informal services for more costly institutional care. Ten states received multiyear demonstration funds, and as of March 1985 all states had terminated the demonstration phase. The program, designed with treatment and control groups, was devised to answer questions that previous demonstrations had not totally answered, such as the cost of case management systems and how best to target community-based services on those who would otherwise be institutionalized. Other questions to be answered by the demonstration included the following. Does channeling reduce institutionalization and hospitalization? Is use of formal health and social services in the community increased? Do formal services substitute for services of families and friends? What impact does channeling have on public and private costs of long-term care, on longevity, improved health status, and overall client well-being?

Results of a preliminary analysis of 3,000 early enrollees in the program indicate that the demonstration identified a very frail population with limited income living in the community. Of this early sample, 52 percent were incontinent, 22 percent were unable to perform activities of daily living, and 81 percent were restricted in mobility. A large majority needed assistance in preparing meals, shopping, and other housekeeping activities. In addition, 57 percent of the sample had income below $500 per month.

Social/Health Maintenance Organization Demonstration

In 1980, the Health Care Financing Administration, HHS, and private foundations began funding the development, planning, and operation of the S/HMO concept for financing acute and long-term care services for an elderly population eligible for Medicare and/or Medicaid. The S/HMO concept builds upon and extends the health maintenance organization (HMO) model for financing acute medical care services. Specifically, an HMO offers health insurance coverage for specific health care services on a prepaid, capitation basis (the premium charge for enrollment) and either provides directly, or arranges to have provided, the health services covered under the insurance contract. The HMO is at risk for the costs of the services it covers; that is, it will experience some level of profit or loss on the basis of its ability to estimate in advance its revenues and the utilization and costs of services it provides.

The success of conventional HMOs in managing acute medical care services and costs suggests the possibility of expanding the concept to include long-term care services. Under the three-year HCFA S/HMO demonstration, four test sites across the country will assume responsibility for financing and providing a full range of medical and long-term care services under a fixed budget that is prospectively determined. The four S/HMO sites will serve an elderly population eligible for Medicare and/or Medicaid. These persons will range from the well to the impaired elderly. Medicare, Medicaid, and private premiums will finance the services.

Long-term care services covered by S/HMOs will include nursing home services, home health services, homemaker or home health aide services, personal care, adult day care, respite care, and home-delivered meals. Each S/HMO site will have its own defined long-term care benefit. Because of limited experience with long-term care insurance and utilization, long-term care services will be covered up to a maximum dollar amount per year and will require a copayment. The limits range from $6,500 per year to $12,000. In addition, S/HMOs will gradually assume full risk for the utilization and costs of covered services.

The four demonstration sites began providing services in 1985 and will continue to do so through June 1988. An independent contractor will evaluate all four sites. In general, the S/HMO demonstration is intended to provide information about the cost-effectiveness of providing services in an integrated and managed system of care, the impact of such a system on the utilization of health and long-term care services by the elderly, and its effect on the quality of care available to the eligible population. Among the specific questions HHS expects this demonstration to address are the following:

- Can comprehensive long-term care insurance be marketed to a significant number of elderly?
- What combination of benefits, eligibility criteria, and premium and marketing techniques produce a viable long-term care insurance plan?
- Can a consolidated, prepaid system of acute and long-term care services produce greater system savings than HMOs serving Medicare beneficiaries with acute care services only?
- Will the new privately financed long-term care benefits significantly reduce nursing home admissions and Medicaid spenddown?
- Can quality of care and service continuity and access be improved by consolidating acute and long-term care in a single managed system?
- Will informal support (i.e., care provided by family members, friends and community volunteers) of chronically impaired elders be enhanced in a prepaid, risk-based, case-managed health care system offering both acute and long-term care services?

State Level Initiatives

The fragmentation and lack of coordination among major federal programs that support long-term care services have provided the states with major implementation challenges. The Medicaid, Social Services Block Grant, and Older Americans Act programs all delegate administration and implementation responsibility to the states and, in so doing, require the states to deal with problems inherent in the different goals of these programs, as well as in their varying eligibility requirements, service benefits, and reimbursement policies. These implementation problems have also resulted from the fact that fragmentation at the federal level has been mirrored in state administration, with major long-term care programs being administered by different state agencies.

Many states have responded to these challenges by enacting legislation or creating initiatives to reorganize and restructure benefits offered through the federal programs. Also, some states have consolidated the administration of various long-term care programs in a single state agency.

State initiatives to alter and coordinate their long-term care policies have been inspired, in part, by federally sponsored demonstration projects begun in the 1970s. For example, demonstrations funded under Medicaid and Medicare waiver authorities and the Older Americans Act research and demonstration authorities have served as models for state-mandated case management systems and nursing home pre-admission screening programs. Demonstration initiatives have also served as a testing ground for new community-based service models. For example, adult day care demonstrations that took place during the 1970s encouraged state and local agencies to merge existing health and social service funds available under Medicaid, Title XX, and the Older Americans Act to create the more than 1,000 adult day care programs now in existence.

Certain parallel activities have been initiated by states without the benefit of federal demonstration funds and without any changes in federal legislation. A number of states have attempted to reduce the need for institutional care by redirecting existing federal program funds or by using existing federal and complementary state funds in new ways. For example, the Virginia State Medicaid agency operates a nursing home pre-admission screening program through local public health departments for persons likely to be admitted to a nursing home but whose needs could be addressed through community-based services. The Massachusetts state agency on aging has established community-based organizations to manage certain key home care services for older persons through creative use of Title III Older Americans Act funds and state funds. The Utah state agency on aging has established a program to identify persons at risk of being institutionalized and has developed alternative community-based service plans using personnel of the state's network of area agencies on aging.

The objective of reducing institutional care costs and diverting potential users to other forms of care has been the impetus behind much of the state effort to alter long-term care systems. Despite unclear evidence about the cost-effectiveness of substituting various forms of community-based care for institutional care, an enormous amount of state effort has been directed at developing community care options.

Some of the themes evidenced in state level initiatives include the following:

- *Control of institutional access through screening and assessment procedures.* Many states have initiated screening and comprehensive medical and social assessment procedures for those at risk of long-term care services in order to ascertain the most effective and least costly care option given the client's needs. Such screening and assessment procedures are generally applied to persons about to enter a long-term care facility. A review of state Medicaid programs in 1981 showed that 28 states had mandatory pre-admission screening programs for Medicaid patients prior to nursing home admission.[9]

- *Reorganizing access to community services.* Some states have devised projects aimed at reorganizing access to community services by providing case management services or "gateway" procedures for clients. This concept has been developed to overcome problems associated with multiple providers and duplication of services that have resulted in client confusion as to the source of care and unnecessary administrative costs among agencies. The availability of Medicaid funds under the 2176 home and community-based service waiver program has recently spurred the development of many more case management systems, but perhaps not on a statewide basis. Of the 95 2176 waiver programs approved as of April 30, 1985, 66 programs offered case management.

• *Cost control mechanisms.* Some states have eliminated the uncertainty whether community care costs will exceed institutional care costs by pre-establishing upper cost limits on such care. For example, community care may be provided only when such care does not cost more than a certain percentage of institutional care. An example of this concept is contained in New York's Nursing Home Without Walls program. This cost control concept has been incorporated into the National Long-Term Care Channeling Demonstration program and is a basic element of the Medicaid 2176 home and community-based service waiver program.

• *Tax incentives for dependent care.* Many states permit favorable tax treatment for families or other caretakers who care for dependent older persons. According to a survey of the National Association of State Units on Aging, 27 states and the District of Columbia have adopted some form of dependent care tax credits, generally designed to assist in the care of dependents by adults who are working or seeking work. Of these 27 states, five have enacted tax provisions specifically designed to assist caregivers with the expenses of caring for older persons. These states are Arizona, Idaho, Iowa, North Carolina, and Oregon.[10]

PRIVATE SECTOR APPROACHES TO FINANCING AND DELIVERY OF LONG-TERM CARE

Budgetary constraints resulting from growing federal deficits and increasing expenditures required under various entitlement programs that currently finance long-term care have served to shift the focus of the long-term care debate from reform of federal programs to consideration of private sector initiatives that might relieve fiscal pressures on public programs and at the same time improve the elderly's ability to finance long-term care. Observers have also noted that the decline in the ratio of workers to retirees and the growth in numbers of the very oldest segment of the population may have a marked impact on the ability of public programs to support long-term care in the future. In addition, others point out that the economic status of future generations of the elderly may improve significantly and that they will therefore be able to pay for a larger portion of the cost of certain long-term care services.

The improvement in the economic status of certain groups of elderly may lead policymakers to target public sector long-term care programs on the most needy income categories of elderly, while at the same time it may encourage various private sector financing approaches that could assure greater protection against the cost of long-term care services for those who are relatively better off. However, at the current time, most elderly do not have the resources to pay for the catastrophic expenditures associated with certain long-term care services over an extended period of time. For many, depletion of assets and income in paying for the cost of care and then subsequent Medicaid eligibility is the only remedy.

A number of private sector approaches have recently been suggested as potentially feasible alternatives for financing long-term care services. These range from ways to pool the risks associated with long-term care need by means of private insurance and life care communities to conversion of an elderly homeowner's equity into a source of funds to pay for care. A discussion of these approaches and their feasibility for financing long-term care follows. It should be noted that these private sector alternatives may have only limited applicability for the large number of elderly who are poor or may become poor in the future. Another method of risk pooling, the S/HMO, was discussed above in the section on public financing and delivery. This report does not discuss still other options suggested as feasible alternatives for enhancing the elderly's ability to finance long-term care expenses, including the various tax code modifications proposed to encourage families to continue providing long-term care services.

Private Health Insurance Coverage for Long-Term Care

Among the private sector approaches receiving increased attention recently as a potential alternative for financing long-term care services is private health insurance. This alternative has been suggested not only because of growing fiscal constraints on public program expenditures, but even more because private insurance coverage is currently available for a wide variety of health care services and catastrophic illness. Private insurance is generally not available, however, for long-term care services or the catastrophic costs associated with long-term care.

Expenditures for long-term services, and especially for nursing home care, not only strain the budgets of public programs, they are also a burden on private resources. In 1983, total national nursing home expenditures of $29 billion were financed about equally by public programs and private sources of payment. Public programs financed $14 billion of the total and private sources $15 billion. Of total private spending for nursing home care in 1983, only 2 percent was paid by private insurance coverage. Ninety-seven percent of the total private spending for nursing home care was paid directly by the consumer out-of-pocket. The average annual cost of nursing home care exceeds $20,000 per year, which is a catastrophic expenditure beyond the financial reach of most of the elderly.[11]

In addition, private insurance coverage has been viewed as a feasible alternative because of general interest among the elderly population in purchasing private insurance to supplement their Medicare benefits. Nearly two-thirds of the elderly currently purchase such "medigap" policies. While these policies generally pay only certain of the deductible and coinsurance amounts for which Medicare beneficiaries are liable and do not cover long-term care, the widespread interest of the elderly in this broader coverage suggests to some observers that a market for long-term care coverage exists and could be increased.

Furthermore, evidence indicates that the elderly will have higher incomes and assets in the future, which will enable them to afford premiums for coverage. One study has estimated that given future income levels and growth of pensions, by the year 2005 approximately 93 percent of all married couples at age 65 and almost 60 percent of all single persons at that age would be able to purchase long-term care insurance with less than 5 percent of their cash income.[12]

Currently, relatively few insurance companies (studies indicate 40 to 70) write long-term care insurance policies that are substantially more comprehensive than standard medigap policies and that go beyond restrictive Medicare definitions for skilled nursing care to include intermediate and custodial care. It is estimated that about 200,000 elderly persons are presently insured under such plans.[13] Premiums for most of the available policies increase with age at initial purchase. The plans vary by length of time benefits are covered, waiting periods before benefits can begin, and the conditions upon which benefits will be paid.

Most plans provide indemnity benefits, paying a fixed amount for each day of covered service, thereby limiting the insurer's liability. In addition, most have utilization controls to further limit the insurer's liability and to protect the insurer against unnecessary utilization of benefits. These include medical screens and physical examinations for utilization of benefits, pre-existing condition restrictions, prior hospitalization requirements, exclusion of mental and nervous disorders, and renewability limitations.

Home care benefits, especially those related to custodial or personal care, are included in even fewer long-term care insurance policies. Often plans that cover any home care at all require a prior stay in a skilled nursing facility in order to reduce the large potential demand for home care among the majority of the covered population that has never been institutionalized.[14]

A number of barriers have been cited as impediments to the development of meaningful long-term care insurance policies.[15] Traditionally, insurers have been concerned about the potential for adverse selection in long-term care insurance, that is, where only persons more likely to need care actually buy insurance. In addition, insurers point to the problem of the induced demand for services that can be expected to be generated by the availability of new long-term care insurance. With induced demand, individuals decide to use more services and/or shift from nonpaid to paid providers for their care because they have insurance. This is especially critical in long-term care, with 60 to 80 percent of disabled or impaired persons receiving home care services from family or friends who are not compensated.

Still other factors are mentioned as problems inhibiting the development of long-term care policies. Many long-term care services that are felt to be critical in enabling frail elderly persons to remain in their homes are custodial and nonmedical. Traditionally these services, such as personal care, homemaker, and nutritional services, are considered noninsurable because of difficulty in confining eligibility to a limited number of people. In addition, observers have noted that, given the nature of many chronic conditions, many people who need long-term care will need it for the remainder of their lives, resulting in an open-ended liability for the insurance company. Moreover, evidence exists that the elderly do not understand their insurance coverage or their potential need for long-term care. Some elderly believe they are already adequately covered for such services under Medicare while others think they have coverage for long-term care with their purchase of a medigap policy.[16] Therefore, they do not demand specific coverage for long-term care.

According to a study of the Health Insurance Association of American (HIAA), one of the most significant barriers to the development of private insurance options is the major role by Medicaid in financing long-term care and especially nursing home services. According to the HIAA report *Long-Term Care: The Challenge to Society*, Medicaid is already viewed by many as a national coverage program for long-term nursing home care, a program used by far more than the low-income population usually thought of as Medicaid's primary clients. In addition, the ability of individuals to plan for the transfer of assets expands the number of persons eligible for long-term care benefits under the program. According to HIAA's report, public programs are viewed as a safety net providing protection against the catastrophic costs of care. The report calls for reduced Medicaid involvement in financing nursing home care so that fewer middle income individuals can view the program as a viable option for their long-term care needs.

As noted above, the number of long-term care insurance policies providing meaningful protection for the at-risk elderly population is very limited. However, recent research suggests that many of the problems that are commonly thought to preclude the development of long-term care insurance are subject to resolution by careful policy specification, including limitations on number of days covered, waiting periods before benefits can begin, and maximum amounts payable.[17] In addition, research has found that significant reductions in annual premium rates could be offered if persons were encouraged to buy at younger ages and to accept longer periods before coverage begins and a shorter length of coverage for benefits.[18] Others have suggested that allowing families to purchase protection for their elderly parents could make long-term care insurance more feasible. Adding adult children, who have a much lower risk of incurring long-term care expenses for themselves, to the pool of the insured could expand premium collections and at the same time make policies more affordable. The adult children could pay for the premiums on behalf of their elderly relatives as well as themselves, but presumably they would not begin to make claims for long-term care services on their own behalf until some future time.

Nontraditional health insurance alternatives have also been advanced as viable options for long-term care financing. Some have suggested that long-term care services can be controlled only in a managed care system, such as an HMO. The S/HMO demonstration project described above will provide information about the feasibility of this approach. In addition, some have pointed to tax-preferred cash accumulation plans, such as individual retirement accounts (IRAs) reserved for long-term care costs, as possible approaches to be considered. Some have suggested that cash accumulation instruments are perhaps most appropriate when there is a very high probability that a person will need a service at some point in time and when the costs of the service are not beyond the means of a person's lifetime savings capacity.[19] Home care services might be a more likely candidate for this form of financing than a long nursing home stay.

It should be noted that while insurers remain reluctant to enter the market for long-term care insurance, states, faced with mounting Medicaid nursing home expenditures, are expressing increasing interest in having such coverage more widely available. According to the American Health Care Association, which represents nearly 8,000 nursing homes in the country and which is a leading advocate of private long-term care insurance, 24 states are currently involved in some activity related to options for enhancing private insurance for long-term care.[20] Legislatures in a number of states have introduced bills that would mandate long-term care insurance coverage for group policies sold in the state. In addition, the National Association of Insurance Commissioners currently has underway a study group to assist state insurance commissioners in evaluating the increasing number of requests by insurers to establish policies.

Life Care or Continuing Care Retirement Communities[21]

One long-term care living arrangement available for financing long-term care services for a limited but potentially growing number of elderly persons is the life care community. Life care communities, also called continuing care retirement communities, are usually situated in a campus-like setting and are established to provide housing, meals, housekeeping, and social activities to older persons for the duration of their lives. In addition to these basic services, life care communities provide a range of long-term care services on the grounds of the facility.

The distinguishing characteristic of life care communities is the guarantee that residents will be provided with a range of services as long as they are residents of the community. Rights and obligations of the resident and the community are defined under the terms of a life care contract. The life care contract sets forth the services to be received by the resident in exchange for financial payments, including an entrance fee and monthly charges. Because the life care contract is intended to provide financial protection against the future cost of long-term care services for each resident, it may be viewed in part as a form of insurance.

Long-term care services provided in a life care community may include skilled and intermediate nursing home care, personal care, and other health care services such as home nursing and physical, occupational, and speech therapy. Life care communities may differ in the amount of prepaid nursing care offered under the terms of the contract. Acute care and hospital care are not provided, and some communities may require residents to share the cost of health or long-term care services they receive from the community. Residents continue to use Medicare and/or private insurance plans to cover the costs of acute and long-term care services.

Generally residents who enter life care communities are relatively healthy, but as their health or long-term care needs increase, they are provided with increased services as stipulated under the terms of the life care contract.

The number of life care communities is currently very small. Two major studies of communities have provided a range of estimates of the numbers of communities—from about 300 to 600, depending upon the definition used. It is estimated that there are at least 90,000 persons residing in nearly 300 such facilities.[22] According to the American Association of Retired Persons, the number of life care communities doubled in the past ten years and is expected to more than double in the next decade.[23] Most of the life care facilities in existence are operated by private, nonprofit organizations, especially religious organizations, although there has been increasing interest on the part of corporations in developing such facilities.

In order to gain access to a life care facility, a resident is required to pay a lump sum entrance fee with monthly payments thereafter, which are usually adjusted for inflation. Fees are generally based on the size and type of living unit (e.g., a studio or a one-, two-, or three-bedroom apartment). In addition, fees are based on some actuarial assumptions, such as life expectancy rates and projected future health care needs.

Some analysts have observed that the entrance and monthly fees may make the life care community option inaccessible to large numbers of the elderly. A 1984 study by Laventhol and Horwath of 600 communities found that the range of entrance fees was between $4,000 and over $100,000, the fee depending upon a number of factors, such as location, size of living unit, and age of facility.[24] Some analysts, however, dispute the claim that life care is only for the relatively well-off elderly. A study of communities by Winklevoss and Powell indicates that although the range of entrance fees is wide, the average fee is moderate. According to this survey, the average entrance fee for 275 communities in 1981 was about $35,000 for one person and $39,000 for two persons, with average monthly payments of $562 and $815, respectively.[25]

Analysts have pointed out that the life care concept can be viewed as a form of long-term care insurance in that residents pool their resources and share the risk of future costs of long-term care services. A portion of the entrance fees and monthly fees paid by all residents is used by the community to pay for the health and long-term care costs of a small number of residents needing more extensive care at any given time. Because only a small number of residents would be expected to need intensive services at a given time, the fees could be considered similar to insurance premiums, which are also paid by an entire group but used by only a small subgroup at a given time. In some cases, participation in a life care community may be viewed as a form of income redistribution, with some portion of the fees paid by all residents being used to subsidize the costs of residents who can no longer afford to pay for their care.[26]

Supporters of life care communities indicate that there are a number of advantages in this mode of long-term care. Life care communities offer continuous and in large part prepaid health and supportive care in a protected setting with personal and financial protection against the costs of future health or long-term care needs. Residence in such a community may offer increased opportunities for elderly persons to maintain their relatively healthy status at entry (since professional oversight is available on a regular basis) as compared to completely independent living in the community (where older persons may not actively seek health promotion opportunities). Residence in a protective community that offers a range of care services may allay the fears that many elderly face of making a sharp transition from their homes to permanent residence in a nursing home when they become suddenly disabled. The pooling of health and long-term care risks may reduce the uncertainties of future costs of care, and the care provided under the terms of the life care contract can supplement coverage of acute care provided by Medicare and private health insurance.

While life care communities may offer an option to some elderly persons, even to increasing numbers in the decades to come, they may not be able to serve a large proportion of the elderly population. Life care is not an option for the poor elderly or those with relatively intense pre-existing health or long-term care needs. The idea of signing over a large portion of accumulated assets in one lump sum to an organization in return for protection against future costs may not be acceptable to large numbers of elderly persons. Turning over assets in such a way may eliminate inheritances for children.

While some elderly persons may not be able to afford the relatively hefty entrance fees, analysts have pointed out that the equity older persons have in their homes may be employed for this purpose. The proportion of elderly persons owning their homes is large and they have substantial equity as a result. Among the 17.7 million households headed by older persons in 1983, 75 percent of the household heads were owners. In 1980, about 84 percent of older homeowners owned their homes free and clear, and in 1981 the median value of homes owned by the elderly was $44,000.[27] One study points out that the high level of net home equity held by the elderly is not held only by those with a higher income. About 65 percent of all elderly poor are homeowners, with 22 percent of the poor having more than $50,000 in net home equity.[28] Other analysts indicate that because future generations of elderly persons will be better off than those of the past, the elderly may be in more advantaged positions to afford this kind of care in the future. Inflation adjusted retirement income under Social Security combined with private pensions and with IRA income may make the inflation adjusted monthly fees associated with life care communities payable by increased numbers in future generations of the elderly.

Experience with life care communities is limited, as are data about their effect on the costs of organizing an integrated, prepaid approach to long-term care service delivery. While it has offered an attractive option to a small number of elderly persons in the past, there have been problems. Some communities have experienced financial problems, in part because of poor actuarial assumptions about the longevity of residents and their future health care needs, which resulted in depletion of funds to cover costs. In view of these considerations, there has been interest on the part of federal and state officials in more oversight and regulation of the development of these facilities in the interest of consumer protection.[29]

Home Equity Conversion

The search for alternative approaches in long-term care services has led some researchers to analyze the feasibility of using the single largest asset most older persons have—the equity in their home. As pointed out in the previous section, about 75 percent of elderly heads of households are owners, and in 1980 about 84 percent of owners had no mortgage debt. The overall homeownership equity held by the elderly is substantial. It is estimated that the total equity held by elderly homeowners with no mortgage debt is about $548 billion. This figure may underestimate the total equity available to the elderly since elderly home-owners with some remaining mortgage debt are not included.[30] Some observers believe that, if converted into a source of cash, homeowner equity could be a tangible means of financing long-term care services for some elderly who are "house rich, but cash poor."

There are two major types of mortgage instruments that may be used to convert equity into income: reverse mortgages and sale/leaseback contracts.[31]

Under a *reverse mortgage*, the homeowner enters into a loan agreement with a financial institution, which uses the property as security for the loan. The older person retains ownership rights to the home, receives a regular stream of income based on the loan, and accumulates a debt on the loan amount. The loan may be calculated so as not to exceed some proportion of the property value. When the loan becomes due, the owner has the option to convert the debt into a regular first or second mortgage, to sell the property to pay off the debt, or to obtain a new reverse mortgage. The time period for the reverse mortgage may range from seven to ten years or for the remainder of the individual's lifetime, depending upon the terms of the contract.

Under a *sale/leaseback contract*, the homeowner sells the equity in the home but retains the right to reside there, usually for life. The buyer of the equity provides the elderly homeowner with a down payment and pays the balance in regular monthly installments. The seller, then, in effect becomes a renter of the home that he or she formerly owned.

In one extensive analysis of the potential for application of homeowner equity toward payment of long-term care expenses, researchers concluded that there is evidence that a large proportion of older persons could use some of their home equity to finance long-term care needs. This analysis showed that about one-third to one-half of all elderly homeowners at high risk of need for home care could finance a portion of home care needs out of homeowner equity. The analysis also found that homeowner equity could be used to pay for long-term care insurance premiums as well as for nursing home care.[32] Another analysis that reviewed the potential for use of homeowner equity to purchase private long-term care insurance showed that home equity conversion could increase the ability of some elderly homeowners to pay for long-term care insurance, but concluded that reverse annuity mortgages and sale/leaseback arrangements do not easily provide for long-term care financing. Since these arrangements provide for payments to individuals for longer periods of time than usually needed to finance certain long-term care expenses, they may not have wide application for certain expenses requiring lump sums of cash over a short period of time. This report suggested that home equity conversion could be more useful if financial institutions permitted owners to use their homes as lines of credit, as necessary, to pay for long-term care expenses.[33]

While the idea of using home equity for payments of ongoing expenses of the elderly has appeared in the literature for a number of years, the actual number of home equity conversion contracts is very limited (estimates range from 300 to 400 contracts at most). Lenders in only a handful of states have offered home equity loans and these loans may not be made on a regular basis.[34] Therefore, actual experience is relatively meager and its specific application to long-term care should be tentative.

Thus far, there appears to be a lack of consumer demand. A number of obstacles have been cited as barriers to the future development of these arrangements. Many of the elderly may be reluctant to enter into these agreements because they wish to pass on some inheritance to their heirs. Also, even if these arrangements were more widely available, the question remains whether the elderly would actually use the funds to pay for long-term care services. Other elderly persons might not participate because they may feel that services available from public sources will be decreased if they use their home equity. Also, they may feel that if they outlive their equity, they may be forced to move. A number of other issues have been raised, including possible depreciation of homes and the concern that the elderly would not receive fair market value for their homes or that the lenders may default on their loans. These issues would require consumer protection measures.

There has been reluctance on the part of financial institutions to offer these instruments, particularly due to the current lack of mortgage insurance on the loans. Also, if the elderly homeowner lives beyond his or her equity, lending institutions may lose money because they may be reluctant to evict an elderly homeowner when the equity is exhausted. Finally, institutions may not want to enter into agreements in cases where the home is not expected to appreciate.

Other issues with respect to the tax implications of home equity conversions remain to be resolved. According to the Department of Housing and Urban Development (HUD), the status of sale/leaseback arrangements under the IRS code is unclear. Questions in need of resolution include the right of the seller–lessee to take advantage of the one-time homeowner capital gains exclusion and the ability of the purchaser–lessor to depreciate the rental property like other rental property.[35]

In 1983, Congress required HUD to develop a report evaluating the use of home equity conversion mortgages for the elderly, including an assessment of the impact on financial institutions and of the potential for acceptance of this concept in the private market, as well as recommendations on the establishment of a federal insurance program for insuring home equity mortgages.[36]

While home equity conversion is not extensively available, such arrangements might be attractive to some elderly for targeted long-term care expenses if the market became sufficiently developed and loans were devised to be responsive to individual needs. Conversion of home equity into cash to be applied toward a down payment for life care facilities was discussed above. Conversion of home equity in order to remain in one's own home may be more attractive in the long-run than using equity to finance a life care facility down payment. Because this option allows house rich but cash poor elderly persons to remain in their own homes by drawing upon a ready flow of funds, it may ultimately appeal to many more persons than life care. It may particularly appeal to those without heirs who would benefit from the sale of the home upon the death of the homeowner. Advocates of this strategy indicate that it could generate a significant amount of funds that, if directed toward payment of long-term care services paid for by public sector programs, could reduce pressure on these programs.

ISSUES TO BE CONSIDERED CONCERNING FUTURE PROSPECTS FOR LONG-TERM CARE

In the past, debate on federal long-term care policy has focused on a number of issues that policymakers still seek to resolve: how to offer more consistent and adequate protection for long-term care expenses, how to strike a balance between institutional and community-based care, and whether community-based care is more cost-effective than institutional care. Whereas in the past these issues were discussed principally in the context of proposals to reform federal programs of support for long-term care, today questions arising from these issues are applied as well to a new dimension of the debate: the extent to which private sector alternatives, such as private insurance, life care communities, and home equity conversion, can improve the ability of the elderly to finance the long-term care services they need and want. Although the debate may have widened to include private sector approaches, it is likely that reform of current federal benefit programs will continue to be an area of consideration because of the large federal investment in long-term care as well as the large numbers of the elderly who depend upon these programs for assistance. Some of the questions that may need to be reviewed in the future are included below.

- What are appropriate roles for public programs and private sector options to play in the financing of long-term care?
- Can comprehensive long-term care coverage be provided without a public mandate and/or subsidy?

The health insurance industry has been reluctant to offer comprehensive long-term care coverage, suggesting that adverse selection and induced demand for services will result in an insufficient pool of premium income to cover anticipated expenditures.

- What measures are necessary to obtain an adequate population base for long-term care insurance coverage that is affordable?
- Is some kind of public mandate required?

Even if the economic status of future generations of the elderly improves significantly, it is likely that they will continue to have differentiated needs and abilities to pay for long-term care.

- How should public programs and private sector options respond to the needs of a diverse population?
- How can they most suitably complement each other?

Currently many elderly persons have no other choice but to incur sizable out-of-pocket expenditures for long-term care, depleting their incomes and assets to become eligible for Medicaid's nursing home benefit. For these persons, Medicaid offers protection of the last resort. It has been pointed out that Medicaid is used by far more than a low-income population and that many middle income individuals are transferring their assets to relatives in order to qualify for Medicaid's nursing home benefits before actually incurring catastrophic long-term care expenditures.

The HIAA has suggested reducing Medicaid's involvement in the financing of nursing home care so that fewer middle income individuals can use the program as a viable option for their long-term care needs. However, little is known about the number of persons who actually transfer assets in order to qualify for Medicaid's nursing home benefit. Out-of-pocket expenditures for nursing home care, on the other hand, amount to half of total national expenditures and are this high because private sector coverage is very limited and elderly persons must deplete their incomes and assets.

- Can private sector alternatives begin to improve the ability of the elderly to finance their own long-term care expenses without reform of federal programs of support?
- How should reform of public programs proceed?

Public programs and limited private insurance currently provide more support for institutional forms of long-term care than for community-based care. Uncertainty about the costs of expanded community-based care has inhibited the broadening of coverage for these services. There appears to be consensus, however, that regardless of the cost of community-based services as compared to institutional care, community care is the more desirable option for most persons with chronic disabilities. Despite the prevalence of chronic conditions, most older persons are in reasonably good health and most chronically ill persons want to be as self-sufficient and independent as possible. There is also substantial evidence that family members would prefer to continue providing support services if some form of assistance were available to make their continued efforts possible.

- What kinds of controls must be in place for home care coverage to be more extensively included in public or private financing programs for long-term care?
- Can expanded home care coverage be included only in a managed care setting much as a S/HMO or life care community?

NOTES

1. Department of Health and Human Services, Health Care Financing Administration, Office of Research and Demonstrations, *Short-Term Evaluation of Medicaid: Selected Issues*, no. 84-9, July 1, 1984.

2. U.S. General Accounting Office, *Medicaid and Nursing Home Care: Cost Increases and the Need for Services are Creating Problems for the States and the Elderly*, GAO/IPE-84-1, October 21, 1983, 25–26.

3. House Select Committee on Aging, *America's Elderly at Risk*, Pub. No. 99-508, July 1985, Washington, D.C. Research analysis completed for the committee by Dr. Laurence Branch, Dr. David Friedman, and Ms. Elinor Socholitzky.

4. Data were compiled by the American Public Welfare Association under its Voluntary Cooperative Information System, under which states voluntarily report data on their social service programs.

Data for recipients are for 32 states and expenditures are for 31 states. Total expenditures, including a combination of state and local funds, federal Title XX funds, and other funds for 31 states, were an estimated $4 billion in 1983.

5. Title III funding also includes appropriations for U.S. Department of Agriculture commodities or cash-in-lieu of commodities; $120.8 million was available in FY 1985.

6. Data are from a random sample survey of 121 area agencies on aging in 1984. Supplied by the National Data Base on Aging, a service of the National Association of State Units on Aging and the National Association of Area Agencies on Aging.

7. Data are from Administration on Aging testimony at a hearing before the House Select Committee on Aging, Sept. 10, 1985. Unpublished hearing record.

8. Information was compiled by the Congressional Research Service from *The Supplemental Security Income Program for the Aged, Blind, and Disabled, Characteristics of State Assistance Programs for SSI Recipients*, Social Security Administration, SSA Pub. No. 17-002, January 1985.

9. Jackson Knowlton, Steven Clauser, and James Fatula, "Nursing Home Pre-Admission Screening: A Review of State Programs," *Health Care Financing Review* 3, no. 3 (March 1982):78.

10. National Association of State Units on Aging, *State Tax Policy Options for the Elderly: A Guide for Aging Advocates* (Washington, D.C., 1985), 46–47.

11. Pamela Doty, Korbin Liu, and Joshua Wiener, "An Overview of Long-Term Care," *Health Care Financing Review* 6, no. 3 (Spring 1985), 74.

12. ICF, Inc., *Private Financing of Long-Term Care: Current Methods and Resources*, Phase I, (Final report submitted to the Office of the Assistant Secretary for Planning and Evaluation, Department of Health and Human Services, January 1984), 79.

13. ICF, Inc., *Private Financing of Long-Term Care*, 12. For a review of plans, see also Mark Meiners, The State of the Art in Long-Term Care Insurance. Long-Term Care Financing and Delivery Systems: Exploring Some Alternatives. Conference Proceedings. Health Care Financing Administration, Department of Health and Human Services, Jan. 24, 1985.

14. *Increasing Private Financing of Long-Term Care: Opportunities for Collaborative Action.* SRI International, Aug. 1985, p. 14.

15. *Long-Term Care: The Challenge to Society*, Health Insurance Association of America, 1984.

16. Mark Meiners, "The Case for Long-Term Care Insurance," *Health Affairs* 2, no. 2 (Summer 1983):57.

17. Meiners, "The Case for Long-Term Care Insurance."

18. Mark Meiners and Gordon Trapnell, "Long-Term Care Insurance: Premium Estimates for Prototype Policies," *Medical Care* 22, no. 10 (October 1984).

19. *Increasing Private Financing of Long-Term Care*, 10.

20. Marion Ein Lewin, reported in preliminary research findings on private insurance for long-term care.

21. Portions of this section were drawn from a forthcoming Congressional Research Service report on life care communities by Evelyn Howard.

22. These estimates are from the following sources. A 1984 study, *Continuing Care Retirement Communities: An Empirical, Financial and Legal Analysis* by Howard E. Winklevoss and Alwyn V. Powell, estimated that there were about 275 life care communities serving about 90,000 elderly persons. Another 1984 survey of the life care industry, *Life Care Industry* by Laventhol and Horwath, estimated about 600 communities.

23. American Association of Retired Persons, *National Continuing Care Directory*, Ann Trueblood Raper, ed. (Washington, D.C., 1984), 5.

24. Laventhol and Horwath, *Life Care Industry*, 1984, Philadelphia, Pa., p. 7. The report makes a distinction between facilities which are "principally life care facilities" and those which are "oriented toward nursing care." The former refers to facilities where there are two or more apartments per nursing care bed, and the latter refers to facilities where there are fewer than two apartments per nursing care bed. The range of fees cited here include both types.

25. Winklevoss and Powell, "Continuing Care," 12.

26. Winklevoss and Powell, "Continuing Care," 13.

27. American Association of Retired Persons and Department of Health and Human Services, Administration on Aging, *A Profile of Older Americans* (Washington, D.C., 1984), 11.

28. Bruce Jacobs and William Weissert, "Home Equity Financing of Long-Term Care for the Elderly." *Long Term Care Financing and Delivery Systems: Exploring Some Alternatives. Conference Proceedings*. Health Care Financing Administration, Department of Health and Human Services, Washington, D.C. Jan. 1984. p. 83.

29. In 1978, the Federal Trade Commission began investigating management and marketing practices of some life care communities. See Senate Special Committee on Aging, *Life Care Communities: Promises and Problems*, S. Hrg. 98-276, Washington, D.C., May 25, 1983. As of August 1985, 13 states have enacted statutes to regulate life care communities.

30. Senate Special Committee on Aging and House Select Committee on Aging, *Home Equity Conversion: Issues and Options for the Elderly Homeowner*, House Pub. 99-513, January 28, 1985, 58. Testimony of Kenneth Beirne, General Deputy Assistant Secretary for Policy Development and Research, Department of Housing and Urban Development.

31. Reverse mortgages are also sometimes described as "reverse annuity mortgages" or "loan plans." For further information, see "Converting Home Equity Into Income for the Elderly: Issues and Options" by B. Ellington Foote, Congressional Research Service Report No. 84-42, April 5, 1984.

32. Bruce Jacobs and William Weissert, "Home Equity Financing of Long-Term Care for the Elderly." *Long Term Care Financing and Delivery Systems: Exploring Some Alternatives, Conference Proceedings*, Health Care Financing Administration, Department of Health and Human Services, Washington, D.C. Jan. 24, 1984. It should be noted that these findings were based on a model of probability of using home equity for this purpose, not on actual experience as to application of equity toward long-term care expenses.

33. ICF, Inc., *Private Financing of Long-Term Care: Current Methods and Resources*, Phase II (Report submitted to the Office of the Assistant Secretary for Planning and Evaluation, Department of Health and Human Services, January 1985), 25–26.

34. According to an information paper of the Senate Special Committee on Aging, lenders in the following states have offered loans: Arizona, California, Maine, Minnesota, New Jersey, Ohio, Pennsylvania, and Wisconsin. See Special Committee on Aging, *Turning Home Equity into Income for Older Homeowners: An Information Paper*, S. Rept. 98-216, July 1984, 12.

35. Senate Special Committee on Aging and House Select Committee on Aging, *Home Equity Conversion*, 59.

36. This provision was included as part of P.L. 98-181, enacted November 30, 1983.

Chapter 13

Impact of Capitated Finance Systems on the Continuum of Care

Robert S. DiPrete

Systems for delivering and financing health care are growing increasingly complex. What were once clear distinctions among types of organizations and arrangements for payment are becoming blurred. Insurance companies are developing their own alternative delivery systems, e.g., Metropolitan Life with its MetLife HMO network and Prudential with its Prucare network. Hospitals are developing their own health plans or are acquiring, or being acquired by, alternative delivery systems. New sorts of partnerships are being developed involving insurers, employers, physicians, health plans, hospitals, and other parties. Many of these emerging health care delivery and finance systems have in common the use of capitation as the form of payment for health services. This chapter examines the effects of capitated financing systems on managing the continuum of care.

DEFINITIONS

Working definitions are provided below for key terms in order to minimize confusion. Many of the terms generally used to describe alternative delivery and finance systems have gradually taken on a number of meanings, and definitions continue to evolve with changes in laws and regulations—and with the development of the marketplace itself. The following definitions will be used for the purposes of discussion in this chapter.

Capitation. A payment mechanism based on fixed reimbursement to providers of health care on a per person (or person per month of coverage) basis rather than on a per service basis. Premium payments to an HMO are a form of capitation payments, since an HMO is a provider as well as an insurer.

Note: The author acknowledges the insightful criticism of Michaela Garvey Hayes and Kathryn A. Poland, who reviewed the draft of this chapter.

Prepaid. A policy or service paid in advance of the period of coverage or in advance of the delivery of the service.

Risk Contracting. The formal agreement between a purchaser and a provider of health care services to furnish needed health care for a payment amount that does not vary with the utilization of services.

Risk Sharing. An arrangement in which two or more parties share (according to negotiated terms) in the savings or losses under a risk contract resulting from a variance between the payment received and the cost of the services provided.

Prepaid Health Plan. A system for both financing and delivering health care. A prepaid health plan is both insurer and provider.

Health Maintenance Organization (HMO). A prepaid health plan that agrees under a risk contract to provide, for a fixed capitation payment, a comprehensive benefit package to persons enrolled in the program. Federally qualified HMOs must cover a minimum benefit package specified by law.

Competitive Medical Plan (CMP). An organization that closely resembles an HMO but may provide a somewhat less comprehensive benefit package to its commercial enrollees. CMPs are authorized to negotiate risk contracts for the enrollment of Medicare beneficiaries. (The federal designation *competitive medical plan* was created by regulation in January 1985.)

Cost-effective. A service, etc., is cost-effective if it results in cost savings with no deterioration of health outcome or in additional health benefits worth the additional cost.[1]

CAPITATED HEALTH PLANS

Capitated finance systems almost always involve prepaid health plans, i.e., HMOs, CMPs, or similar health plans that have not been certified or licensed by the federal government. There are essentially four prepaid health plan models:

1. The staff model, in which the plan physicians are salaried employees of the plan and other services may be provided by plan providers or by subcontracting providers
2. The group practice model, in which the plan contracts with one or more medical groups for the provision of physician services to its enrolled members
3. The individual practice association (IPA) model, in which the plan contracts with an individual practice association for the provision of physician services to its enrolled members
4. The direct contracts model, in which the plan contracts directly with individual physicians to provide physician services to its enrolled members.

There are variations on the four types of prepaid health plans described above, and hybrids are still being developed. For the purposes of this discussion, the important element is the presence or absence of compensation through capitation payments to providers of various types. Preferred provider organizations (PPOs) are excluded from this discussion because they lack the "lock-in" enrollment feature that makes capitation workable. On the other hand, exclusive provider organizations (EPOs), which require the use of an EPO provider network as a condition for any coverage at all, may be viewed for the purpose of this chapter as the functional equivalent of HMOs.

A capitated finance system ties payment for health care services to a fixed amount per eligible person per period of coverage (usually a month). Capitation payments are typically prepaid. An important characteristic of capitated finance systems is that payment of providers is separated from the delivery of services and is based instead on the period of coverage. Thus, the health plans participating in capitated finance systems combine characteristics of insurers and providers. That is, the health plan receives a monthly premium (as does an indemnity insurer) as payment for a month's health coverage and is also responsible for the provision of needed health care services (unlike an indemnity insurer).

The fact that capitated finance systems separate payment for health coverage from the delivery of services means that the amount of payment does not vary with the level of utilization of services by the population enrolled under the coverage. This is what is meant by the *bearing of risk* in capitated finance systems. Although risk may be buffered under the terms of a particular contract, the typical capitation-based agreement places the provider of services (i.e., the contracting health plan) substantially at risk. Thus, if the cost of needed health care services used by the covered population exceeds the contractually set capitation payment amount, the provider (whether an HMO or an individual physician) absorbs a loss. Conversely, if the cost of services is less than the contractually set capitation payment amount, the provider enjoys a gain. While capitation payment amounts may change from one contract period to another to reflect changes in the expected level of services utilization, within a given contract period the capitation payment amount remains fixed.

The provider of health care services under a capitation-based agreement cannot increase current compensation by providing more, or more costly, services to the covered population. Instead, the fewer services provided (and the less costly those services), the greater the provider's realized income. This represents a marked change from the economic forces at work in a fee-for-service reimbursement arrangement. Since fee-for-service reimbursement ties payment directly to the provision of services, the purely economic incentive is to generate more income by maximizing the number and cost of services provided to the covered population. This difference in economic incentives is at the center of some of the major forces shaping the finance and delivery of health care today.

Many purchasers of health care coverage and services are moving to capitated finance systems (under risk contracts) as a way of transferring their own risk to the provider of health care services. One particular example of this trend is especially pertinent to the management of the continuum of care: Medicare risk contracting. The federal government (more specifically, the Health Care Financing Administration [HCFA]) has been experimenting for a number of years with the coverage of Medicare beneficiaries through HMOs. Recently, however, these research and demonstration projects have become a national initiative that is having a growing impact on the health care industry in general. In effect, the financial risk for the cost of health care services provided to Medicare beneficiaries is being decentralized, spreading from the federal government to a growing number of HMOs and CMPs.

In January 1985, HCFA published in the Federal Register the final regulations for Medicare risk contracting under Section 1876 of the Social Security Act. These regulations specify the conditions under which a federally qualified HMO or a federally certified CMP may contract with HCFA to enroll Medicare beneficiaries under a risk contract. Capitation payments for these contracts are based on the health plan's community rate (the rate it charges to its non-Medicare enrollees), adjusted for Medicare utilization levels and Medicare intensity of care factors. The limit on the capitation amount is currently 95 percent of what the HCFA actuaries have projected the federal government would have paid under fee-for-service Medicare reimbursement for those Medicare beneficiaries who choose to enroll in the HMO or CMP. Thus, the federal government has determined (to the extent actuarial art allows) that the Medicare program will realize a 5 percent savings on those beneficiaries who enroll in a risk contracting health plan.

In addition to this 5 percent savings, the federal government also benefits by passing its risk, through the contract, to the HMOs and CMPs. The contracting health plan is obligated to provide at least as comprehensive a Medicare benefit package as that provided to Medicare beneficiaries not enrolled in an HMO or CMP, and it must manage the delivery of health care carefully in order to keep costs within the capitation payments it receives from the federal government.

Medicare is one of three major kinds of health insurance coverage for the U.S. population; the other two kinds are Medicaid and commercial (either group or individual) accounts. In all three kinds, capitated finance systems are becoming more common.

Medicaid programs in many states are contracting with health plans for the enrollment of Medicaid recipients; reimbursement is in the form of capitation payments. As of mid-1986, states with such health plan enrollment options for Medicaid recipients included Arizona, California, Florida, Illinois, Minnesota, Missouri, New Jersey, Ohio, Oregon, Utah, and Wisconsin.

Commercial account enrollment in health plans that are under capitated finance systems is also growing. Many corporations and businesses are encouraging or even requiring new employees to enroll in an HMO. Lockheed has required HMO enrollment of all new employees since 1984, and Hughes Aircraft began the same requirement for its new employees in 1986. Even some self-insured employers are offering employees a capitated finance system alternative by developing an in-house health plan. McDonnell Douglas developed such a company HMO in 1985. Confidence in the cost-efficiency of capitated finance systems is by no means universal among major employers. Eastern Airlines recently made clear its suspicion that its contracting HMOs are enrolling employees who require less costly health care services than the capitation payments assume. In any case, capitated finance systems offer the prospect of reducing the health care purchaser's costs and risk; although the evidence may yet be inconclusive, the potential for cost-containment is difficult to deny.

The economic incentives for providers and purchasers of health care services are an important feature of capitated finance systems. Equally important are incentives to manage and maintain the health of the population enrolled in a capitated finance system. Besides the economic aspects, the following are often claimed as advantages of HMOs:

- emphasis on preventive medicine
- maintenance of health
- accessibility and availability of services
- case management by primary care physicians
- continuity of care

Viewed in the most flattering light, HMOs appear to offer the provision of quality health care services by a team of providers under the management of a primary care physician who is fully informed of the patient's medical history and present condition.

It should be noted that skepticism about capitated finance systems has not been lacking. There is persistent questioning of claims of the savings to purchasers of health care, and there is skepticism about the quality of care provided under capitated finance systems. The quality of care issue is a critical one for the federal initiative to enroll Medicare beneficiaries in HMOs and CMPs under risk contracts. In order to be federally licensed, an HMO or CMP must have in place an approved quality assurance program. Since the economic incentives inherent in a capitated finance system encourage the effective control of services utilization, quality assurance is examined closely. Also, since Medicare beneficiaries typically need more health care services from more types of providers, quality assurance is of special concern for this population.

In managing a continuum of care, the delivery of appropriate health care services in the appropriate setting is important. Referrals to specialty providers, hospital discharges, skilled nursing facility admissions, and the general planning of treatment all require attention to the patient's changing condition and to the best use of the available resources. In a capitated finance system, the role of the attending physician is often quite sharply defined in terms of management responsibilities, and treatment decisions should be watched closely for financial consequences and quality of care implications.

LONG-TERM CARE COVERAGE

The financing of long-term care is a major issue affecting capitated finance systems. While maximizing continuity of care may represent a promising approach to the management of long-term care in a comprehensive setting, it does little or nothing to address the problem of who pays the long-term care bill. As of this writing, Medicare covers in full only the first 20 days of skilled nursing facility care, and then requires a copayment by the beneficiary of $61.50 per day for days 21 through 100. After the 100th day, Medicaid covers additional days only if the Medicare beneficiary is also eligible for Medicaid coverage.

Putting aside questions as to the sensibility of this division of coverage, the transition from Medicare coverage to Medicaid coverage is a substantive issue when the skilled nursing facility patient is enrolled in a prepaid health plan under either Medicare or Medicaid. Since Medicare is the first payer in this situation, Medicaid acts in effect as a supplemental coverage to Medicare. As there becomes an increasing number of persons who are eligible for both Medicare and Medicaid and who are also enrolled in a prepaid health plan, this issue will take on greater importance. Also of concern is that the transition from Medicare-covered long-term care to Medicaid-covered long-term care is often economically devastating to the patient. The cost of nursing home care sometimes exceeds $1,200 per month for the ''private pay'' patient, and Medicaid means tests exclude from eligibility any patient with moderate or better personal resources. Thus, a lifetime's savings may be expended in bridging the gap between Medicare and Medicaid coverage of long-term care.

In recent years, a special variety of HMO has emerged that is designed to address directly the continuity of care issues (such as long-term care) that particularly affect the frail elderly and disabled populations: the social/health maintenance organization (S/HMO). A S/HMO combines the usual HMO benefit package with intermediate and long-term care, as well as services addressing the comprehensive health care needs and related social support needs of the target population. Thus, a S/HMO's benefit package might include adult day care, homemaker services, nonemergency transportation, home-delivered meals, and respite care in addition to a comprehensive range of medical services—all within one capitated finance system. In this setting, institutional care needs can be minimized as management of the continuum of care is combined with coordination of benefits.

Long-term coverage is an issue that is receiving increasing attention from state and federal government, from indemnity insurers, and from capitated finance systems. Legislation was proposed but not passed by Congress, that would have created a federal obligation to cover long-term care beyond the present Medicare and Medicaid coverage (H.R. 2293 and S. 1378, introduced in the 99th Congress by Representative Ron Wyden of Oregon and Senator David Durenberger of Minnesota, respectively). Insurance regulators at the state level are beginning to examine the implications of offering long-term care insurance privately rather than publicly. Some states are considering incentives that would encourage the development of the private long-term care insurance market.[2] Given the substantial liability borne by states under title XIX, as well as the widespread concern about financing the Medicare program, this interest in alternative funding of long-term care is not surprising.

INCENTIVE IMPLICATIONS OF CAPITATED
FINANCE SYSTEMS

Capitated finance systems have substantial implications for managing the continuum of care. These implications affect everyone involved, including administrators and managers, clinicians, providers, insurers, purchasers, and the patients themselves. Perhaps the most significant implication has to do with the economic incentives resulting from capitation payments. These incentives are markedly different from the economic incentives inherent in fee-for-service reimbursement.

Fee-for-service reimbursement ties payment made to providers directly to the provision of health care services. For example, a physician will receive a discrete payment for each office visit or procedure according to a fee schedule or a payment formula based on billed charges. This means that such a payment method increases a physician's income in direct proportion to the number and relative intensity of services furnished to patients under the fee-for-service coverage. Similarly, an insurer that reimburses providers on a fee-for-service basis will pay out more money in direct proportion to increases in the number and relative intensity of services provided. Since the insurer has received a fixed premium payment for each covered person, increased payments to providers directly decrease the insurer's reserves and/or profit margins. In brief, fee-for-service reimbursement entails that the insurer (or the direct-pay patient) and the provider each will gain financially only at the other's expense.

With capitation payment, however, the case is different. For example, a primary care physician is paid a fixed dollar amount per person per month in return for whatever primary care services might be needed by those persons enrolled with that primary care physician. The physician is contractually obligated to provide primary care as medically necessary without increased reimbursement for increased services. The insurer (in this case, the prepaid health plan) receives a fixed premium per person per month, and in turn pays a fixed capitation amount per person per month to the primary care physician. The risk for the cost of primary care has been transferred from the purchaser to the insurer, and in turn from the insurer to the provider. Under this payment arrangement, the physician has an economic disincentive to provide unnecessary primary care services, since to do so will mean expenditure of the physician's resources without any corresponding increase in payment.

Capitation, it would appear, rewards the provider for doing nothing, just as fee-for-service reimbursement would seem to reward the provider for doing anything. Fortunately, things are not quite so. The number and kind of services being provided to the covered population is monitored closely by both indemnity insurers and prepaid health plans. Underutilization of services and overutilization of services are equally indicative of problems in the management of health care delivery. Prepaid health plans must guard against underutilization, since the incentives of capitation payment lead in this direction. Similarly, indemnity insurers must guard against overutilization, since fee-for-service reimbursement creates incentives leading in that direction. Under either payment system, physicians have professional standards and ethical concerns that operate against inappropriate utilization of health care services.

Primary Care Physician Incentives

The incentives created by capitated finance systems are especially important in their impact on physicians. Physicians are arguably the most influential of all providers in determining which services are provided, when they are provided, and in what setting they are provided. It is not surprising, then, that physician incentives are a matter of great and growing concern to all involved with the delivery and financing of health care.

It is important to note that physicians themselves are aware of the sometimes insidious connections between economic incentives and the frequency and intensity of services provided. Under fee-for-service reimbursement, these economic incentives often are connected with the relative opportunity to hospitalize patients. In a *New England Journal of Medicine* editorial entitled "Which Rate Is Right," John Wennberg, M.D., discusses the connection between the availability of hospital beds and the incidence of hospital admissions for certain kinds of medical conditions:

> Admission rates for more than 80% of medical conditions, including most orthopedic injuries, such as fractures of the ankle and forearm, and knee and back injuries, and for manifestations of chronic cardiovascular disease other than acute myocardial infarction, such as chest pain, atherosclerosis, and congestive heart failure, are highly variable. For these, the need for hospitalization is less clearly defined and physicians differ from area to area on when hospitalization is appropriate. The admission rates for these sorts of medical conditions correlate positively with the number of beds per capita.

Unless the medical profession accepts responsibility for the question of "which rate is right" and addresses these issues within the current cost-containment context, others will see to it that "the least is always best" theory dominates by default. After all, if physicians can't agree on what is best, why do more?[3]

Capitation payment of primary care physicians is quite often accompanied by the contractual requirement that the primary care physician act as medical case manager. This "gatekeeper physician" role for the primary care physician is an important issue in managing the continuum of care. Contractual requirements regarding medical management are often extensive, including such elements as the following:

- responsibility for making necessary referrals to specialty physicians
- responsibility for specifying the scope of consultations by specialty physicians
- responsibility for assuring physician availability 24 hours per day, seven days per week
- responsibility for providing or authorizing emergency services
- responsibility for authorizing decisions to hospitalize
- responsibility for authorizing treatment plans, whether inpatient or outpatient
- responsibility for authorizing decisions to discharge from hospital
- responsibility for arranging for admissions to intermediate care facilities or skilled nursing facilities
- responsibility for arranging for home health care services

The medical care management responsibilities of primary care physicians are taken seriously by many successful prepaid health plans. It is important to note that many hospital and community-based programs have recently initiated their own formal case management programs. This development may well conflict with the simultaneous requirement that primary care physicians assume greater responsibility for case management under prepaid health plan contracts. Administrators of health care organizations offering a continuum of care should be aware of this potential conflict.

When the primary care physician is paid through capitation payments, the prepaid health plan has removed an economic incentive that might interfere with the physician's cost-effective medical case management. The primary care physician's economic incentives are even more aligned with the prepaid health plan's own economic incentives when the primary care physician shares in the risk for specialty and inpatient services. Such risk-sharing arrangements take many forms, but their intent is to bring about an increased awareness of the costs of all categories of care. A typical risk-sharing arrangement might include contract clauses like the following:

• If, in the aggregate, the actual expenditures for specialty physician care exceed the budgeted amount for all enrollees associated with a particular primary care physician, then the Plan and the physician will share the resulting losses 50-50, up to a maximum loss to the physician of X dollars (or Y percent of Plan payments to that physician).

• If, in the aggregate, the actual expenditures for inpatient care exceed the budgeted amount for all enrollees associated with a particular primary care physician, then the Plan and the physician will share the resulting losses 50-50 up to a maximum loss to the physician of X dollars (or Y percent of Plan payments to that physician).

• If, in the aggregate, the budgeted amount for specialty physician services exceeds actual expenditures for all enrollees associated with a particular primary care physician, then the Plan and the physician will share the resulting surplus 50-50.

• If, in the aggregate, the budgeted amount for inpatient services exceeds actual expenditures for all enrollees associated with a particular primary care physician, then the Plan and the physician will share the resulting surplus 50-50.

Risk sharing of this type does much to ensure that the provider most responsible for managing the frequency, intensity, and categories of services used will strive for cost-effectiveness. There is, however, the possibility that the cost-containment encouraged by such risk sharing may get out of hand. For example, an aberrant physician might decide against a medically indicated hospital admission in order to maximize his or her share in savings as determined by contract clauses like the sample clauses above. Putting aside the question of whether such practice is in fact cost-containing in the long run, it is certainly not responsible. The possibility of this sort of mismanagement of care motivates purchasers and regulators to demand effective quality assurance programs in capitated finance systems.

Specialty Physician Incentives

The incentives under capitated finance systems are not always as clear for specialty care physicians as they are for primary care physicians. Specialty care physicians are seldom reimbursed through capitation payments and are seldom given case management responsibilities. Prepaid health plans that place a substantial medical case management responsibility on the primary care physician often do not require risk and reward sharing of participating specialty care physicians. Risk and reward sharing are more appropriate with those providers who manage utilization of services. For example, when a prepaid health plan requires primary care physician authorization for all specialty and inpatient care as a condition of payment, it makes sense to share risk or rewards with specialty physicians and hospitals only if they are significantly involved in developing or structuring the treatment plans for patients enrolled in the prepaid health plan.

The incentives for specialty care physicians under capitated financing systems are related to their role as providers in a continuum of care. While the primary care physician is typically the medical case manager, the specialty care physician is consulted at points of transition from one segment of the continuum of care to another. These transition points include the following:

- admission to the hospital
- discharge from the hospital
- placement in a skilled nursing facility
- change in the focus or direction of a treatment plan

In brief, the specialty care physician is in most cases a fee-for-service provider operating within the capitated financing system. This means that the specialty care physician's economic incentives may be at odds with those of the primary care physician, and are often at odds with those of the prepaid health plan itself. However, the specialty care physician's economic incentives are usually aligned with those of other fee-for-service providers within the prepaid health plan, including hospitals, skilled nursing facilities, and home health care agencies.

Hospital Incentives

Hospitals fall into two major categories regarding economic incentives that arise from their relation to capitated finance systems. First, there are hospitals that are partners in a capitated finance system, e.g., hospitals that have started an HMO or CMP, either unilaterally or through a joint venture. Second, there are hospitals that interact with capitated finance systems exclusively as contracting providers.

Hospitals in the first category stand to gain or lose financially in tandem with their capitated finance systems. Although these hospitals may be reimbursed fee-for-service for the services they provide, they also stand to share in aggregate savings on the cost of all services provided to those enrolled. When a hospital owns an equity share in a prepaid health plan, its economic incentives as a partner in the insurance of health care will be to

- maximize occupancy
- minimize admissions per capita for plan enrollees

- minimize length of stay for plan enrollees
- minimize intensity of services provided to plan enrollees
- minimize readmissions of plan enrollees

However, the hospital's economic incentives as a provider will differ from its incentives as an insurance partner, just as the economic incentives for hospitals in the second category will differ from those of the insurers with whom they contract as service providers.

Hospitals in the second category will have different economic incentives depending on whether they are reimbursed through capitation payments or fee-for-service (and depending also on the type of fee-for-service payments). If a hospital's reimbursement is through capitation payments, its economic incentive will be to minimize the number of bed days used, the intensity of services provided, and any avoidable addition of marginal costs in the provision of services. If its reimbursement is fee-for-service, the type of fee-for-service reimbursement will determine the economic incentives. Consider the following three types of fee-for-service hospital reimbursement:

1. DRG-based reimbursement ties the amount of payment to the type of condition for which the patient is hospitalized, without regard to actual length of stay or intensity of services provided.
2. Per diem reimbursement ties payment to the number of days in the patient's hospital stay, without regard to diagnosis or intensity of services provided within a per diem payment category (e.g., medical/surgical, obstetrical, psychiatric).
3. Charge-based reimbursement ties payment to the hospital's billed charges for a particular stay.

The economic incentives associated with each of these fee-for-service reimbursement types are as follows:

1. DRG-based reimbursement: The incentive is to select the diagnosis that maximizes payment and minimizes the number of bed days and the cost-intensity of services provided.
2. Per diem payments: The incentive is to maximize the number of bed days and minimize the cost-intensity of services provided.
3. Charge-based reimbursement: The incentive is to maximize the number of bed days and the cost-intensity of services provided.

Note that the economic incentives for hospitals under reimbursement through capitation payments include an element that is not intrinsically associated with any of the three types of fee-for-service reimbursement: minimizing admissions.

Incentives for Other Providers

In addition to physicians and hospitals, there are several other providers that play important roles in a continuum of care. These include intermediate care facilities, skilled nursing facilities, adult day care centers, home health agencies, and hospices. These providers share one characteristic: they are in nearly all cases less expensive than hospitals with regard to the type of care in which they specialize. Often these providers are also alternatives to one another at the time a patient is discharged from a hospital. Their future is therefore closely connected with the future of hospitals.

Hospitals are changing as institutions. Much of this change is due to the effects of capitated finance systems on the health care marketplace. Initiatives for cost-containment usually identify the reduction of hospital inpatient utilization as a primary management goal—and every capitated health care finance system is an initiative for cost-containment. Most urban areas have a surplus of hospital beds. As has been noted earlier, the incidence of hospital admission for the majority of medical conditions seems to vary directly with the availability of hospital beds. This correlation may be due primarily to medical or to economic factors; in any case, hospitals with low occupancy rates are anxious to fill empty beds, and capitated finance systems (and other parties active in health care cost-containment) are anxious to eliminate hospital admissions for which there is a more cost-effective alternative.

When the decision is being made to discharge a patient from a hospital, one important consideration is whether the patient should be discharged to another care facility, to home with home health care services, or to home with no further treatment or care arranged. In a prepaid health plan, some, all, or none of the options for continuing care may be available under capitation payment. If the patient's primary care physician is the patient's case manager, that physician will have an economic incentive to arrange for continuing care reimbursed through capitation if he or she shares in the risks and rewards associated with the costs of continuing care. In any event, a primary care physician case manager who is cost-conscious will seek to place a patient in the least costly appropriate setting where needed care can be provided. Note that if the patient is referred outside the health plan for services not covered by the health plan, the cost may be substantial to the patient.

Since home health care represents a markedly less expensive alternative to continued hospitalization, it affords a good example of how economic incentives operate in the selection of a setting for continuing care. Mary Jane Koren, M.D., touched on the relevance of economic incentives in an article in *The New England Journal of Medicine:*

> Most referrals to home care programs are by nurses or social workers who may work for the agency to which they refer patients. Also, home

health agency staff are often involved in discharge planning and treatment planning, evaluating need and establishing frequency of visits and duration of placement.[4]

The factors noted by Dr. Koren are likely to be displaced by new incentives brought on by two developments: (1) Many prepaid health plans are seeking to negotiate capitation reimbursement agreements with home health providers, and (2) many hospitals are developing their own home health care agencies.

As home health care is brought within vertically integrated hospitals' portfolio of services and is covered more often under capitation payment agreements, it is likely that home health care will be used at least as often as now, but in response to different economic incentives. When a hospital refers a patient on discharge to the hospital's own home health care agency, the hospital continues receiving revenue. Similarly, when a prepaid health plan discharges a patient from a hospital bed to home health care reimbursed under a capitation agreement, savings may result.

Skilled nursing facilities also are relevant examples of the effect of capitated financing systems on managing a continuum of care. As was noted at the beginning of this chapter, the coordination of long-term care benefits between Medicare and Medicaid is a point of economic tension, in large part because of the high morbidity and mortality rates for this population. HCFA data illustrate this rather strikingly: "After standardization for age, the data indicated that the death rate was 50% higher for the dually eligible than for those eligible for Medicare only."[5]

Incentives for Consumers

Consumers of health care services are attracted to capitated finance systems by some combination of the following:

• low price
• extensive benefits package
• greater convenience
• absence of claims and bills
• accessibility and availability
• emphasis on health education and preventive care
• reputable providers

Enrollees in prepaid health plans usually understand full well the promised availability of a wide range of services at little or no cost per episode of care. They also expect that whatever array of providers they may require will be arranged for by the health plan. In some instances this is a drawback since enrollees may have to give up their former physician for a participating health plan physician. Since their health care needs are paid for in advance under the implied responsibility of the health plan to keep them healthy, the enrollees' incentive is to use primary care services whenever they perceive the need; postponement of care makes little sense. Prepaid health plan enrollees are therefore likely to complain if they feel that either the accessibility or availability of health care services is being compromised. (Sophisticated consumers of prepaid health plan services, however, do tend to expect some difficulty in getting referred on demand to specialists.)

Medicare beneficiaries appear (at least anecdotally) to be especially attracted by the absence of patient responsibility for handling claims and bills. Traditional fee-for-service Medicare imposes a heavy claims-processing burden on the beneficiary, and freedom from this burden is a likely motive for enrolling in an HMO or CMP.

UTILIZATION CONTROL AND QUALITY ASSURANCE

In practice, economic incentives that might encourage either overutilization or underutilization are counterbalanced by two factors. First, there is the individual commitment on the part of the vast majority of providers of all types to place the health and well-being of the patient above economic considerations in furnishing and arranging for medical care. Second, there are the effects of utilization control and quality assurance programs.

Utilization control is increasingly common with indemnity insurers and nearly universal with capitated finance systems. In both cases, the goal of utilization control is to guard against inappropriate utilization of services and especially to monitor for overutilization.

Quality assurance programs monitor for substandard care. With capitated finance systems, quality assurance typically includes an increased surveillance for the omission of needed health care services. The most effective quality assurance program is one that recognizes and addresses the economic incentives at work. The author knows of no convincing evidence that providers of medical care are either more or less susceptible to economic incentives than the general population.

Quality assurance programs will probably turn their attention more and more to the management of the continuum of care. The forces acting on health care finance and delivery will continue to cause change, and this change will affect the transition points between the various segments of the continuum of care. Effective quality assurance programs will monitor the efficacy of coordination of care, the health outcomes of patients with various conditions treated at various levels of care, and any significant changes in the rates of utilization of services in the various segments of the continuum of care.

Case Examples

The effects of capitated finance systems on the continuum of care include both problems and opportunities. Perhaps the best example of this is the medical management responsibilities of the primary care physician in many prepaid health plans. Medical management responsibility is in part economically motivated: It is a mechanism for controlling utilization and cost of services. However, medical management is also designed to maximize coordination of care and to prevent slippages and gaps in the continuum of care. It is the responsibility of the medical manager to take full advantage of all levels of care available to the patient. When this responsibility is carried out effectively, the likelihood is increased that care will be of high quality and cost no more than is necessary; when it is not, substandard care is the likely result, probably at excessive cost.

Consider two examples that together indicate how capitated finance systems can affect the management of the continuum of care for ill or for good.

The first example is a prepaid health plan with the following characteristics:

- Primary care physicians have full responsibility but little authority for case management.
- Protocols and documentation requirements for specialty care referrals, hospital admissions, and other treatment planning decisions are weak or unclear.
- Risk and reward sharing arrangements are ill conceived, penalizing or rewarding providers for the wrong sorts of practice; economic incentives are not aligned to encourage responsible cost-containment by all participating providers.
- Utilization targets are set too low.
- Clinicians are not trained in multidisciplinary teamwork.
- Reimbursement of participating providers is inadequate or of the wrong type to encourage responsible cost-containment.
- Quality assurance is ineffective.

The result of such an array of weaknesses would be mismanagement of the continuum of care, characterized by substandard care, omitted care, services provided at an inappropriate level or in an inappropriate setting, and fruitless expenditure of resources.

The second example is a prepaid health plan with the following characteristics:

- Case management responsibilities are judiciously designed and are matched with appropriate authority.
- Protocols and documentation requirements for specialty care referrals, hospital admissions, and other treatment planning decisions are clear and adequate.

- Risk and reward sharing arrangements are balanced, and incentives are aligned to encourage responsible cost-containment.
- Utilization targets are neither too high nor too low.
- Clinicians are trained appropriately in multidisciplinary team management.
- Payment levels are adequate and encourage responsible cost-containment.
- Quality assurance is effective.
- The plan has providers under contract who cover the entire continuum of care.
- The plan has risk contracts for Medicare, Medicaid, and commercial groups.
- The plan is paid premiums that reasonably reflect the coordination of benefits among Medicare, Medicaid, and commercial coverage.

Such a prepaid health plan would be capable of effective management of the continuum of care.

FUNCTIONAL REQUIREMENTS OF CAPITATED HEALTH SYSTEMS

Although it is not intended that this chapter serve as a guide to the development of a prepaid health plan, the following is offered as a brief summary of the necessary elements. Consulting the legal and regulatory requirements for federal qualification of an HMO and federal certification of a CMP is recommended as a way of getting a more complete picture. In brief, the successful operation of a prepaid health plan requires good administration in the following areas:

- financial management
- risk management
- rate development/actuarial analysis
- marketing
- management information system (MIS) support
- membership management
- provider relations/contract management
- utilization management
- quality assurance

Providers and organizations contracting with prepaid health plans should examine proposed contract terms as to their implications in each of these areas.

CONCLUSION

It is not reasonable to expect that capitated finance systems will entirely replace fee-for-service reimbursement. Neither is it reasonable to expect that capitated finance systems will go away, or even that they will stop growing in enrollment in the near future. Health care providers and health services delivery organizations should therefore plan for both types of reimbursement, and for the tensions between them. Government initiatives in Medicare and Medicaid and private sector commitment to cost-containment suggest that capitated finance systems will demand increased attention from those who manage the continuum of care.

NOTES

1. Adapted from Peter Doubilet et al., "Use and Misuse of the Term 'Cost Effective' in Medicine," *New England Journal of Medicine* 314, no. 4 (January 23, 1988).

2. Laurence F. Lane, "Insurers Response Growing to Consumer Demand for Long-Term Care Plans," *Business and Health*, January-February 1986: 49.

3. John Wennberg, "Which Rate is Right?" *New England Journal of Medicine* 314, no. 5 (January 30, 1986).

4. Mary Jane Koren, "Home Care—Who Cares?" *New England Journal of Medicine* 314, no. 14 (April 3, 1986).

5. Alma McMillan et al., "A Study of the 'Crossover Population'; Aged Persons Entitled to Both Medicare and Medicaid," *Health Care Finance Review* 4, no. 4 (Summer 1983).

Chapter 14

Computer Applications within the Continuum of Care

Mary C. Kreger, MPH
Lawrence J. Weiss, PhD

The term *management information system* (MIS) is commonly used to refer to computerized systems for ordering information. Although computerization is not a prerequisite, it is essential that information be gathered and organized in a manner that enables it to be retrieved and employed for the appropriate task or decision. MISs are also communication systems. Communication among departments, within departments, and over time (i.e., historical information retrieval) is enhanced. A variety of routinely used systems are examples of MISs: libraries, medical records, staffing schedules, and accounts payable and receivable.

In the complexity of the horizontally and vertically integrated health and social service systems of today, communication among departments and services is a prerequisite for managing and integrating a system. The capabilities of computer networks that can access and integrate data from services within a continuum of care and a community are especially relevant. An MIS is particularly valuable in dealing with chronic conditions that may evolve slowly and therefore be more difficult for health and social service personnel to keep track of. The sequence of relevant events in chronic illnesses may be separated by months or years. The computer system allows information about these events and related financial data to be integrated, tracked, and organized appropriately by time or event. Figure 14-1 shows the software components in the On Lok Senior Health Services System.

An MIS should improve the decision-making process in ways that are relevant to the programs involved. At a minimum, the system should improve internal decisions with regard to finances and client care, as well as providing the capability for accurate reporting to funding or regulatory agencies. In the case of internal decisions, the system should improve client information, making possible improved decisions regarding care; also, financial decisions should be improved by having timely information. External decisions should be improved by allowing timely and precise responses to reporting agencies.

Figure 14-1 The On Lok Information Management System: Major Software Components

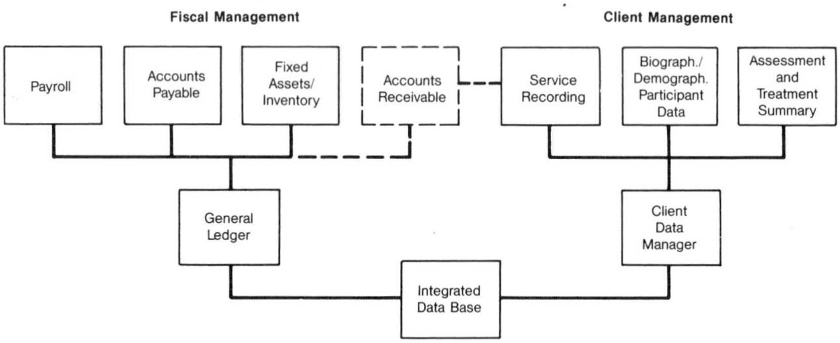

Fiscal Management   Client Management

| Payroll | Accounts Payable | Fixed Assets/ Inventory | Accounts Receivable | Service Recording | Biograph./ Demograph. Participant Data | Assessment and Treatment Summary |

General Ledger

Client Data Manager

Integrated Data Base

Source: Reprinted from *Computerized Information Management in Long Term Health Care: A Case Study* by R.T. Zawadski and S. Gee, with permission of On Lok Senior Health Services, © 1982.

This chapter is divided into several sections. In the first, the history of the computer field is explored briefly. In the second section, clinical applications relevant to a continuum of care are discussed. Specific uses as well as the ramifications for clients and service providers are presented. The third section considers examples and the importance of operational applications. The fourth section discusses research and planning applications. The fifth section discusses important steps in designing an MIS for a continuum of care. The final section is a resource guide to individuals and organizations that may be able to provide further computer assistance in design or applications relevant to the continuum of care.

HISTORY OF THE FIELD IN RECENT YEARS

This section provides a brief chronology of the development of MISs. The magnitude of the revolution that is occurring in the financing and delivery of health care is matched, if not surpassed, by the magnitude of the continuing revolution in the technology of data management. Late in the 1960s, MISs were designed that would conduct operational tasks and also provide supportive services for managerial and planning activities. While the processing and operational activities, including issuing paychecks and other routine and predictable accounting tasks, were generally successful, the higher level managerial and planning designs usually did not meet expectations. In recent years, the sophistication of systems has greatly increased. The more predictable, operational tasks are handled now by systems programmed to deal with structured problems, while managerial and planning functions are handled by strategic planning systems that enable a sophisticated integration of data. Now computer systems are capable of providing timely, appropriate analysis to assist in the development of a continuum of care in the rapidly changing health care environment. Computers in the 1950s and 1960s were difficult to house, expensive, and required specialized knowledge to operate. With the development of the microprocessing chip and user friendly programs, sophisticated computer applications are now widely available. As a result, health and social service personnel are now actively involved in the use of computer systems for client care.

Large businesses and state and federal agencies have used mainframe computers to perform highly structured activities since the 1960s. This type of data processing is generally accepted as being cost-effective and accurate. However, problems with these systems may still exist, as when it is necessary but difficult to correct information. Hospitals use computers in the monitoring of patients (e.g., in cardiac monitors and as aids in diagnosis and treatment) and in transfering patient information among hospital departments (e.g., laboratory data from a client's tests). However, use in multiple multidisciplinary health and social service settings is just beginning to develop.

Since hospitals are the largest, and historically the most profitable, entities within the health care market, the greatest energy has been expended in this sector. Nursing homes and home health agencies, being smaller segments of the market, offer less profitability for developers of hardware and software systems. Therefore, very little has been done in developing their potential. This does not mean that the appropriate technology does not exist, but when designing systems for these services, it is usually necessary to put together a variety of components initially designed for slightly, or even drastically, different purposes. Programming for the specific application or modifying a standard program may be necessary in these situations.

CLINICAL APPLICATIONS

A continuum of care matches the need of a client with the appropriate level and type of medical, health, or social service(s). This matching of needs with services requires the distilling of a great deal of information in a timely manner. Coordination among services requires even more. Even for a single service, gathering and processing this information is a labor-intensive and time-consuming task. The expansion of hospitals and other providers into horizontally and vertically integrated service systems intensifies the need for case management and communication among departments, including the concomitant transfer of information. For example, an individual who is seen in the emergency room needs to have his clinical record available to providers in the outpatient clinic, the inpatient setting, and other services within the continuum. A common clinical record is the underpinning of continuity of care.

Just as the paperless hospital is now possible, whole networks of integrated service systems will soon be able to function with computer supplements to or replacements of the traditional paper charting system. Two factors are driving these advances. First, the technology has developed to enable expansion. Second, the change from cost-based to prospective pricing reimbursement and the competitive environment in health care makes it necessary for data to be analyzed in new ways. Under cost-based reimbursement, the unit of analysis is the department, and census and financial statements constitute the requisite data. Under prospective pricing, it is desirable and necessary to track data and costs by patient and by diagnosis for all services provided in the continuum. These changing data requirements are necessitating new measures of quality, as well as new measures of task performance on an individual and systemwide level. These requirements are especially pertinent to a continuum of care, because of its complexity and its interlocking levels of service provision.

Common applications of an MIS to clinical needs occur in the following areas: medical and health history, service coordination, and tracking and monitoring. Each of these is discussed below. Additionally, separate sections discuss the ramifications of an MIS for health and social service personnel and clients.

Client Records

There are three primary advantages of computerized medical records, medical record summaries, and health status records. First, evidence suggests the time required for chart review is decreased. Second, medical logic can provide prompts or assistance in client diagnosis and treatment. Some programs can also predict outcomes—based on other individuals in the data base—for specific conditions or treatments. Third, the disease process itself can be studied and better understood. The clinical data base can present relevant information in a time-oriented or symptom-oriented manner, thereby increasing the efficiency of analysis of various aspects of the disease.[1]

Computerized health and social service records can be divided into medical records, medical record summaries, and health status records. Software programs for all three types of records are discussed below. Medical record programs exist that can perform the functions of the paper chart. One limiting factor is the escalation of costs that occurs as the number of records increases. Additional research and development to allow for expanded applications is underway.

A medical record summary provides a list of important events and dates. This saves storage space and facilitates finding major events in the complete record. Retrieval can thus be achieved faster, since the number of entries is reduced.

Health status records present a profile of relevant client information. In certain situations, clinical assessments are able to be replaced by data from self-administered questionnaires that provide longitudinal data of clients' medical and social conditions. This type of program can be used to track changes in conditions and, when analyzed in conjunction with changes in status or utilization data, to predict future changes in health status or utilization of services. Health maintenance organizations and preferred provider organizations frequently compile this type of information to aid in screening and monitoring enrollees.

As it becomes increasingly important to measure the efficiency and effectiveness of health care provision, additional thought will be given to defining meaningful measures of client activity. There are three types of units that can be used in defining client contracts. They are visits, episodes of illness, and time periods (usually one year).[2] Visits are the standard measure of client encounters used in all of the software program examples cited later in this section.

For chronic conditions, great advantages exist in the categorizing of episodes of illness or care. Such data provide utilization per problem or symptom and are useful in comparing outcomes according to the number and types of procedures and tests employed, complicating conditions, and total resources used. However, the definitions required for delineating episodes are not agreed upon, especially for ambulatory services. For example, what defines an episode? What connects events so that an episode is formed? How are episodes with multiple diagnoses or presenting symptoms that do not lead to a clear diagnosis dealt with? The yearly basis of aggregating care is helpful for capitation but may arbitrarily cleave related events that occur in two different years. Also, care within one year may relate to multiple illnesses or symptoms.

Several examples of computerized client records follow. Included are brief overviews of the Total Medical Record, COSTAR, Regenstrief, HELP, and PROMIS.

The Total Medical Record (TMR)

The Total Medical Record, often referred to as TMR, was developed at Duke University starting in 1972. The goal of this system is to supersede the paper chart. TMR includes the following information: demographic data, diagnoses, procedures, laboratory and other tests, therapies, results of physical examinations, appointments, and accounting information. History and data collection protocols exist for specific types of problems. Recall of this information can be accomplished by time, problem, or encounter. In the TMR system, a dictionary, which is defined by the user, controls the modules that manipulate the data. Changes in the orientation of an inquiry can be accomplished easily, without a significant amount of reprogramming. The administrative function that performs billing and scheduling tasks can offset some of the maintenance costs of the system by reducing the costs of billing and scheduling. The program works on either a mini- or a microcomputer, although applications are more limited on the latter. For statistical analysis, the system can be linked to a mainframe computer.

COSTAR

From 1968 to 1978, the Massachusetts General Hospital Laboratory of Computer Science developed COSTAR (COmputer-STored Ambulatory Record) in conjunction with the National Center for Health Services Research, the Digital Equipment Corporation, and the Mitre Corporation. To date, it is the most widely used clinical data base. Its goal is to supplement the paper chart; increase clinicians' access to information by improving the legibility, systematization, and recall of clinical data; and support accounting, budgeting, planning, and research functions. Data can be entered or recalled by batch before or after a visit or online during a visit. Reports can be generated for specific encounters or as status reports, which include pertinent information (e.g., medication and test results). Due to the Robert Wood Johnson Foundation Program for Hospital Initiatives in Long-Term Care, COSTAR has now been modified to enable assimilation of data for acute and chronic care issues. Geriatric assessments, plans for care, and issues relevant to social workers and nurses have now been incorporated into COSTAR. To accomplish this, both the system and the vocabulary have been enlarged. This system is being used by the three Massachusetts General Hospital Community Health Centers. As with TMR, COSTAR's administrative functions can help offset the costs of operating the system. Since COSTAR's design and development were financed partly by the federal government, the software is considered to be in the public domain. The ramifications of this status, however, are unclear, and the firmware—the link between hardware and software—might not be considered in the public domain. Both mini- and microcomputers can be used with COSTAR.

Regenstrief

The Regenstrief Medical Record system is used at the Regenstrief Health Center in Wishnard Memorial Hospital, an affiliate of the Indiana University School of Medicine. Development of the program was started in 1973. The goal of this system is to assist in the incorporation of information into, and to foster appropriate use of, the medical record by health and social service personnel. Protocols, written by physicians, remind clinicians to check for certain conditions or to order specific tests based on the data previously entered, the specific diagnosis, or the presenting problem. Prompts range from preventive care through appropriate follow-up decisions during therapeutic or diagnostic interventions. In research, this program can determine predictors of specific outcomes or events within certain diseases or under certain protocols of treatment.

HELP

This system was developed at the Latter Day Saints Hospital at the University of Utah in Salt Lake City starting in 1970. The system provides a medical data base, as well as administrative and research functions. The medical decision logic can search and mark irregular results and provide guidelines for diagnosis and treatment. At the Latter Day Saints Hospital, data on all medications are entered into the computer before the medications are dispensed. In this way, there is a check whether the medications might result in synergistic or allergic reactions and whether the individuals have contra-indicative conditions. Prescribed medications and dosing schedules are listed for each patient for each nursing shift. The system assimilates information from many hospital locations and creates a unified data base.

PROMIS

Development of PROMIS (Problem-Oriented Medical Information System) started in 1968 at the University of Vermont. Since 1970 it has been in use at the Medical Center Hospital of Vermont. This program classifies information according to problem and lists the problems, plans, and progress notes. Data are presented in various summarized formats. The convenience of these summaries acts as an inducement to use the computer. Medical and business audits, as well as epidemiological studies, can be performed on this system.

HELP, COSTAR, Regenstrief, and PROMIS each provide some form of medical logic that helps guide health and social service personnel through medical histories and diagnostic and treatment procedures. HELP, in addition to providing "if-then" statements, can give probability statements regarding outcomes. COSTAR contains flow charts for common conditions and diagnoses. PROMIS, TMR, and COSTAR provide summaries of client information. For example, COSTAR produces status reports that contain summary information required for monitoring or treating a client. TMR and COSTAR allow the user to define or adapt various functions. Most programs use coded data. This serves to standardize entries and reduce errors. COSTAR, in addition to using coded data, allows for the use of text. Each of these programs allows for interactive entry and recall of data during client visits. COSTAR also allows data to be entered in batch form after client visits.

Service Coordination

The uses of MISs for service coordination include client follow-up instructions, scheduling, and communication among various providers within a continuum of care. Each is discussed below.

Follow-up instructions and reminders for clients can be generated easily in an MIS. Reminders or prompts regarding appropriate preventive, screening, or follow-up techniques can also be provided to health and social service personnel at timely junctures in client care. This capability can also be used as a marketing tool by the hospital to direct specific information to clients who are most likely to benefit from it.

Client and personnel scheduling can be handled more efficiently on a computer system. This function involves scheduling clients' appointments and planning appropriate staffing levels. Additionally, scheduling among various services in a continuum can be accomplished in such a way as to achieve the maximum benefit of resources. For example, services that frequently require the most intensive scheduling are transportation and homemaker or chore services. To ensure that the service is available when needed and that it is timed appropriately requires precision. Scheduling on the computer can be much more accurate than with a manual system. On Lok Senior Health Services in San Francisco estimates that their manual information system was 90–95 percent accurate. Their computer information system, in contrast, is 99.5 percent accurate.[3] This increased accuracy is important for scheduling as well as for maintaining records of clients' addresses and telephone numbers, which are essential for routine contacts and home-delivered services.

Another area of importance in coordination is communication among providers. One of the advantages of keeping progress notes in the computer is the ability to update information, print the information, and send copies to other providers. This can be accomplished easily for providers in a continuum of care or for other organizations in the community. Of course, the process can also function in reverse, with community organizations referring clients to services and being able to easily and rapidly transmit information.

Tracking and Monitoring

Tracking and monitoring of clients in a continuum of care permits increased accuracy in historical data, scrutiny of functional levels, and integration of health and social service data with financial data. Each area is discussed below. Examples of programs that employ tracking and monitoring functions conclude this section.

Monitoring the treatment of continuing clients allows for up-to-date information, which is especially important in maintaining quality of care. For example, a current list of medications can alert health and social service personnel to potential adverse drug reactions before they occur.

Previous encounters with any level of a continuum of care are essential to know about in providing appropriate and timely health and social services. It is important to know whether a client had a heart attack years ago that led to hospitalization or had functional problems several weeks ago that resulted in a screening appointment, as well as knowing about the care provided and the results. Creating historical files on clients involves aggregating and integrating data in new ways. The pattern of relationships of information becomes more important. Systems of data collection and analysis that previously operated independently, such as clinical and financial information systems, need to be integrated. Only by this integration will it be possible to aggregate costs by clients and diagnoses. This type of individual patient data will allow the assessment of ways of identifying costs and the designing of ways of treating clients more efficiently and effectively.

Tracking of patients through the network of services and providers will allow analysis of changes in function or status and of the quality of care provided. The pooling of client information by diagnoses, treatments, tests, procedures, and results will allow better coordination and management. The management and coordination will also affect the types of planning that are done for an individual entering the system. Planning for relevant procedures and treatment allows required resources to be routinely anticipated. Budgeting of time and resources can thus be accomplished earlier in the client care process, in part because of the expanded types of client information available.

The tracking of clients will allow for the monitoring of each client's medical and social history. The service coordinator will be able to take a proactive position regarding treatment and intervention, in contrast to the currently common reactive stance. For example, when multiple chronic conditions manifest themselves, the service coordinator can plan with the client to ensure that functioning remains as normal as possible, as opposed to waiting for function to deteriorate and then taking steps to improve it. Similarly, awareness of social factors that affect the health or function of an individual need to be monitored for potential problems.

An MIS should integrate information on the client, the provider, the care process, and costs. From an analysis of this information, identification of elements that explain variations in the outcome of diseases, in care interventions, and costs should be possible. For example, the ability to compare clients with the same diagnoses adjusted for length of stay, for complicating factors, and by provider is a routine matter for an MIS. These functions enable several subsequent processes to occur: (1) for uncomplicated cases, protocols that outline appropriate care can be written to facilitate the care process; (2) cases that exceed routine parameters can be screened; (3) reasons for these variations can be probed; (4) screening for quality assurance can be accomplished; and (5) provider productivity can be measured. The advantage of an MIS in a continuum of care is that information on clients is available for the periods before and after hospitalization. This can provide useful variables in analyzing the course of illness or care.

A significant advantage of an MIS is its ability to connect resources used in client care with the result of care. This type of analysis, which has not been easily done up to this time, can demonstrate the tradeoffs among various options. For example, does the use of telephone calls to check on elderly clients decrease the frequency of necessary visits? Can a nurse coordinator effectively postpone or prevent hospitalization or nursing home admissions for certain types of clients by increasing the effectiveness of the informal support network? Guidelines for appropriate care, including measures of efficacy, efficiency, and professional and cultural values, can be developed from these analyses.

Tracking patients through a continuum becomes especially important if payment for services is on a capitated or single-payment basis. Capitated plans need aggregate data to determine capitation rates and to monitor the use of costly services. Only by having a record of services across the continuum can the aggregated amount of services be totaled. By studying specific patterns of expenditures, strategies for substituting one type of service for another or for designing complementary services can be developed and analyzed for efficiency, cost-effectiveness, and quality of care. Additionally, the most efficient use of resources and personnel can be studied. The Group Health Cooperative of Puget Sound, a health maintenance organization, has designed a data base that incorporates clinical data relevant to its prepaid coverage system. Again, this type of record is especially valuable for tracking and monitoring clients and developing an historical record.

Clearly, there is wide latitude in the design of systems for institutions. Development of an MIS should be guided by which current issues require information for the purpose of analysis. At present, important reasons for monitoring clients include the following: (1) to examine the efficacy of treatments and procedures; (2) to determine appropriate levels of utilization by diagnosis and severity of illness; (3) to measure provider productivity; and (4) to increase provider productivity. Regarding provider productivity, it is important to determine the reasons for differences in practice patterns. Demographic variables, case mix, and number of ancillary procedures performed constitute three possibilities for variation. Also, specific information can be generated regarding the costs of specific configurations of diseases and functional impairment. Identification of which practice patterns and resource allocations yield the greatest advantage is possible.

A specific example of an on-line medical record and client tracking system is the one used in the cardiovascular disease program at Duke University since 1969. It is used to track everyone suspected of having cardiovascular disease. Since 1974, it has provided "prognostigrams," which describe projected outcomes, at each stage of evaluation, for those involved in the cardiovascular disease evaluation program. As the program expanded and all clients suspected of having a cardiovascular condition were evaluated, the system was combined with TMR. It is now a significant tool that supports multiple care-related functions.[4]

Another example of files created to track clients' activities is the system designed by the Mount Zion Care Account at the San Francisco Institute on Aging, Mount Zion Hospital and Medical Center, San Francisco. Component files used for client tracking, utilization, and expenditures are categorized (according to subject matter) as either client health status files or financial and service utilization files.

The following are examples of client health status files:

- The Client Application file provides selected information from the client's application to join the Mount Zion Care Account. Name, medical record number, address, insurance information, and the dates enrollment procedures were completed are recorded in this file.
- The Demographics file provides information on demographics, such as language spoken, marital status, living arrangements, income, and primary physician.
- The Provider file lists the primary physician and the specialists the client sees, as well as the frequency of visits.
- The Health Status and Medical Record file lists a number of categories of health problems and the client's status with respect to these. This information is compiled from the Health Status Questionnaire, which is self-administered annually.
- The Other Information file provides additional information on recent stressful events, personal habits, psychosocial conditions, and regular social contacts.
- The Personal Information file gives information to Care Account personnel on assistive equipment needs, activities of daily living, independent activities of daily living, and dietary habits.
- The Assistance Provided file provides information on the types of assistance given, the provider, and the relationship to the client.
- The Coordination Plan file reports the client's status with respect to relevant health status measures, contacts with the nurse coordinator, and risk level, as well as the status of notes in the chart.

A variety of financial and service utilization reports also exist, including the following:

- The Service Utilization file provides a list of clients and for each health and social service, the units of service used.
- The Financial and Service Utilization by Individual file occurs in two formats: one lists each unit of service separately, the other aggregates units from the same service.
- The Summary of Financial and Service Utilization by All Patients file lists the units of all services used by specific clients.

Figure 14-2 shows examples of the client files used by Mount Zion Care Account.

Utilization Review and Quality Assurance

Utilization review and quality assurance functions can also be expedited in a continuum by an MIS. In utilization review, an MIS enables analysis of utilization

Figure 14-2 Selected Health Status Data for Enrollees in the Mount Zion Care Account

Mount Zion Care Account Personal Information

Q.93 Bathe	Q.101 1. Other
Q.94 Dress	
Q.95 Move	TQ.102 a. Handrail
Q.96 Eat	
Q.97 Bathroom	Mount Zion Care Account Other Information

Mount Zion Care Account Other Information

Q.70 Smoke

4 Q.79 Downhearted   Q.84 Irritable
2 Q.80 Happy   Q.85 Demands

Q.98 Walk
Q.99 Bladder
Q.100 Bowels
Q.101 Transp.
Q.101
Q.101
Q.101
Q.101
Q.101
Q.101
Q.101
Q.101
Q.101
Q.101

Mount Zion Care Account Medical Record

Q.29 Fatigue	Q.48 Swelling of feet	Q.55 Dental prb.
Q.30 Insomnia	Q.49 Pain in legs (walk)	Q.56 Loss of apt.
Q.31	Q.50 Pain in legs (rest)	Q.57 Weight loss

Q.32
Q.33
Q.34

Mount Zion Care Account Demographics

Q.35
Q.36
Q.37
Q.38
Q.39

Last Name: MITHRIDATES
First Name: JOAN
Middle Initial: E
Medical Record: # 99999   # of Calls: 0

Q.13 Sources of income
T Social Security
F SSI
T Pension
F Wages

Q.40
Q.41
Q.42
Q.43
Q.44
Q.45
Q.46
Q.47

Q1. Race/Ethnicity 5 Other
Q2. Religion 2   Other
Q3. Language 1   Other
Q4. Speak English? T
      Read English? T
      Write English? T
Q.5 Marital status 3
Q.6 Housing 1   Other
Q.7 Ownership 1
Q.8 How long lived there? 5
Q.9 Living arrangements 1
Q.10 # of people in house 0
Q.11 Schooling 4
Q.12 Income 4

T Interest
F Investment
F Rental property
F Family
   Other
Primary occupation: SALESMAN
When retired 01/01/75
Name: DR. L. WEISS
Addr: 20 GEARY BLVD
City: SAN FRANCISCO
Sta: CA Zip 94116
D Phone: (415)929-0000
E Phone: (415)929-0000
Relat: PERSONAL PHYSICAN

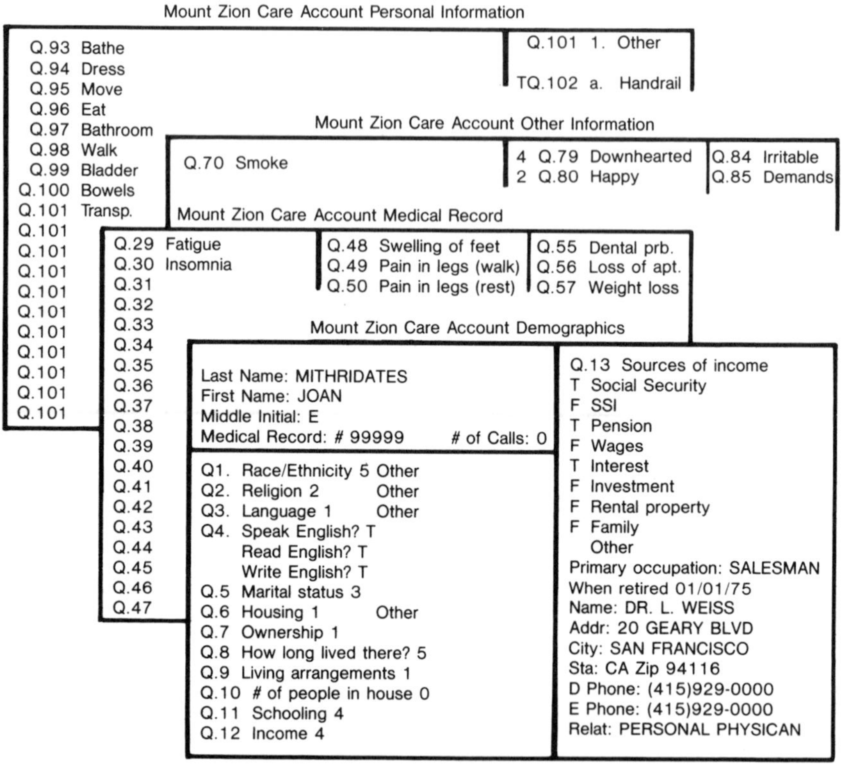

by type of client, whether individual or grouped. This is essential for cost control. Similarly, in quality assurance, analysis of symptoms and diagnoses in conjunction with treatment procedures allows for quality of care to be assessed by client, provider, or treatment mode.

Ramifications of an MIS for Service Personnel

The tracking of clients through the range of services in a continuum greatly facilitates the practice of health and social service personnel. Information regarding all aspects of the client's care allows all providers to have access to relevant information about a given client. The coordination of medications alone affords the opportunity to reduce the risks associated with different clinicians prescribing medications for different conditions without being aware of possible synergistic reactions among drugs. Similarly, clinicians will become increasingly educated about the "total patient." Information that previously was limited within disciplines or services becomes available in a convenient form and without the need for lengthy meetings and conferences held merely to inform participants. Of course, it is still necessary for personnel to discuss cases. However, less time need be spent sharing initial information regarding recent client procedures and treatment. This increase in the types and flow of information among providers facilitates the delivery of appropriate care. Better clinical judgments can be made faster than is possible under the constraints of fragmented information systems.

Computer capabilities are not used just to track clients. All levels of care providers need to be tracked to determine associated costs and performance. This can be achieved by integrating clinical and financial data bases. This information allows analyses for determining which clinicians and services reduce costs or generate profits or losses, as well as for determining efficiency measures that could be implemented. Analysis of practice patterns or portions of practice patterns is facilitated by computer systems, and quality of care becomes easier to monitor.

To date, clinical data bases have been used very little in educating medical and social service providers. Libraries now routinely conduct literature searches for articles; at some point they may be able to provide access to the actual data upon which articles are based. The ability to update information easily also means that computers could be used to supply care providers with recent advances in diagnosis, treatment, and service provision.

Ramifications for Clients

Clients benefit from an MIS in several ways. Paperwork is decreased, since demographic data can be retrieved, checked, and updated instead of needing forms to be completed for each service and during each episode of illness. Health and social service personnel have demographic and previous medical or social information readily accessible. Therefore, the time spent reviewing the chart is decreased without sacrificing the quality of the information retrieved. Additionally, health and social service personnel seeing clients are aware of the clients' social support networks, contacts with other services, primary and specialist physicians, and previous medical and social history. Many of these benefits could occur with the use of identification cards each containing a computer chip. The chip stores relevant information about medical conditions and events and is read by a computer upon the client's request for services. Thus, even if a client is unable to speak, certain information can be transmitted to providers. In summary, computer applications in a continuum will allow for increased access to care, more accurate historical data, and decreased paperwork, especially in the admissions process.

OPERATIONS APPLICATIONS

As stated previously, computer processing of information has been widely accepted in activities that are highly structured and repetitive. The accounting done in a business office or billing office comprises many functions of the kind that are adaptable to computer programs. In hospitals, these applications tend to be ones that have been in place the longest and are therefore the most widely accepted. Operations procedures that are facilitated by an MIS include both traditional ongoing operations and some new business operations.

Ongoing Operations Applications

- *Accounts Receivable.* This operation includes the types of billing and types of reports needed by the various services and providers in a continuum.
- *Accounts Payable.* An MIS can track current and projected accounts payable and cash flow needs.
- *Payroll.* This operation was one of the first areas of use for data processing in the 1960s. In addition to the accuracy an MIS offers, the payroll can easily be broken down into units to determine the personnel costs associated with various service centers, an important activity in this era of prospective pricing.
- *General Ledger.* An MIS can be helpful here, as it can keep the general financial records relevant to the service system.

Newer Applications

New areas of application for computer technology include inventory control and purchasing, assigning charges to the appropriate client, budgeting by cost center, and planning appropriate staffing levels.

- *Inventory Control and Purchasing.* The use of an MIS for this operation is currently expanding in pharmacies. Also, there is great potential for use in central supplies. Computer systems are useful for keeping track of inventory, as well as for deciding appropriate levels of inventory to maintain. Purchasing can also be conducted at the most efficient levels for maintaining quality and cost controls.
- *Client Charges.* An MIS allows for charges to be accurately assigned to the appropriate client. It is costly if the wrong client is charged, which can also result in billing losses if the appropriate client cannot be identified.
- *Budgeting by Cost and Revenue Producing Centers.* An MIS allows for comparisons among cost centers or revenue centers, including the costs of various inputs.
- *Planning Appropriate Staffing Levels.* As hospitals expand to include larger numbers of services (delivered directly or through contractual arrangements), being able to accurately determine staffing levels is important for cost-effective management. An MIS can help in this process.

Each of these applications become increasingly important as competition in the health and social services arena increases and a premium is placed on management of internal revenues. The operations applications also provide essential information for planning and research activities.

PLANNING AND RESEARCH APPLICATIONS

Planning

As horizontal and vertical integration of institutions and services continues, the information needs for internal operations and for survival in the increasingly competitive environment will be dramatically greater. The ability to track costs by client, by diagnosis, by service, and by payer adds significantly to the tools available for planning. Developing tools for performing community needs assessment, developing marketing strategies for specific segments of the population, and analyzing the types and extent of competition are additional tasks that will become commonplace because of the computer's capability to organize and analyze data.

Common planning applications made possible by an MIS include the following:

- *Analysis of Trends in Practice Population.* An MIS allows for analysis over time of the type of patients being treated, which in turn provides information for planning and marketing.
- *Analysis of Competition.* Tracking the participation and performance of competition in the market-place, analysis of market share, and assessment of costs by personnel, by admissions, and by number of beds provides invaluable information for strategic planning.
- *Assessment of Marketing Strategies.* Simulation of outcomes is possible before putting strategies into practice. This enables assessment of alternative strategies before the costs of implementation are incurred.

The purpose of an MIS (or decision support system in the planning process) is to improve the following processes:

- By analysis of data relevant to a continuum, problem areas can be identified.
- Potential marketing strategies can be developed by integration of data from a continuum and from the community or region. For example, identification of patient characteristics by services can be determined. The incidence of occurrence of the characteristics in the community can be determined and an appropriate marketing strategy developed.
- Alternative planning strategies and their ramifications for the continuum can be simulated.

Since a computer system facilitates the allocation of costs and the tracking of utilization through a continuum, the data required to analyze pertinent issues are available. In the past, aggregated data was used for these purposes; however, under prospective pricing arrangements the data must be broken down into more meaningful units.

To be able to monitor the environment, track costs associated with clients, and track service personnel and their costs, new and more specific measures of performance are required. Meaningful measures or composites of measures need to be developed that analyze efficiency and effectiveness for the total system and that track production line costs, (i.e., the costs of producing a product or service, including goods and personnel). Measures that are becoming more important are the following: (a) the number of outpatient visits, (b) the cost of these services, (c) the comparison of the cost of inpatient to outpatient services, (d) the number of admissions to services compared with capacity, (e) the census measures by service by payer, (f) the number of full-time staff days required per admission according to service, (g) the total cost per admission to a service according to diagnosis, and (h) the timeliness of completion of billing forms or medical records.[5] Analysis by payer is important in negotiating contracts and discounts with specific payers. Costs that are less directly associated with client care are also important. For example, the costs incurred from incomplete medical records or billing forms may result in unpaid claims and a loss in revenues. These measures of performance, of course, should be known for competitors within the service area as well as for the organization.

Two issues that are relevant for planning are cross subsidies and the determination of fixed, variable, and marginal costs. In the past, hospital costs and charges had a low correlation. Confusion still exists, because the terms are often used interchangeably. The charges associated with providing services in hospitals were often defined as costs. Also, cross subsidies were built into charges for many areas. An MIS system allows for more accurate allocation of costs and, if cross subsidization is practiced, a more accurate means of determining the subsidies. Second, in the current competitive environment, the need for information on fixed, variable, and marginal costs has also increased. With such information, providers can make decisions about the efficiency of providing services at optimum volume levels. As the costs of individual tests, procedures, and visits are able to be determined, there will be ramifications for decisions regarding volume and, subsequently, staffing, scheduling, and service provision. The MIS enables this type of analysis to be done in preparation for planning decisions.

Marketing is another area where an MIS system can greatly enhance productivity and appropriate use of resources. A computer system can facilitate the identification of service needs and of specific subpopulations at which marketing efforts should be directed. If desired, marketing efforts can also be monitored to determine the results of various strategies. While these are not new endeavors in the field of marketing, computer capabilities make it significantly easier to amass data and analyze it. Within a continuum of care this is especially important, as the tradeoffs among alternatives may be complex. For example, in a given environment, is it better to market the continuum of care with equal emphasis on all services or to highlight a few services and let the remainder serve as a backdrop? Analysis of approaches to this issue may involve patterns of service use, perceived need of services, satisfaction with services used, and insurance coverage of services. An MIS can assist in this type of broadly focused data collection and analysis.

Additionally, it is important to understand the environment within which a continuum of care exists. Pertinent aspects of this environment are federal and state regulations and their reimbursement provisions. Types of information that are especially relevant to policymakers from the continuum of care include the linkage of client characteristics, utilization patterns, and structural properties of the health and social service system. A related type of information is the breakdown of clients' characteristics by the characteristics of providers that are used as the routine source of care. The same type of information is desirable with respect to specialty care providers and, over time, for both primary and specialty providers.

Research Applications

An MIS allows for the pooling of data across time, and so it is an appropriate device for the kind of analysis required in research. There are several types of research in which an MIS is most commonly used. The first type consists of "process" studies. These examine, for instance, the process of using a computerized clinical record or the process of prescribing and monitoring medication used by geriatric clients. A second type of study is traditional hypothesis testing, where clients are assigned to either an experimental or a control group and receive care or treatment according to the group. The use of the MIS in these studies is primarily to aggregate and perform statistical analysis on the data base. If the data are gathered on the computer, compilation is, of course, made simpler. A third type of study enables the hook-up of a local system with a national data base. Results of diagnoses and treatments can then be compared and projections made based upon the national data base. A fourth type of study uses the data base itself as a reference pool for aggregating data. Comparisons can then be made with similar cases that have occurred. Some systems provide predictors of likely outcomes based on this historical data. (This is discussed above in the section "Clinical Applications.") Also, some systems allow the comparison of results and costs by client, diagnosis, payer, etc. (This aggregation of costs or outcomes by other variables is discussed in "Planning.")

The first and fourth types of research are the more important ones for a continuum of care. An example of a process study was previously cited. The aggregation studies attempt to link types of procedures or events with an outcome event or to analyze events or conditions that covary with an outcome event. The Duke Databank for Cardiovascular Disease is used for this type of research (see "Clinical Applications"). One example of an MIS used for research on treatment efficacy is the American Rheumatism Association Medical Information System (ARAMIS).[6] This uses the Duke Databank for Cardiovascular Disease program adapted for rheumatism. This data base contains approximately 6,000 records, performs literature searches, and compares types of treatment and effectiveness of therapies for similar types of patients. Additionally, comparisons of treatment and outcomes among various services can be made, e.g., home care versus inpatient care. These predictive studies do not provide the scientific validity of random and clinical trials; however, under conditions of rapidly developing technology, they provide an alternative to the time and monetary expense of randomized clinical trials. Since third party payers end up paying for the use of technology in clinical settings and the elderly are major recipients of these therapies, it would seem especially important for them to fund studies that assess appropriate technology within the continuum of care.

Additional possibilities for profiling specific communities to determine their epidemiology suggest themselves. Once such profiles exist, strategies for providing appropriate care could be devised. One issue that needs to be resolved is how to gather this type of data. If self-administered questionnaires prove an effective, valid, and reliable means of procuring this data, a major hurdle will have been overcome.

STEPS FOR DESIGNING AN MIS SYSTEM FOR A CONTINUUM OF CARE

This section outlines the components relevant for an information system, the requirements for a continuum of care, important issues in developing a computer information system, network capabilities in the continuum, potentials for misuse of the system, and an example of the system development process in the San Francisco Institute on Aging.

Components of an Information System

Data that are relevant to the delivery and financing of health and social services make up a computer data base for a continuum of care. The type and extent of the detail incorporated into the data base depends upon the purpose the data base serves. A clearly defined purpose will provide guidelines for analyzing the compromises to be made among the hardware, the software, and the design of the data base. With hardware, the cost increases as the sophistication of the functions the computer is to perform increases and as the latitude of the data base expands. Often a time lag exists between the development of hardware and software, with hardware being developed first. In considering software, it is important to determine the time period over which data will be collected. If this period is lengthy, the variables important to the data base may change. Software that can adapt to such changes in variables without major program changes is preferable.

There are four primary processes essential to the functioning of an information system: data acquisition, data entry, data storage, and retrieval of data. Each is discussed below.

Data Acquisition

In designing a system for acquiring data, definition of the variables and the manner in which they will be collected is necessary. Careful evaluation of the purpose of the data base is required in order to collect the appropriate amount of data. The actual process of data acquisition can be accomplished during the client care process or from documents such as health-related questionnaires. Data that are gathered during the encounter (and the quality of such data) can be monitored by the systems already in place to assess quality of care. When accomplished as part of the clinical process, the data base can assist in providing reminders, summary information, and in billing. One disadvantage of this technique is that health and social service personnel are required to gather the data. A less time-consuming technique for staff is to use self-administered questionnaires where appropriate.

Data Entry

Entering data should be as easy and efficient as possible. Clearly, if built into the client encounter process, entering data into the data base must be efficient, requiring minimal time and effort and providing easy access to the system, both physically and psychologically. Coding is often used to simplify the data entry process. One keystroke can be used to represent a word or diagnosis. This saves time and reduces errors. For variables with normal ranges, appropriate limits can be programmed so that the user is notified if values beyond the normal range are entered. This provides a means of verifying data that is outside the normal limits. The screen can also routinely verify data as it is entered and prompt the user for additional data when required. With the advent of light pens and other methods of data entry, this process may become increasingly efficient. In general, programs need to be as interactive as possible, providing prompts to notify the user of access to other menus for help or explanations.

Data Storage

Storage can be organized in either fixed or variable length records. Each format has certain advantages. Variable length allows for text and is used for wide latitude applications, whereas fixed length is appropriate for more limited applications. Variable length allows for more compact storage, whereas fixed length makes it easy to select specific data groupings and recall data accordingly. Optical discs now create the possibility of maintaining larger numbers of files, some active and some inactive. Also, expansion of storage capacity as the system grows must be planned.

Retrieval of Data

The ability to retrieve data is critical to a well-functioning data base. If retrieval needs to be accomplished during client encounters, it is necessary for the system to be on-line. In general, data should be able to be retrieved in a format appropriate for the purpose to be served. This may require flexibility in providing data for service reports and for sophisticated computations on the data base. At a minimum, retrieval within a continuum needs to be able to be done by client, diagnosis, symptom, provider, payer, and time period.

Unique Requirements of the Continuum of Care

Because a continuum of care is a complex system, involving a range of multidisciplinary services and a large variation in types of services provided and lengths of stay, designing an MIS involves several issues rarely encountered in acute care settings. Specific requirements need to be met in the areas of centralization, flexibility, and utility.

Centralization

- Billing and payments need to be centralized, itemized, and dated, in contrast to a system that only maintains an open balance. Specific payments need to be credited to the appropriate line item.
- Adjustments to bills throughout the continuum that apply to all clients within a certain group, like an insurance plan or preferred provider organization (PPO), need to be made appropriately.
- Changes in information relevant to billing should easily be done, especially if the client is involved in a lengthy treatment course or has had multiple admissions and discharges. Type of insurance is an example of this kind of data.

Flexibility

- Simultaneous enrollment in multiple services is also a key design issue. Patients need to be able to be admitted and discharged from services while they are still enrolled in other programs. For example, inpatients may be admitted into an outpatient program while they are still inpatients (to ease transition problems, or for other reasons). Similarly, a client may be receiving services from multiple services simultaneously. This capability needs to be planned for.

Utility

- Utility in the arrangement of data is also important. Demographic, clinical, and financial files need to be separable, so that the demographic and clinical data can be used for future encounters.

Important Issues in Developing Computer Information Systems

Consideration of several issues relevant to developing a computer system are essential during the developmental and implementation stages. Without careful consideration and planning, the many components can become dysfunctional and fail to contribute to the overall purpose of the total system.

As mentioned previously, defining focused goals for the computer system is necessary to guide the planning process. There can be a temptation to attempt to collect all possible data. If well-defined goals and objectives are articulated, appropriate data needs can also be specified. Anticipated changes in goals and variables can also be planned for so that the computer system continues to be useful in a continuum of care. Part of the process of defining goals and objectives is to consider the level of decision making for which the system provides information. Policy level information should provide information for the general framework of the continuum of care, including financing, reimbursement, and service provision issues. Information for planning should enable the continuum to maximize current resources and marshal new ones to better fulfill the policy level goals. For example, appropriate avenues of expansion can be explored to increase the continuum's market share of the elderly population. Management level decisions pertain to the organization of the goods, services, and procedures required for the continuum to function. The dovetailing of each level with the preceding one is required for efficient information flow through the continuum.

Once the immediate and future needs are outlined, predicted growth should be analyzed. Attempts should be made to evaluate as many options and systems as possible without giving special preference to those systems individuals have had experience with. Request for proposals for vendors can then be developed that specify what functions should be handled in-house, with support, or as shared services. Careful evaluation of in-house expertise and outside supportive services is critical. It is important to ask vendors how they will meet needs, what type and how much training is provided, what supportive services they provide, how timely are their responses to software or maintenance questions, whether the documentation provided is adequate, how adaptable the system is to anticipated future needs, and what costs will be incurred if the system is expanded.

Personnel considerations are also a critical element for a computer system. Included under the rubric of personnel issues are the requirements for the team in charge of developing the computer system and the management of relations among the personnel in the continuum vis-à-vis the computer system. Designing the system requires team members with a range of skills: (1) health and social service personnel responsible for thinking about the direction and the types of data that are relevant for the computer system; (2) managers, planners, and marketing specialists responsible for the definition of the relevancy of the system to their work; (3) a computer specialist responsible for designing the system in accordance with the needs of the continuum; and (4) a statistician (familiar with health and social service issues pertaining to the aged) responsible for design issues that relate to analysis and for the analysis of the data itself. It is especially helpful if each participant in the planning-implementation team has an interdisciplinary background, which facilitates communication. In many situations, this will necessitate team members learning how the computer functions and what tasks are appropriate to expect it to perform. Throughout the duration of this team, leadership will be required to keep discussions focused and the process moving toward the desired objectives.

A different type of personnel issue is the education of personnel in the continuum, and the attendant reduction of anxiety, regarding the computer system. Since learning to use the system requires an investment of staff time, the benefits to be gained from the computer system should be stressed. Also, this educational process probably proceeds more smoothly if the computer is viewed as a tool that can help the staff. During the planning and implementation stages, it is good to investigate the computer sophistication of the potential users. An understanding is needed of what computers can accomplish and what the staff's expectations are with respect to the computer system. This evaluation needs to assess the time, energy, and commitment available to create a working computer system. Users of the system should be involved in the entire development process. This allows for participation and for an overview of the purpose and of the changes that will occur as a result of having the computer system.

The stability of the funding for the computer system is another important issue. Successful computer systems tend to have a stable funding base. Since setting up the data base can be a lengthy process, and some types of funding require that the data base be operational before the funding is provided, planning is clearly required. Sometimes research on a limited topic can be merged with a larger project to obtain funding. Other times multiple funding sources are put together to provide increased stability. Since administrative and research priorities can change during the lengthy developmental and data collection stages, it is important to create a flexible system.

Determining the value of the benefits to be derived from the computer system is the ultimate test of whether it is worthwhile for a continuum of care to develop the system. This determination of value can be difficult to make. Assessment of value can be facilitated by defining specific goals and objectives and specific designs for data collection. Thus, determination of success can be measured more readily. Benefits such as increased revenues from third party payers, decreased costs for payroll and other accounting functions, and increased speed of recall from client records are areas where specific measures of performance can be made. Judgments regarding the overall effectiveness of the system need to be broken down with respect to these types of areas to determine the value and efficiency of the system to the continuum. Ultimately the value of the computer system is judged by whether it can address the issues for which it was designed to provide information.

Networks

Tracking clients through a network of services is rarely done at present. Standardization of data elements is required for this to occur. The electronic capability for rapid transmittal is now starting to be available commercially. One advance is the connection machine, which allows high-speed computing to occur by employing thousands of processors simultaneously.[7] This not only dramatically affects the speed of information retrieval, but also the types of modeling and image processing that can occur.

A local area network allows display terminals, microcomputers, printers, and data storage units to be linked together. This is accomplished by specific hardware, software, and a cable connection (or telephone connection). Figure 14-3 shows one configuration of a computer network for a continuum of care.

Advantages provided by such a computer network include decreased costs, simultaneous access to data, and increased flexibility.

- *Decreased Costs.* A network allows one terminal to connect to multiple systems without a separate system being required for each function. For example, a terminal in client care can access information in the financial or transportation system. This can significantly reduce costs. The costs saved by not being required to have a printer for each computer station alone may save a substantial amount of money.
- *Simultaneous Access to Data.* Several locations can have access to a data base without having to copy and store the data at each location. Instantaneous transfer of information can occur among hospital departments, as well as locations outside the hospital. Not even multiple copies of a paper charting system can offer this type of information transfer, since all copies of the paper chart must be updated individually.

Figure 14-3 A Computer Network for a Continuum of Care

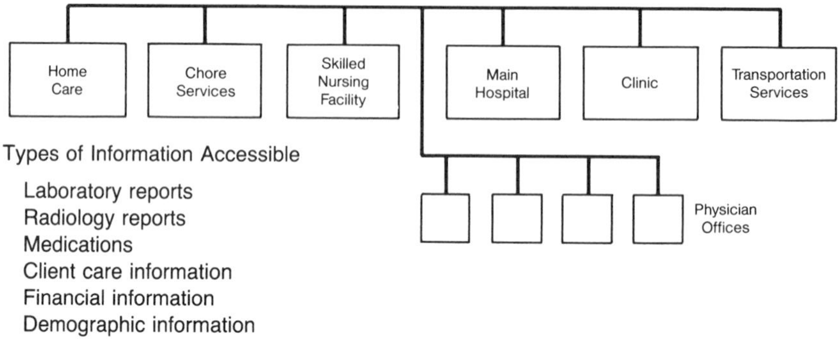

Home Care | Chore Services | Skilled Nursing Facility | Main Hospital | Clinic | Transportation Services

Types of Information Accessible

Laboratory reports
Radiology reports
Medications
Client care information
Financial information
Demographic information

Physician Offices

- *Increased Flexibility.* The components of the system can be rearranged if the volume changes or the capabilities of the system need to be expanded.

Inpatient departments that are finding these networks effective in coordinating information are dietary, radiology, and pharmacy. Also, as more hospitals affiliate, the rapid and accurate transmission of information among different locations becomes increasingly critical. Similarly, physicians need to be able to connect their offices with hospital laboratory and radiology services. As the technology improves and costs decrease, networks within a continuum and among community providers will become commonplace.

Potential for Misuse

With the integration of computers into the fundamental communication and decision-making processes of our culture, it is wise to consider the negative potential of these systems. Within the health and social services arena there are three primary issues of concern:

1. concentration of data by location
2. control of access to data
3. power derived from access to data[8]

Very few people in the field actively deal with safeguarding against the negative potential of these systems. While there are certainly concerns about many different stylistic issues, little concern is expressed about whether the final consequences of computer technology conform to accepted ethical standards. Weizenbaum cautions against the substitution of computer technology for human traits such as respect or love, especially in situations where an urgent need is not demonstrated and concomitant misuse can be envisaged. The debate about possible negative consequences needs to be entered into by individuals, including health and social service personnel, of diverse views.[9]

Example: Developing an MIS for the San Francisco Institute on Aging

The following section describes the initial information-gathering and decision processes used to determine the common needs among services and to define a common goal among the geriatric services of the San Francisco Institute on Aging, Mount Zion Hospital and Medical Center, San Francisco.

Computerization does not magically satisfy all needs or bring order out of chaos. The ease of creating a computerized MIS is significantly affected by the state of the manual system for organizing information. Mount Zion's long history of providing geriatric services (with the accompanying needs for service information by funding agencies, by internal management, and for research) is an invaluable source of experience in information gathering and retrieval. The individual geriatric services within the San Francisco Institute on Aging are the following:

1. Acute Geriatric Assessment and Rehabilitation
2. Adult Day Health Center
3. Alzheimer's Day Care
4. Artworks
5. Consortium for Elder Abuse Prevention
6. Geriatric Assessment Service
7. Geriatric Patient and Family Services
8. Geriatric Medical Clinic
9. Home Care
10. Information, Counseling, and Referral
11. Lifeline
12. Linkages
13. L'Chaim Senior Center
14. Mount Zion Care Account
15. Multipurpose Senior Services Program
16. Senior Health Screening and Referral

Given this array of services, the desirability of shared information and coordination among the component services is evident. The following section will outline the process being used by the San Francisco Institute on Aging to assess the functions that could be performed by an MIS. The first step was to conduct interviews with each of the geriatric service coordinators to determine the types of data they gathered and the purposes it served. The list below identifies some of the key elements that were defined in this process.

Planning Stage 1

Among the things defined or determined were

- the information gaps in the current system
- the types of data that would fill these gaps
- who would need to be involved in the development process
- the goals and objectives for the system

Planning Stage 2

Among the things defined or determined were

- the types of information to be collected
- who the users of an MIS would be
- who would gather data and how this would be accomplished
- the functions the system would need to perform (e.g., reports and analyses)
- the format required for reports or statistical analyses
- the frequency of use of the system (e.g., would daily, weekly, or monthly reports need to be generated for specific individuals?)
- the amount of time needed to enter and to obtain data from the system
- the location of the terminal to be used and the location where the data would be stored
- the costs and benefits of different systems
- whose support would be required for advancement to the next level

As part of Planning Stage 2, the forms used to gather data within each service were collected. Next, a matrix was created that identified variables and which services used each variable. This also provided the frequency with which a variable was used across services.

Information that had common applications across services included

- Chart and Referral Applications—the demographic face sheet, instructions for making referrals to other geriatric programs, and the patient chart
- Statistical Analyses and Funding Reports Applications—statistical reports required by funding sources, the hospital, and for fund-raising purposes; research applications; and informational files (e.g., a list of the physicians that accept assignment or a list of discounts offered at various pharmacies)

After completion of the planning stages, design; development; and implementation processes follow. Under each stage are issues that must be addressed.

Design Stage

- descriptions of reports that can be designed to provide useful information
- the types of hardware and software that are required

Development Stage

- determination of who will do the programming
- documentation for testing the system
- the timeline for development

Implementation Stage

- the projections of staff time for the implementation stage
- time the computer system should be operational
- types of transition steps necessary to smooth the conversion for staff and to facilitate information processing between manual and computer systems
- method of system evaluation, and
- method of using data from evaluation to improve the functioning of the system

It is helpful if the entire planning and development process is mapped out at the beginning. While adaptations will doubtless be required, initial mapping allows the participating individuals an overview and some indication of the time and resources required.

SUMMARY

At present, the general state of the MIS field still involves a patchwork of elements. In order to turn this patchwork into a smooth, efficient system, it is necessary to clearly articulate needs and available resources. Since these systems are costly in both dollars and time, careful planning more than adequately pays for itself. While an MIS is clearly an investment of major proportions, it is also indispensable in managing services in a system as complex and diverse as a continuum of care.

Computer systems are now available that facilitate client care and increase the efficiency of potential operations, planning, and research in the health and social services. The potential for improving care and efficiency among the interlocking levels of a continuum has been barely tapped. Computer technology should be considered part of the present, not just the future.

RESOURCES

The following organizations and people may be able to provide assistance in the design and use of computer systems for a continuum of care.

San Francisco Institute on Aging
Mount Zion Hospital and Medical Center
P.O. Box 7921
San Francisco, California 94120
(415) 885-7800

On Lok Senior Health Services
1441 Powell Street
San Francisco, California 94133
(415) 989-2578

Dick Schoech
University of Texas
Arlington Schools of Business, Social Work and Urban Studies
P.O. Box 19129
Arlington, Texas 76109
(817) 273-3964

NOTES

1. D.B. Pryor et al., "Clinical Data Bases: Accomplishments and Unrealized Potential," *Medical Care* 23 (May 1985):623–647.

2. D.M. Steinwachs, "Management Information Systems: New Challenges to Meet Changing Needs," *Medical Care* 23 (May 1985):607–622.

3. R.T. Zawadski and S. Gee, *Computerized Information Management in Long Term Health Care: A Care Study* (San Francisco: On Lok Senior Health Services, 1982), 22.

4. Pryor et al., "Clinical Data Bases."

5. K. Sandrick, "Information Needs Change," *MULTIS* 2 (August 1985):M10–16.

6. Pryor et al., "Clinical Data Bases."

7. M.M. Waldrop, "The Connection Machine Goes Commercial," *Science* 232 (May 1986):1090–91.

8. D. Bell, "Thinking Ahead," *Harvard Business Review* 57, no. 3 (1979):20–42; D. Schoech, *Computer Use in Human Services: A Guide to Information Management* (New York: Human Sciences Press, 1982), 312.

9. J. Weizenbaum, *Computer Power and Human Reason* (San Francisco: W.H. Freeman, 1976), 300.

Chapter 15

Care Coordination: An Integration Mechanism

Lawrence J. Weiss, PhD

One of the critical integrating components of a continuum of care is care coordination. In today's complex health environment, which includes diverse medical service specialties, intricate financing, and intense scrutiny of practice, professional skills and knowledge are required to work with the maze of services in order to obtain the most appropriate level of care, ensure quality and continuity, and still control health care costs. This chapter's main premise is that if a continuum of care is to be successful from the perspective of both patient and provider, it must incorporate care coordination, which promotes cost-containment and preserves quality. Care coordination is defined as an integrating mechanism that incorporates a systematic process of assessment, risk appraisal, care planning, service procurement, monitoring, and reassessment.

Care coordination addresses an individual's basic need to understand, trust, and manipulate his or her environment. Within our increasingly complex system (or "nonsystem") of health care delivery, the bewildering array of options and services becomes even more distressing and complex when health decisions must be made during times of acute or even chronic need. Often, health care consumers do not seek professional advice until their problem has become acute. Thus opportunities for prevention or early intervention are lost, resulting in the delivery of more intense and expensive services. Care coordination can introduce appropriate and efficient allocation of resources in the uncontrollable and ill-defined fee-for-service system.

This chapter focuses on the roles, functions, and responsibilities of care coordination within the continuum of medical, health, and social services. The stage is set by a discussion of the history and background of care coordination. A definition is presented. Its fundamental components, such as assessment, risk appraisal, care planning and team conferencing, service referral and procurement, monitoring, and reassessment, are addressed. Sponsorship, organizational positioning, and financial considerations are also considered. Finally, examples of successful operational programs are offered.

HISTORY AND BACKGROUND: APPLYING AN OLD CONCEPT TO A NEW ERA

The concept of providing resources that are individually tailored and meet the needs of the "whole" person is not new. Historically, the general practitioner physician, the public health nurse, and most certainly the social case worker all have, in doing their job, selected from a wide range of services those that served most to mitigate functional dependency and enhance the quality of life for the patient. Before the proliferation of specialties, advanced technology, and third party health insurers, the health professional's goals were

- to achieve a maximal level of physical, emotional, and social independence with the most accessible, appropriate, and least costly resources available
- to treat the individual as a whole person, with unique needs and an informal support system
- to enhance prevention and early intervention through participatory problem solving and decision making
- to improve continuity and quality of care through constant monitoring and personal coordination and follow-up

Recently, the growth of complexity in the health industry, in part due to the explosion of knowledge, the increase in health expenditures, and the proliferation of treatment options, has necessitated the evolution of a professional manager or coordinator. This coordinator provides linkages between systems, focuses on the whole person, helps the person navigate through the array of complex services, and facilitates the delivery of quality care.

Even though the roots of care coordination can be traced to traditional general practitioners, community social case workers, and public health nurses, the new generation of professional care coordinators has evolved into "indirect" service providers. They utilize computer technology to flag risk, to monitor service use, and to locate resources; they also have more client contact via the telephone than traditional case workers. Because today's delivery systems must be maximally efficient, increased utilization of technology is a requirement. However, the personal and human component should not be lost.

During the 1970s, community organizations providing coordinated care systems emerged through the help of federally supported research and demonstration programs. The federal government under the Medicare and Medicaid health insurance programs began to experiment with alternative delivery systems that used service coordination as a means of attempting to reduce health expenditures. The programs focused on the elderly, particularly the chronically ill or disabled population, who use the greatest amount of resources. From 1976 to 1983, the Health Care Financing Administration (HCFA) funded thirteen demonstration projects (e.g., Triage, Conn.; Access, N.Y.; MGSP, Ca.; Project Open, Ca.).

The research evaluation focused on service effectiveness, cost reduction, and patient functional outcomes. Not unexpectedly, given the diverse models (ranging from state-sponsored programs to hospital-based programs), the results were mixed. Despite the lack of systematic experimental methodology, the various demonstrations showed cost savings, easier access to services, maintenance of functioning level, and, most importantly, the value of care coordination or a managed care approach.[1]

In the early 1980s, the Department of Health and Human Services funded ten "channeling" sites nationally. One of the objectives of the channeling demonstrations was to compare coordination models. One-half of the projects provided management services with no authority to pay for expanded services, while the other half was allowed both to arrange and provide reimbursement for expanded services. The results indicated no cost savings or differences between the management models. In spite of these results and other data from research evaluations,[2] the popularity and success of care coordination is evidenced by its continued proliferation in many types of health and social service settings.

Hospital-based coordinated care programs were quite limited until 1984. At this time, the Robert Wood Johnson Foundation funded National Initiatives in Hospital-Based Long-Term Care and required care coordination as a component in programs at 24 sites. Subsequently, a groundswell of interest in long-term care has developed among hospitals, hospital systems, venture capitalists, private businesses, insurance companies, and public employee retirement systems. Austin suggests that the reason that management services or care coordination is becoming so widely accepted is that it is seen as incorporable into existing service delivery systems without major system or structural changes among services or providers. However, she maintains that care coordination has the capability of becoming a powerful change agent with providers. If care coordinators are given the authority to allocate services, delivery systems would change.[3] In fact, care coordination provides an avenue through which everyone benefits: Payers can exercise legitimate influence upon health care utilization patterns and reduce costs; providers gain more time for direct, comprehensive patient care and experience fewer consumer problems (including lawsuits) because of increased communication and consumer participation; and consumers are provided with a concerned, accessible professional who can give advice and direction and simultaneously help to reduce expenses.

DEFINITION AND FUNCTION

One of the major conceptual problems with care coordination is that there are as many definitions as there are programs and practicing coordinators. This section will discuss the various definitions and components, including the roles of the professional, paraprofessional, and volunteer, as well as the informal support system.

Even in this book care coordination is referred to by many different names. *Service coordination*, *case management*, and *service management* are only a few such terms of reference. Perhaps the most common name is *case management*. This term is not employed here for two reasons: People generally do not like to be referred to as *cases*, nor to be *managed*. Care coordination is a more consumer-sensitive term, one appropriate to associate with a person-oriented system of care.

Care coordination is not a discrete service such as cataract surgery or a home-delivered meal. It involves the delivery of an alternative support system that selects from the total array of services and service settings within a continuum of care. Care coordination connects the person or consumer of services with the appropriate resources within the continuum or with other community services. It also helps facilitate the utilization of informal or family support, which is critical in the overall care of the person, especially within a home environment. Some programs may take care coordination to be identical with the acute care hospital discharge function, or with traditional social work, or nursing service, or even primary physician care. Rather, care coordination incorporates these functions and coordinates aspects of all of them. It involves orchestrating all providers and disciplines (sometimes simultaneously), with the goal of providing effective quality care that maximizes efficient use of services.

An operational definition of care coordination is as follows:

> *Care coordination* is an integrating mechanism within the continuum of services that provides the optimum in appropriate, effective, and cost-efficient care. Medical, health, and social services are organized to meet individual needs and promote independent functioning. This is done through a systematic process of assessment, risk appraisal, care planning, service procurement, monitoring, and reassessment.

A comprehensive care coordination system moves beyond simple information and referral programs or crisis intervention strategies. It focuses on prevention and early intervention in the lives of those people who have been identified as high-risk. Prior utilization screens and risk appraisal techniques are used to target care coordination services to those who most need them. Once care coordination participants are identified, they are assessed in depth using multifunctional assessment tools and clinical data from current providers. All available data are gathered and distilled in a care planning process. The care plan usually involves the appropriate professionals (such as a nurse, social worker, physician, psychologist, and occupational, speech, or physical therapist). The care plan objective is to establish the priority of needs, type and amount of service, and the measurable goal or outcome of the service.

Negotiating the care plan with the consumer and the family is the next step, which involves both education and advocacy. Once there is a mutually agreed upon plan of care, service procurement follows. Since the professional care coordinator is knowledgeable about the variety of service options available, and since resource directories are readily available (perhaps even automated), referrals or arrangements of services occur as appropriate. Once a service or package of services is defined and arranged, the coordinator tracks and monitors service utilization and progress toward meeting service goals. The coordinator adjusts the plan of care as needed through routine reassessment and various tracking mechanisms.

Care Coordination Process

The care coordination process consists of six fundamental components: functional assessment, risk appraisal, care planning and team conferencing, service referral and procurement, monitoring and tracking, and reassessment. Even though there is general agreement on the six components, there are many interpretations as to how each should be operationalized. A comprehensive review is not attempted here, but a representative approach is suggested for each component.

Functional Assessment

The first and most critical component of the care coordination process involves assessing a person's functional level from a multidimensional perspective. To obtain a picture of a person's health status, it is not sufficient to define the medical diagnosis. (It is especially important to keep this in mind when dealing with chronic diseases and conditions.) Assessment of physical, emotional, and mental function and of the functional capacity of the informal support system is necessary to develop a comprehensive care plan. Therefore, a comprehensive assessment involves obtaining medical information as well as information on routine activities of daily living, such as ability to walk, cook, or use transportation. There are many assessment tools and methods available.[4] In-home assessments are usually performed by a professional care coordinator or a team of professionals, but some programs utilize paraprofessional assistants or volunteers to collect the information.[5]

Depending upon the complexity and intensity of the person's condition, various levels of assessment may be employed. Perhaps the most cost-effective method is to use self-administered health status screens upon entry into a system. The San Francisco Institute on Aging at Mount Zion Hospital and Medical Center uses this approach effectively within their care coordination system. If a person is unable to fill out a questionnaire, or his or her health status or history reflects the need for additional, more intense assessment, the service coordinator performs additional evaluations. The goal of the assessment process is to obtain comprehensive data on a person's functional abilities and inabilities and to accomplish this in the most efficient manner possible.

Risk Appraisal

One method of achieving efficient use of professional staff is through the development of automated screens or risk appraisal mechanisms. If care coordination is to be effective, methods must be established to screen out those persons who do not need such help. One method is to provide clear eligibility criteria that single out only those who need coordination services. Unfortunately, imposing strict intake criteria tends to complicate, rather than simplify, the process. For example, the San Francisco Institute on Aging has four care coordination programs. All have different eligibility criteria. This complexity does not necessarily facilitate easy access to the appropriate service.

Instead of imposing intake eligibility criteria, it is suggested here that baseline screens be established on all persons, applications, or enrollees associated with the service system. Risk appraisal methods would then be applied to the baseline assessment data or any routine follow-up assessment data. The appraisal would identify factors that would put the person "at risk" of needing more intensive and dependent levels of care. For example, acute hospital episodes, emergency room use, mismanagement of medication, and lack of social support at home all could lead to more expensive and intensive services if not managed properly. The risk appraisal serves as an identifying mechanism through which areas needing more intensive assessment would be flagged. The care coordinator would identify those persons at risk and perform, or refer to the specialist to perform, the appropriate in-depth evaluations. Through this risk appraisal mechanism, care coordination would be applied to a broad-base population, yet utilized only by those who need it most.

Care Planning and Team Conferencing

Once a person has been comprehensively assessed and his or her level of risk identified, the next step is to develop a plan of care. The care plan delineates the needs, the type of service to meet those needs, the expected amount of service, and the goals or measurable objectives of the service; it also specifies possible providers of service, including both formal and informal resources (see Table 15-1). The plan of care is more extensive in scope and duration than traditional treatment or discharge plans utilized in social work, nursing, or medicine. The care plan encompasses traditional medical services performed for acute needs, as well as nontraditional informal or supportive services needed for assisting persons with chronic conditions. A discharge care plan ends with post-acute placement (e.g., in home health care or a skilled nursing facility), while a care plan within the continuum of care extends for as long as it takes to procure the needed services and stabilize the person's situation. Even when the person's condition stabilizes, adjustments to the plan of care occur periodically; thus the coordination process can continue on either an active or inactive basis.

Table 15-1 Care Plan: Mrs. A.

Date	Problem	Goal	Responsible Person	Plan	Date Resolved
2/06/86	1. Wants new primary doctor.	To assist family to find competent care-giver whom they trust.	GNP	After review of medical problems, offer daughter names of 3 physicians to interview.	2/10/86
2/06/86	2. Reduced functional status, past stroke, mobility balance, adduction of shoulders is 30 °	Increase walking to 20 ft. without tiring; increase range of motion of shoulder to ease dressing—adduction is 60°.	PT	Refer to Home Care.	4/14/86
			OT		
2/06/86	3. Word finding problem.	Improved ability to communicate; improved self-esteem.	ST	Refer to Home Care.	
2/06/86	4. Incontinence of urine probably secondary to decreased mobility.	Continence.	GNP	Evaluate 3 weeks after PT begins, contact MD at that time if not resolved.	3/10/86
2/06/86	5. Depression, feeling of worthlessness, social isolation, major move to a new home.	Improved morale; discontinuance of antidepressant medications.	GNP/ Daughter	Weekly visits by GNP, bring friends into home, refer to ADHC, ASAP.	
2/10/86	6. Congestive heart failure, polypharmacy.	Resolve.	MD	Hospitalization.	2/13/86

(continues)

Table 15-1 Care Plan: Mrs. A. (continued)

Date	Problem	Goal	Responsible Person	Plan	Date Resolved
3/04/86	6. Congestive heart failure.	Resolve without hospitalization.	MD/ GNP/Daughter	Daily nursing monitoring, evaluation of status and medication.	3/11/86
4/14/86	2. Continued reduced functional status—walking 20 ft., no stairs. ROM shoulder at 40°, house care discontinued.	Stair training, ambulation to 40 ft.	PT	Refer to ADHC.	
4/14/86	3. Word finding problem.	Improved communication speech group and 1:1 therapy.	ST	Refer to ADHC.	
	5. Depression, social isolation.	Contact with peers, women's group, stroke group.	Recreation Therapist/ Social Worker	Refer to ADHC.	

The care planning process varies widely. Depending on the organization, the team may involve a nurse, social worker, physician, physical therapist, occupational therapist, recreational therapist, psychologist, or pharmacist. Generally, a nurse and social worker compose the basic team and then consult with other professional specialists. The team conference is held regularly and reviews particularly complex or difficult situations. This team conferencing is essential and the results may be extremely educational for all team members, producing the continuity of care necessary in a well-executed care plan.

Other persons who should be included in the development of the care plan (and usually are not) are the current caregivers (e.g., homemaker), the family or support network, and the identified "patient." In traditional health care practices, many forget basic principles of open communication and decision making. The persons themselves are ultimately responsible for their own health care practices. Therefore, they should be, when possible, included as active members of the care planning process. Family members have an historical perspective on functioning levels and assume most of the burden of care at home; therefore, they too should be included in the care planning. Finally, current providers of service have a perspective on ongoing behavioral patterns that could contribute extremely valuable information to the development of a workable plan of care. The primary task of the care coordinator in developing the plan of care is not only to collect the assessment information from all available sources, but also to provide realistic and practical approaches to meeting needs. Incorporating the identified patient, the family, and other service providers as members of the team in the care planning process assures the follow-through needed in the implementation of the care plan.

Service Referral and Procurement

After the care plan has been developed and accepted by the client, the next step in the care coordination process is to see that the client actually secures the services identified as appropriate. Working from the individual care plan with the established priority list of services, the coordinator arranges for the services. Depending on the availability of services, the continuum's service network, and the particular model of coordination, the professional care coordinator not only makes referrals to existing services but also pays for such services. In some health plans that provide a care coordination service (e.g., French Health Plan, San Francisco; Senior Health Plan, Minneapolis), the extended services may be covered within the plan's benefit package through letters of agreement or contracts with community services. The plan may also purchase those services on a case-by-case basis through another benefit fund (e.g., chronic care package). If not, the care coordinator still makes the referral and helps with service procurement, informing the client and the family of the expected cost. Since the care coordinator knows the community resources well and works with a volume of referrals, he or she generally has negotiating ability in both accessing the service and reducing its cost. The amount of direct care responsibility and purchase authority in the allocation of services varies from one care coordination model to another. The differing models of care coordination are discussed below in more detail, but it is important to note here that the amount of help provided to the client will depend not only on the client's needs, but on the organizational model as well. At the most basic level, a referral is made. At a more involved level, the model provides the direct service as well as payment for it.

To utilize the available resources and fulfill service goals, the informal network needs to be thoroughly tapped by the care coordination system. This informal network includes the immediate family, friends, and other relatives, as well as church groups and volunteers from all sectors within the human service field. For example, a spouse may provide personal care, but may only be able to do so with the aid of a homemaker who visits three times a week. A stroke survivor may only be able to function alone at home if he or she has the help of several volunteer services (e.g., Meals on Wheels, paratransit services, the senior companion program, and the American Heart Association's stroke exercise program). Maximizing both the family and informal community supports in the referral process is critical to achieving an efficient and cost-effective system.

Monitoring and Tracking

One of the unique features of the care coordination process is service monitoring to assure appropriateness, continuity, and quality of care. Appropriateness of the services provided is determined by monitoring the service objectives and assessing outcomes. Services must be continually fine-tuned for efficient and effective utilization. Continuity of care is established by having the care coordinator know what services are being rendered, how much of each, by whom, and where. If discontinuity occurs, the care coordinator can intervene. For example, if several different physicians were to prescribe contra-indicated medications, the coordinator could inform the primary physician accordingly. Finally, quality care assurance is inherently built into the monitoring and tracking function. If a particular service is not meeting the needs of the client or is not being rendered in the amount or kind required, the care coordinator can adjust or advocate for adjustment accordingly.

In order to aid the care coordinator in the monitoring and tracking functions, a well-devised computer information management system should be incorporated into the continuum of care. The computer information system needs to synthesize all historical and current functional health data, service utilization data, provider data, and interactive information with the care plan. Such a system is an integration tool that enables the care coordinator to distill a tremendous amount of individual data on a large number of people. (Refer to Chapter 14 for a more detailed description, including current operational models.)

In short, monitoring and tracking assures quality care, responses to changes in status, communication between all formal and informal providers of service, and a mechanism for prevention and early intervention.

Reassessment

Periodic reassessment evaluates whether services are meeting the person's needs. Such periodic reassessment may involve an abbreviated form of the initial assessment. Reassessment thoroughly evaluates ongoing methods of treatment; adjusts the plan of care; recommends more, less, or different services accordingly; and, if necessary, loops back through the care coordination process.

Reassessment may be warranted at times other than regularly scheduled intervals. Any time the person's condition changes—either a current condition increases in intensity or in acuity or a new condition develops—a reassessment is appropriate. When a medical condition necessitates an acute hospital admission or a caregiver notices a significant change in behavior and brings it to the attention of the care coordinator, the reassessment process can facilitate the development of a new care plan. Access to appropriate services results because the coordinator has historical assessment and service utilization data as well as current knowledge of the environmental and support system.

The reassessment process must occur in an efficient and timely manner, otherwise labor expenses make it prohibitive. In fact, the periodic reassessment could be self-administered (as could the initial assessment) unless major changes and/ or disabilities do not allow it. In addition, only areas that reflect change have to be addressed.

Who Provides Care Coordination?

As previously stated, the historical roles of physicians, nurses, and social workers all could be described as care coordination. However, the current roles and responsibilities of members in each of the disciplines necessitate their performing certain specialty functions that do not allow for extensive coordination of the kind being discussed here. A physician's efficient use of his or her time does not allow for the arrangement of homemakers or Meals on Wheels for a home-bound patient. A discharge planner barely has enough time to see that all persons who are ready to leave the acute setting and are appropriate for placement in home health care or a skilled nursing facility receive this care, let alone follow through for six months and arrange for long-term maintenance community services.

Social workers, perhaps, perform the function most similar to care coordination. But social work roles are usually limited to the arrangement of social support services. For example, social workers traditionally provide information and referrals, mental health counseling, and arrangement of in-home support services. However, to provide the direction, management, information, and advice necessary for people who have complex chronic conditions and who cycle in and out of acute stages, a coordinator must have a firm grasp of clinical medicine and nursing. Generally, physicians listen to or communicate more effectively with nurses than with social workers. Therefore, the nurse, social worker, and physician need to work closely as a care coordination team. Each has traditional training and areas of expertise to bring to the table.

The roles and responsibilities of the care coordinator (of whatever discipline) need to be defined within the continuum of care. A social worker within a home health care program may provide some coordination functions, but only a piece of what is needed within a coordinated care system. Discharge planners may also perceive themselves to be care coordinators and may even extend their responsibility and provide some follow-up to their discharge plans. But neither the home care social worker nor the discharge planning nurse perform the functions required of a comprehensive care coordination system. If they were to assume the responsibilities of a care coordinator within a fully functional system, they would need to redefine their roles, distinguishing them clearly from the traditional roles of nursing and social work within an acute hospital or home care program. In short, care coordination has its own identified functions; it is not merely an extension of the activities of already existing social work or nursing roles. An interdisciplinary team is needed with at least the nurse and social worker as basic participants. The physician and other specialists are incorporated as consultants and clinicians where appropriate, but not as care coordinators.

The care coordinator must assume multiple roles with corresponding skills. The care coordinator needs to be an assessor (or evaluator), planner, data collector and provider, problem solver, negotiator, mediator, manager, counselor, confidant, educator, and advocate. With any one individual, the coordinator may be many of these things, or just one. Help from the team, including professionals, paraprofessionals, volunteers, and family, is critical in fulfilling all of the functions. For example, an individual may need to be contacted once a day via telephone for reassurance, a duty which a paraprofessional or volunteer could perform. The same person may need a hot meal delivered to his home or transportation to a medical appointment. A family member, friend, or volunteer could carry out such tasks. The professional coordinator orchestrates these activities, monitors the person's functioning levels, informs the physician of areas of patient noncooperation with medical treatments, and educates the person and the family on ways of working with his or her disability.

Who Receives Care Coordination?

Since the concept of care coordination is fairly complex and difficult to grasp, it is not easily sold to the public, unlike a hot meal or surgical operation. Consumers may become aware of or active participants in a successful coordination process without knowing quite what it is. They are merely aware of receiving help in locating a particular resource or service and of the assistance of a nurse or social worker. As a result, the care coordination program needs to be packaged or bundled within a service system.

Since care coordination is too costly to provide to everyone and not appropriate for independently functioning persons, the previously discussed system of risk appraisal serves as one model for selecting those for whom coordination is appropriate. Other methods of selecting who should receive coordination can be determined through a combination of entrance criteria, prior or current use of services (based on frequency, duration, or specific types of service), perceived need, and level of independence. Those persons who have chronic conditions that limit their activities of daily living are appropriate. For example, persons who have had a stroke, chronic heart failure, COPD, or have Parkinson's disease, fractured hips and other orthopedic illnesses, neurological problems, or degenerative diseases are appropriate persons to receive care coordination. In addition, those who require long-term follow-up and have little or no family support are at risk and need help coordinating their care. Each program or system should establish its own criteria for identifying appropriate persons.

Some organizations are providing limited care coordination in order to cut costs of high utilizers and to provide a utilization review function. For example, Ford Motor Company has adopted a care coordination program. This type of program can be useful in cutting costs, but the overall goal of care coordination must not be forgotten: to achieve the maximum benefit from available resources, while simultaneously maximizing independent functioning without sacrificing quality care. If employers like Ford Motor Company, insurers like Blue Cross and Blue Shield, or public employee retirement systems develop coordination or managed care approaches, they must not lose sight of this goal.

An Example of Care Coordination: Mrs. A.

Mrs. A. is an 80-year-old widow. She is a retired state employee who has lived in San Francisco for eight months, moving there from Sacramento. Mrs. A. suffered a stroke, with right-sided paralysis, ten months ago. She has a prior history of hypertension and arteriosclerotic heart disease with congestive heart failure, for which she was once hospitalized more than a year ago. She had an extensive evaluation at time of stroke, with one month rehabilitation prior to her move.

Mrs. A. came to San Francisco to be cared for by her unmarried daughter. The doctor who was recommended to them repeated the extensive evaluation, ordered no rehabilitation, and referred her to a neurologist for evaluation, to an orthopedist for swelling of her right knee, and to a psychiatrist for treatment of depression. At this point, she was taking 11 prescribed medications. Her mobility, balance, and shoulder range of motion were worse than they had been at the time of her move, and she was suffering from urinary incontinence due to her inability to get to the bathroom. Mrs. A. was receiving attendant care around-the-clock so that her daughter could work.

Four months ago, Mrs. A.'s daughter called Mount Zion Care Account on the advice of an elderly friend who was a program participant and had already experienced Mount Zion Hospital's care coordination process. Mrs. A.'s daughter was looking for comprehensive care; she felt that her mother's needs were not being met and that neither mother nor daughter were being included in decision making. Her daughter noted that Mrs. A. was becoming weaker each day.

Mrs. A.'s daughter spoke with the care coordinator and a home visit was arranged. The evaluation revealed Mrs. A.'s need for occupational therapy, physical therapy, speech therapy, and an evaluation for polypharmacy. Mrs. A. was noted to have symptoms of mild congestive heart failure (possibly drug related) and to be socially isolated and depressed.

A plan of care was established after the first visit. Mrs. A.'s daughter selected a new primary physician with her mother's input and approval. The physician and the care coordinator agreed to obtain home care services and eventually adult day health center placement.

After their first meeting, the physician admitted Mrs. A. to acute care for congestive heart failure and polypharmacy. She went home three days later with only four medications. Home care occupational therapy, physical therapy, and speech therapy were arranged. Her hospitalization was abbreviated by three days as a result of service coordination made possible by prior knowledge of her environmental situation, especially the family support available at home.

Three weeks later, Mrs. A. was found by the care coordinator to be again in mild congestive heart failure. A second hospitalization was avoided by the care coordinator's ability to evaluate the client in the home, contact the physician, and modify medications and the established supportive services. Nursing visits were made daily for four days and then tapered off.

Six weeks later, Mrs. A. was well enough to attend an adult day health center two times per week, which also provided respite (and support) for her daughter. Within that setting, Mrs. A. received occupational therapy, physical therapy, speech therapy, and social support via a stroke group, a women's group, and nursing monitoring. Her depression began to lift as her functional abilities improved. Her attendant care in the home was reduced to six hours, three days per week. She was able to stay at home, avoiding entry to a skilled nursing facility, and her (and her daughter's) satisfaction, morale, and energy levels improved significantly.

A cost review reveals that the family escaped substantial out-of-pocket costs, and the health insurance organizations saved as well. Physician office visits were reduced from six per month to one or two per month and were performed by a physician who accepted Medicare assignment. The cost of prescription drugs decreased from $135 to $49 per month. Hospitalization decreased from six days to three days (a hospital savings of approximately $4000) for one stay, and another admission was avoided completely (a Medicare and insurance savings of approximately $8000). Attendant care costs were reduced from $490 to $135 per week, while her weekly adult day health care costs were $70 per week. Adult day health care costs added to attendant care costs totaled $205 per week, or an out-of-pocket savings of $285 per week.

In short, Mrs. A. not only improved her functional abilities, quality of life, and degree of contentment by participating in the care coordination program, but she was also able to save money for herself, the health insurance company, and ultimately Medicare.

SPONSORSHIP AND ORGANIZATIONAL POSITIONING

Depending on the organizational structure of a continuum, care coordination can be positioned in many different ways. The corporate entity may assume responsibility, especially if centralized intake or processing is required from many vertical or horizontal organizations. If the continuum contains joint affiliation with an insurance company, employer(s), or a retirement association, the most appropriate locus of the care coordination component might be in one of them. The two most crucial factors are, first, that consumers perceive that care coordination is a *benefit* and does not inhibit receiving service, and, second, that the care coordinator has the *authority* within the system to provide the variety of functions necessary to accomplish the appropriate tasks. This includes access to, as well as power to utilize (and perhaps even to prescribe) the array of services within the continuum. If the care coordination program has these features, its actual position within the continuum is less important.

Recently, hospital-based coordination programs have begun to develop. In a survey performed by the American Hospital Association, 55 percent of the community hospitals said that during the period 1983–1985 they had improved the internal coordination of already existing services. In addition, 64 percent of the responding hospitals reported that they had some kind of ''case management'' program for all ages. However, only 3 percent had a program specifically for seniors.[6] (As mentioned earlier, the Robert Wood Johnson Foundation has encouraged the development of care coordination programs within acute care hospitals.)

Hospitals are positioning the care coordination programs in diverse ways depending upon their interpretation of the service. Generally, the coordination component is located at the department level of such direct service units as home health care, nursing services, social service, patient and family relations, discharge planning, and geriatrics. Other hospitals or health systems have chosen different approaches and have subsequently defined the service differently. For example, a few hospitals have positioned care coordination within the marketing and membership services departments, where capturing market share or patient retention is a dominant motivating factor. Other organizations have contracted with free-standing community agencies to provide coordination services for their patients and members. Whether the coordination component is purchased externally or situated within the organization, a clear understanding as to the authority of the coordination program and the payment mechanisms for services must be established. The amount of understanding, receptivity, and participation by the many different departments or service entities will impact on the overall success of the care coordination.

One method for securing the authority needed by the care coordination program is to establish contractual agreements that clearly designate the roles and responsibilities for both internal and external operations. Internally, a patient flow mechanism needs to be established. Intake mechanisms, referrals or transfers from departments, patient data–sharing on common computer information systems, utilization review, and quality assurance mechanisms all need attention within each of the multiple services of the continuum. Since care coordination hinges on accessing appropriate services, building strong formal and informal affiliations with all services is critical to the success and effectiveness of the program.

Another method for assuring the authority of care coordination is providing it with payment or reimbursement capability for services. Many programs, particularly state Medicaid systems (e.g., California Multi-Purpose Senior Service Program; Wisconsin Community Options Program) and health maintenance organizations (e.g., Minneapolis's Senior Health Plan) provide the care coordinator with the ability to authorize payment for health and social services. Availability and access to services, especially community services, increases with the ability to reimburse for those services instead of making a simple referral. However, even referrals, if done in volume, make a difference to most providers.

FINANCIAL CONSIDERATIONS

Who Funds Care Coordination Programs?

Currently, very few organizations fund care coordination. Some foundations (e.g., The Robert Wood Johnson Foundation) provide initial development money. Federal or state research and demonstration monies have been available in the past, but are not currently. Some state Medicaid, Title XX, or Older Americans Act block grant programs (e.g., in California, New York, and South Carolina) provide funds for care coordination, generally for the economically disadvantaged.

Hospitals are beginning to recognize some of the benefits of care coordination and are funding them under the auspices of marketing, patient and family relations, or discharge planning. Since most health care financing organizations do not routinely recognize care coordination as a distinct reimbursable service, funding is often incorporated into administrative overhead. This expense must be justified. A reduction in direct services (e.g., average length of stay within an acute hospital) or in administrative costs (e.g., duplication in processing admissions) or an increase in revenue (e.g., increased volume of Medicare paying patients to inpatient services or physician offices) can provide this justification.

The financial benefits of funding coordinating programs have been demonstrated by past research. For example, the Mount Zion Hospital and Medical Center program (Project OPEN), a five-year research demonstration funded by HCFA, provided data on an experimentally controlled sample of frail elderly persons that revealed a 15 percent total dollar savings within the fee-for-service setting. The savings occurred through a decrease in acute admissions, readmissions, lengths of stay, and outpatient services, especially physician office visits.[7]

All variations of care coordination require ongoing cost data collection and evaluation. The care coordination system, if set up properly, incorporates a management information system that provides this capability. If high-risk, high-cost patients are discharged more quickly into appropriate subacute or community settings, this might be the only benefit needed to justify the program. However, a word of caution to planners regarding the motivation for developing a care coordination program: The evidence to date is unclear as to cost benefits of care coordination, and therefore the objectives of the program should also include some emphasis on improving client satisfaction and quality of care.

More recently, several other sources of funding for care coordination have emerged among private sector payers. Insurance companies, employers, HMOs, public retirement systems, and consumers themselves have become interested in paying for coordination on a limited basis. Prudential Insurance Company, Ford Motor Company (through Blue Cross/Blue Shield of Michigan), and French Health Plan in San Francisco all have developed some form of care coordination with the intent of saving money. Adding the potential for savings on direct service costs to the potential for increased productivity from persons in the work force who serve as caregivers might make corporations even more interested in funding care coordination programs. For example, the Travelers Corporation in Hartford, Connecticut did a survey of the caregiving responsibilities of its employees. It found that one in five were caregivers to an elderly person and that eight out of ten said that it interfered with their lives, precluding vacations for over a year.[8] The relationship of caregiver strain to work productivity needs further scientific study, but there is likely to be a direct negative correlation. This, in turn, should provide some incentive for employers to fund care coordination as one method for helping their employees maintain high levels of productivity.

Another source of funding for care coordination services is the consumer and his or her family. Private fee-for-service care coordination is currently limited but growing. If issues related to the intangibility of the concept, efficiency of labor, targeted marketing, handling of product liability insurance, capitalization, and creative methods of payment could be addressed, then fee-for-service care coordination would grow rapidly.

How Much Does Care Coordination Cost?

The cost for private fee-for-service care coordination ranges from $35 to $75 per hour, depending on the level of staff professionalism, profit status, amount subsidized by donations or grants, and types of activities performed. It has been estimated that a care coordinator costs $35,000 to $72,000 per year, including indirect expenses. This figure varies on a per client per month basis, depending on the number of participants who use the coordination service. Traditional caseload sizes range from 40 to 60 active clients, with some more innovative and cost-conscious programs reaching the hundreds or even thousands. Capitman, Haskins, and Bernstein recently reported that care coordination costs within the demonstration programs ranged from $40 to $105 per client per month.[9] Therefore, in order to compare and plan for care coordination program expenses, a detailed description of objectives, staffing patterns, services provided, reimbursement mechanisms, and number of clients to be served would need to be provided.

MODEL PROGRAMS

California's Multi-Purpose Senior Service Program (MSSP)

In 1979, California piloted an eight-site Medicaid demonstration to test care coordination as a means to prevent unnecessary institutionalization of the frail elderly and disabled adult population. MSSP pooled funds from Medicaid, Title III of the Older Americans Act, and Title XX social service funds to purchase a broad range of community services. The results generated savings for the extremely frail (nursing home certified) and for high-risk participants. Recently, the California legislature has expanded the program.

Wisconsin Community Options Program (COP)

In 1978, Milwaukee, Wisconsin, started a 2176 Medicaid waiver demonstration program called the Milwaukee Community Care Organization (CCO). The CCO provided care coordination service along with extended Medicaid benefits to the chronically ill, frail elderly with the intent of preventing institutionalization. The demonstration was successful enough to go statewide in the early 1980s. The program is now called the Wisconsin Community Options Program, in which

CCO contracts with the state on a per diem basis to provide service to Milwaukee's elderly residents.

The South Carolina Community Long-Term Care Project

The South Carolina program was one of the thirteen original HCFA-sponsored demonstrations. The project used pre-admission screening to skilled nursing facilities in order to target appropriate clients for care coordination. Its community-based approach has been so successful that it has been adopted statewide.

New York State's Nursing Home Without Walls

This program, established in 1979, focused on Medicaid patients eligible for nursing home placement. It provided care coordination and extended home care benefits through the department of social services. It has also been very successful at reducing expenditures.

Connecticut Community Care, Inc., Bristol, Connecticut

In 1974, Triage, Inc., in Connecticut, was one of the first long-term care research demonstration projects that provided care coordination services to persons 65 and older. This demonstration provided a home care prototype that was licenced by the state health department as a case management organization, Connecticut Community Care, Inc. Cost savings as high as 30 percent have been found for some of the targeted populations using care coordination.

On Lok Senior Health Services, San Francisco, California

Starting in 1972 as a consolidated direct-service model, On Lok has continually demonstrated its value in cost savings and functional maintenance. Recently, it became a Medicare prospective payment system for long-term care services similar to a S/HMO.

Social/Health Maintenance Organizations (S/HMOs)

A S/HMO provides a comprehensive package of social and health services to a Medicare population on a capitated, prepaid basis. Care coordination is incorporated into the prospective payment. Four S/HMO projects exist:

1. Elderplan, Metropolitan Jewish Geriatric Center, Brooklyn, New York
2. Medicare Plus, Kaiser Center for Health Research, Portland, Oregon
3. SCAN Health Plan, Senior Care Action Network, Long Beach, California
4. Senior Health Plan, Ebenezer Society and Group Health, Inc., Minneapolis, Minnesota (see below)

Senior Health Plan (SHP), Minneapolis, Minnesota

SHP is an HMO that integrates acute and long-term care. It is a HCFA demonstration site that is testing a "prior use" capitation funding approach. SHP has over 40 care coordinators serving 5,000 Medicare beneficiaries. In addition, SHP is conducting research on the effectiveness of care coordination in four different settings.

Senior Care Plus, French Health Plan, San Francisco, California

French Hospital claims to be the oldest health plan in the country, and since 1984 it has been serving the Medicare population. This staff-model HMO has 4,000 Medicare enrollees and employs geriatric nurse practitioners as care coordinators. A high-risk screen filters through those persons who need care coordination the most. The benefit package does not include chronic care, but community services are utilized on a fee-for-service basis.

Mount Zion Care Account, San Francisco Institute on Aging, Mount Zion Hospital and Medical Center, San Francisco, California

Project OPEN at Mount Zion Hospital was a demonstration program that started in 1978. That demonstration led to the Mount Zion Care Account (funded by the Robert Wood Johnson Foundation), which is a preferred provider organization that has 17 geriatric services within the system and contracts for other services to provide a very comprehensive benefit package to the Medicare population. Care coordination is provided to those who are picked out as being high-risk. A cost-benefit analysis has demonstrated its effectiveness, and it is funded, in part, by hospital marketing services.

NOTES

1. Rick T. Zawadski, ed., *Community-based Systems of Long-Term Care* (New York: Haworth Press, 1984).

2. J.A. Capitman, B. Haskins, and J. Bernstein, "Care Management Approaches in Coordinated Community-oriented Long-Term Care Demonstrations," *The Gerontologist* 26, no. 4 (1986):398–404.

3. Carol D. Austin, "Case Management in Long-Term Care: Options and Opportunities," *Health and Social Work* 8, no. 1 (Winter 1983):16–30.

4. Rosallie A. Kane and Robert L. Kane, *Assessing the Elderly: A Practical Guide to Measurement* (Lexington, Mass.: Lexington Books, 1981).

5. Raymond M. Steinberg and G.W. Carter, *Case Management and the Elderly: A Handbook for Planning and Administering Programs* (Lexington, Mass.: D.C. Heath & Co., 1983).

6. William A. Read and James L. O'Brien, *Emerging Trends in Aging and Long-Term Care Services*, The Hospital Research and Educational Trust, American Hospital Association, Hospital Survey Series (Chicago, Ill., 1986).

7. Lawrence J. Weiss and June O. Monach, "San Francisco's Project OPEN: A Long-Term Care Health System Development and Demonstration Program for the Elderly," *PRIDE Institute, Journal of Long Term Care* 4, no. 1 (Winter 1985):13–23.

8. "The Travelers Employee Caregiver Survey" (The Travelers Corporation, Hartford, Conn., 1985).

9. Capitman, "Care Management Approaches."

Part IV

Human Relations

The human dimension is the most perplexing and time-consuming aspect of the continuum of care. It is also the most rewarding. The primary rationale for health and social service care is, after all, to help people meet their needs — mental, physical, functional, financial, and emotional. Although this book was written for managers, we must remember that the primary focus of our efforts is the patient. Thus the opening chapter of this part describes the family and client view of the continuum.

In creating a continuum of care, the most challenging management issues— and the ultimate key to success—are the human relations issues. Managers must define, coordinate, and maximize the talents of the individuals and disciplines involved. In new service programs, role definition and resolution are always a challenge, particularly in interdisciplinary efforts. This part thus describes personnel issues from the perspective of major disciplines. The differences in the issues and the approaches taken by the authors are indicative of the diversity, and also of the breadth, of talent that can be drawn upon— and of the challenge in doing so.

Chapter 16

The Continuum of Care: The Patient and Family's View

Paul Torrens, MD

Just like everything else in life, the continuum of care for the elderly looks different to different people. For family members and the patient or client, it looks and operates in one fashion, while for others it may be seen in an entirely different light. The physician in the office, the insurance executive, the parish priest, the home health agency administrator . . . all have their own view of what it is and how it functions.

It is the patient and the family members' view, however, that is the most important—because they are the people most centrally involved in its functioning. It is they who must live and struggle under the shelter of its varied services; it is they who must pay a large part of its cost directly out of their pockets; indeed, it is they who give it a reason for existence. Therefore, it is important to understand how the patient and the family view the continuum of care; its ultimate success or failure can only be judged in their eyes. Health and social services systems really exist for the benefit of those being served, not for those doing the serving—a fact that is sometimes forgotten by the servers, but nonetheless central to an appraisal of a health care system.

THE CASE OF MRS. R.

Old age and its attendant infirmities do not arrive overnight. Growing old is a gradual, multistaged, progressive process that usually moves slowly (and inexorably) to a conclusion. Too often, when people not directly involved in the process look at this progressive life drama, they focus on the concluding years and the most serious end-stage conditions. They sometimes forget the initial and the middle stages that have preceded these end-stage problems, thereby missing the opportunity to intervene when intervention may be most fruitful and when constructive action may make future care easier and more productive.

As a case in point, and as an example of how the patient and the family view the continuum of care, let us look at the situation of Mrs. R., a 90-year-old woman currently residing in a nursing home and very much at the end of the continuum of care (and most probably at the end of her life). Let us trace the progress of her life and of her aging in relationship to the continuum of care and let us examine how it has been viewed by the patient and her family.

Mrs. R. was 70 years old when her husband died—at age 78. He had worked until 72 in one capacity or another, and although the victim of a mild heart attack at 68, he had remained comparatively quite healthy until two years before his death. He had a moderate stroke at that time, which left him somewhat incapacitated but generally functional.

Mrs. R. herself had been a vital, active, and healthy woman up until the time of her husband's retirement. She was not really prepared for that change or for her husband's subsequent episodes of disabling illness. She had never had any substantial preparation for his retirement or her own, and she had moved into the years of retirement without a good understanding of what problems were ahead or what could be done about them. Although she had been active in civic affairs and women's groups for years, she had no idea what resources were available in the community to help her.

Like many wives, she had to learn to cope with her husband's depression following his retirement from an active work life and with his subsequent bouts of illness. She had to learn how to arrange for medical care when he had his heart attack and how to obtain nursing care at home when he returned from the hospital. When he had his stroke, she had to learn how to seek out and maintain certain home health care services and, eventually, the services of a daily attendant at home. Beginning at age 60, she increasingly had to learn how to manage all aspects of their financial life and also how to deal with the complicated paperwork, including insurance forms and billings of one kind or another.

Overall, Mrs. R. managed to cope rather well with her husband's health and life problems. In addition, the experience gave her the first insights into what her own aging process might involve in the future. It is a sad truism about aging and the elderly that many women first learn about what is ahead for them by living through the decline and death of their mates.

Following her husband's death, Mrs. R. functioned quite well for a number of years, with only occasional and minor health problems. She maintained a large home in the city, and managed to find household help and neighborhood handymen and gardeners to help with the ongoing maintenance that her husband had formerly done or that she was either not skilled or no longer physically able to do. She was fortunate to have two interested and supportive sons, but both lived at some distance from her, so she mostly had to cope on her own for many years.

A major feature of Mrs. R.'s life after her husband's death was the gradual constriction of her social contacts. While her husband was alive, they had maintained an active schedule of attendance at church, at movies and shows, and at community and professional gatherings of one kind or another. Many of the social events had revolved around her husband's business or fraternity friends. With her husband's death, Mrs. R. was less willing and less motivated to move out of her house in the evening, and she also had fewer invitations or opportunities. Thus, she began to limit her activities considerably.

At the same time, many of her friends, as well as siblings, began to have serious health problems of their own, to limit their own contacts, to move into retirement communities or nursing homes some distance away, and, in some cases, to pass away. Mrs. R.'s own mobility outside of the house suffered a further restriction—a great one—when, at 82, she agreed to stop driving her own automobile. She had been involved in a series of small accidents and finally had realized that she was no longer safe to herself or to others on the road.

The restriction of her driving brought a major change in her existence, although at first its magnitude was not fully appreciated. It was only by accident a year or so later that one of her sons realized that her food and dietary intake had been considerably reduced, since she was no longer able to go to the market herself and select her own food. This had been a pleasant pastime for her in earlier years, not just because of the food itself, but also because of the opportunity for social contacts and for exercising, in some small degree, choice (and therefore power) in regard to her own life by way of the purchases she made.

Mrs. R.'s condition began to deteriorate further, and it was next realized by one of her sons that she could no longer manage her financial affairs and that she was also probably in need of more regular supervision at home in the evening. The problems with her financial management were made apparent when certain utility bills were not paid in a timely fashion and services were actually shut off. (Subsequently, her son enrolled in a program offered by the utility companies that automatically informs an authorized party if bills have gone unpaid for more than one month.) The need for more regular supervision at night was made apparent by neighbors who reported to her sons that she had begun to wander aimlessly out of the house in the evening, clearly not knowing exactly where she was going or how she would get home.

Her sons arranged to take charge of her financial affairs, a feat that was not easily accomplished, as it entailed Mrs. R.'s giving up the last vestiges of control over her personal life. For a woman who had saved carefully for "my old age" and who had managed her financial resources with great thought and skill, relinquishing the handling of her financial affairs was a sad admission of her weakening abilities. After an initial round of resentment and resistance, she quite surprisingly gave over all control to her sons and, seemingly quite relieved, never evidenced any further interest in her finances.

From the sons' perspective, the legal and tax aspects of accomplishing this were as challenging as the personal aspects. The sons, both professionals with advanced degrees in their own technical fields, had to make decisions about issues such as trusts, power of attorney, inheritance obligations, etc. To determine how best to handle their mother's affairs required that they first begin to educate themselves about these issues, which neither had needed to know much about, other than how to maintain adequate life insurance to protect his own family. Finding appropriate legal and tax counsel was in itself a problem, as they discovered, since the majority of lawyers, accountants, and investment advisors are also not familiar with the combined technical and psychological complexities of managing the affairs of an aging family member. Fortunately the brothers—and their wives and the other family members—got along well. There were no divisive disputes about who should be responsible for handling their mother's affairs on a daily basis, about the division of other responsibilities, or about the division of the inheritance.

CONSTRUCTING A CONTINUUM OF CARE AT HOME

Supervision of Mrs. R.'s status in the evening was accomplished by recruitment of a young college student to live with her and to be present in the evening. The student also took charge of buying the groceries (usually on the weekends, with Mrs. R. along) and of getting Mrs. R. to church on Sunday, an important occasion for her.

During the next year or two, it became necessary to add a second college student in the house, to be sure that someone was present every evening. Towards the end of this period, as Mrs. R. began to show signs of decreasing awareness of what was going on and increasing feebleness, it was necessary to recruit an attendant to stay with her during the day.

This situation remained stable for approximately a year until Mrs. R. had the first of three hospitalizations that occurred over the course of two years. The first was for a minor cardiac problem, but as it was the first hospitalization for Mrs. R. since the birth of her children more than 50 years before, it was a difficult experience, both for her and for her family. This hospitalization was followed soon afterwards by another one for evaluation of a possible malignancy (which proved benign) and eventually by a hospitalization for a moderately severe stroke.

During the period right after the hospitalization for the cardiac problem, it was required that more active nursing care, including more attention to problems such as increasing incontinence and potential bed sores, replace the care by home attendants. Several months after her return home from the hospitalization for her stroke, it was finally determined that she would probably continue to need around-the-clock nursing care if she stayed at home. It was decided that this probably would not be practical, because of the expense involved, the difficulty in ensuring reliable full-time nursing care on a continuous basis, and the reluctance of the students living in the home to take on the major responsibility of coordinating all aspects of Mrs. R.'s life and care. After considerable discussion and anguish, Mrs. R.'s sons searched for an appropriate institutional program of care and eventually placed her in a nursing home located fairly near her former residence. Mrs. R. made the transition to the nursing home relatively easily, scarcely understanding what a major change had taken place in her life.

THE IMPLICATIONS

The case of Mrs. R. represents a composite of important episodes from a number of patients and families. Her hypothetical case provides a useful vehicle for examining the patient and family's view at various stages in the process of aging and at various places in the continuum of care.

Knowing What to Expect

Mrs. R. and her sons agreed that they were really unprepared for the changes and complexities brought about by Mrs. R.'s and her husband's aging. Like many people of similar age and background, they simply did not know what to expect, how to handle different events as they happened, or (most important) where to look for advice and guidance. All through her husband's illness (and eventually through her own), problems were handled one by one on an ad hoc emergency basis without any specific source of continuing advice, assistance, or support. One son summarized the situation very well when he said, only half jokingly, "My cars get better continuous attention than my parents. At least when I have questions about my car, I know that I can call the American Automobile Association and get good advice on what to do and where to go. I also know that state laws protect me from being taken by bad workmanship and outrageous prices. With my parents everything is a new challenge; I have to handle it alone and without much guidance. And I never know what the final bill will be."

This very accurately points out one of the greatest deficiencies in the continuum of care at present, at least from a family's point of view: There usually is no easily accessible system of advice and assistance that a family can connect with while the patient is still healthy and before there is a real need for service. When crises come, families are forced to find the needed connection for the first time, acting under great pressure from current events.

Assessing Change

A second feature of Mrs. R.'s case was the gradualness (almost imperceptibly), of the deterioration of her physical and mental state in the years following her husband's death. This meant that both she and her sons didn't fully realize the degree to which she was not able to function, until some major event brought her real condition to full view. With her husband, Mrs. R. had been present every day, 24 hours a day. She was able to detect his aging by experiencing the subtle changes in day-to-day living. She could compensate by gradually assuming more responsibility herself—and she become acutely aware of how little free time she had compared to earlier years. However, neither of Mrs. R.'s sons lived near enough to see her often, and when they were together, it was "a family event," not a routine day.

Looking back long after the fact, one of her sons observed that it would have been nice to have had some type of objective measure of her real functioning ability, somewhat like a periodic driver's test, so that he and his brother could have known more accurately how she was actually doing. Like many families, the only two contacts that Mrs. R. had with potential evaluators were with her parish priest and her family doctor. Although both of these were very good in their specific functions, neither was able to provide an objective evaluation of her living abilities to a degree that would have been useful to her sons and would have alerted them to the need for some organized intervention at an earlier stage in her process of gradual decline. Subsequently they learned of a geriatric assessment team at one of the local hospitals that offered a comprehensive evaluation of health, mental health, social, and functional status. Had the family been able to take advantage of this service, they would have felt reassured in having more thorough knowledge of their mother's status; more importantly, they might have been able to act more quickly to provide some of the functional assistance and support that she needed.

Arranging Services

One of her sons commented upon the fact that his mother's living condition really began to deteriorate after her decision to stop driving. Rather suddenly, her range of social contacts and daily activities became markedly more constricted—and she became rather depressed. Without social stimulation, her mental functioning began to decline more rapidly. He pointed out that had he been aware of the importance of that change, he would have been much more aggressive in arranging substitute transportation for her on a regular basis.

Indeed, both sons commented on the degree to which certain small services, when finally initiated, had made a major change in her mood and condition. Assistance with food shopping, preparation of meals, and transportation were important early; it became important for someone to stay in the home overnight later on and, much later on, for someone to handle her finances.

"Some of these are really not very complicated technical things to get done; yet, we didn't do them because we didn't know they were so important and we didn't know where to get help when we finally realized what was going on," one of her sons said, echoing the feelings of many families in similar situations. "We were constantly handling crises, putting out fires, rather than being out in front of things and taking care of them before a crisis would come up."

The problem pointed to partly reflects the changing pattern of American society. When families remained in one town, when fewer women worked, when families were larger, stronger social networks supported the older members of a family and community. For the two sons—living at a distance, unaccustomed to the caregiver role, and unfamiliar with the array of social support activities (many of which are known about through women's social networks)—arranging the appropriate support services for their mother was difficult, time consuming, and frustrating. Moreover, once services were ordered, the sons were never quite sure of the quality of care or sensitivity of the providers until after the service had been provided and paid for. At the same time, the attention required by Mrs. R. detracted from the time her sons spent with their own families and their own careers. One weekend a month was devoted to a visit to Mrs. R. Although their wives understood—because they were often busy performing similar duties for their own parents—their children did not fully appreciate why their father had to spend a whole day taking grandma to church when the family could have gone off skiing for the weekend instead.

Later on, when Mrs. R.'s problems became more medical in nature and her care required professionals, the situation was not much easier. "When we brought my mother home from the hospital the first time, one or another of us had to be in the house constantly until we could get people to come in and take care of her. We had to interview potential home attendants without even knowing what to ask, without knowing what their duties were or what we should pay. We were lucky we found some good ones, but nobody at the hospital or doctor's office was very helpful with the problems we were facing; they seemed as bewildered as we about how to find or evaluate help. The ladies in the various offices offered their personal suggestions, but there was no organized or professional assistance."

Eventually, the family found several attendants to share Mrs. R.'s care. Two were students, who thus had other obligations and time commitments. Two of the four were immigrants, which posed a set of problems in itself. While the cost was more affordable than the $7.50 per hour charged by private home care agencies, finding the right people had been done through friends and the grapevine, and without the ease, screening, and ongoing supervision provided by using a formal agency. Payment had to be by cash rather than check, which was more difficult for the sons to arrange at a distance. The sons had been concerned that the difference in the language and customs of the daytime attendant (who was Hispanic) might pose problems for Mrs. R., since she spoke no Spanish. Fortunately, in the earlier years she seemed to enjoy occasionally trying to learn Spanish words. The issue of the "green card" arose. The one attendant who had supervised daily activities returned overseas when she could no longer get an extension on her visa, requiring the family to find a suitable replacement.

Fortunately, one of the home attendants had taken care of an elderly person before and had learned how and where to order medical supplies, how to get them delivered, and even what Medicare would and would not pay for. One of Mrs. R.'s sons said, "I only wish we had found her a lot earlier—it would have saved a lot of time and worry!"

Legal Issues

In addition to the financial issues, the brothers also realized that there were several legal issues to be dealt with attendant to their mother's health status. In their state, a *living will* was recognized, as was a *durable power of attorney for health circumstances*. Issues involving these could have been discussed with their mother, and even their father, if the sons had known about them earlier, and they could have been handled as family affairs prior to anyone's illness. Rather than the sons later trying to project what their parents would have wanted, they would have known.

Finances

Mrs. R. was fortunate in having no financial problems. As with many older persons, she owned her home free and clear. Until she became ill, her monthly expenses were primarily for food, utilities, and, until she stopped driving, her car. Her husband had been a successful businessman, and he had left Mrs. R. a sizable estate. He had also had good investment counselors, and they continued to manage Mrs. R.'s portfolio so that she had a regular income based on interest, while protecting the principal. Mr. R.'s company had been far ahead of its time in developing a retirement pension and making actuarial projections that made the pension still financially viable. Thus, unlike many older persons, Mrs. R. received a regular monthly pension payment from her husband's former company.

When Mr. R. had a heart attack, and later a stroke, the majority of his hospital expenses were paid for by Medicare. Mrs. R. was able to provide most of his support care after the stroke, so the expenses for direct medical care were primarily physician's fees and drugs. Although only about half of the costs were paid for by Medicare, the remaining expense was not significant compared to Mr. and Mrs. R.'s total monthly income.

To cover the costs of her own medical expenses, Mrs. R. had Medicare Part A, Medicare Part B, and a supplemental insurance policy that covered the Medicare co-pays and deductibles. At some point she had also purchased an insurance policy for "cancer care." Although her sons thought at the time that it was a sham, the policy did indeed cover many of the procedures and tests that she had during her second hospitalization, which was due to a potential diagnosis of cancer.

The hospital, lab, drug, and physician fees for Mrs. R.'s acute episodes of illness were high—but Medicare covered about half the costs, and private insurance also contributed. After her second hospitalization, her sons considered enrolling their mother in one of the recently opened Medicare HMOs. However, this would have meant that she could no longer go to the physician who had been caring for her for 30 years, a change they felt would cause more harm than the financial benefit was worth. The HMO package offered direct access to some services, such as home health, which would have decreased the brothers' work in selecting and coordinating services on their own. However, the services paid for by the HMO did not exceed by much the services that were covered for Mrs. R. under her own private insurance policies.

The significant cost of maintaining Mrs. R.'s health was not for acute medical care, but for the in-home support services. Mrs. R. lived in a city that had a very active health care community, and the brothers had frequently read about grants awarded to one agency or another to "demonstrate the alternatives to institutionalization" and the "cost-effectiveness of maintaining the frail and chronically ill in their homes instead of in institutions." But as the family discovered, the cost of enabling Mrs. R. to remain head of her own household was considerable. Moreover, no insurance paid for it.

In her last years at home, Mrs. R. had two full-time students living in her home. In exchange for fixing her meals, the students were provided with all of their meals free of charge. The grocery bill totaled about $400 per month. The utilities for the large frame house, with two active boarders, averaged $200 per month during the winter and $100 during the summer. Weekly long-distance phone calls to and from her sons came to an additional $50 per month. During the day, Mrs. R. had a housekeeper. For five days a week, this cost $250 per week. Eventually Mrs. R. found it more comfortable (and safer) to use a hospital bed with electric adjustment, and this added $50 per month. Mrs. R. used a cab for transportation, even to nearby locations, and taxi expenses ranged from $30 to $50 per month. In addition, of course, Mrs. R. paid for all drugs, physician visits, eye glasses, and other medical expenses, including monthly insurance payments. Just these basic costs totaled nearly $1800 per month. This did not include extra, but common, expenses (e.g., an occasional new dress, painting the house, the annual pruning of the trees, and all the other expenses incurred in operating a household or maintaining a social life), let alone the extraordinary expenses, such as unexpected hospitalizations. Mrs. R. could afford the $21,600 per year. The majority of women of her age, however, would not have been able to afford the high financial cost of maintaining their independence and remaining in their own homes.

THE CAREGIVERS

A previous comment by Mrs. R.'s son highlights one aspect of the care of aging relatives that is frequently passed over as unimportant: the amount of time and energy that the children and the families of the elderly actually spend taking care of their aging relatives.

Impact on Productivity and Life Style

In a recent survey of their employees, the Travelers Corporation, an insurance company in Hartford, Connecticut, found that as many as one in five of their approximately one thousand employees in the home office was providing care to an elderly relative. Fifty percent cared for relatives living in their own homes, 20 percent for relatives living with them, and 15 percent for relatives in nursing homes. Four in ten employees managed the older person's finances, and three in ten provided some direct financial support. The survey found that the average time spent caring for an elderly relative was 10 hours per week, but 8 percent of the employees surveyed said they devoted as many as 35 hours per week. The greatest amount reported (by one employee) was 80 hours a week. Only 20 percent of employees giving care to the elderly said it did not interfere with their family life.

This involvement in the care of elderly relatives takes its toll on the caregivers. According to a survey by the New York Business Group on Health, 64 out of 96 U.S. companies surveyed believed that employees providing care for older relatives were more often late to and absent from work than other employees. A survey conducted at the University of Michigan School of Nursing found that people caring for the aged were three times more likely to suffer from depression than the relatives they were caring for. A study by the Duke University Center on Aging showed that 33 percent of the people caring for relatives suffering from Alzheimer's disease used prescription drugs to cope with depression, compared with 10 percent for the U.S. population as a whole.

Financial Costs

Caring for an older relative can also be a financial burden. In the case of Mrs. R., each of her sons commited himself to visit one weekend per month. For one son, this meant driving two hours each way. For the other, it meant a monthly plane trip and car rental. Long-distance telephone calls, not only to the older relative, but also to neighbors, health care organizations, physicians, lawyers, accountants, and a host of others, can mount up. Many families do the shopping or prepare meals for their frail family members, do small but potentially costly errands (like picking up the cleaning), and regularly provide transportation. While the day-to-day costs may not be substantial, for families with children or on tight budgets an extra $50 to $100 per month can mean foregoing purchases required for other family matters.

Health care programs, if they are well-organized, comprehensive, and efficient, may be able to save some of the direct out-of-pocket costs of health care.

An organized continuum of care, which includes case management and access to available community social supports, may also save family members both time and dollars.

LEGAL, FINANCIAL, AND ETHICAL DECISIONS

Not knowing what to expect in the care of an elderly relative and not knowing where to get the services that are needed when a crisis arises are two major problems for caregivers. However, probably the most difficult challenge for a family member caregiver to handle is to assume the role of decisionmaker, thus taking from the elderly person control over his or her own life. For concerned and compassionate children of aging parents, this aspect of care may be the most stressful of all.

In the case of Mrs. R., there were several key points where this type of stressful situation occurred. The first was when her sons began to realize that she was no longer capable of driving. They knew that it would have an impact on her life to stop driving, but they were reluctant to push the point too hard. They also realized that she still felt she was totally in control of her life and that she could make her own decisions, their role still being that of supportive "outsiders." Fortunately, Mrs. R. came to the conclusion on her own that she should no longer drive. Her sons often wondered how they would have handled the confrontation if she had not. As mentioned above, they also had no idea of the magnitude of the negative impact of not driving—something that they might have helped to mitigate had they been more involved in resolving the issue with their mother.

The decision to take control of Mrs. R.'s finances was equally difficult. It required several years of effort. Mrs. R. was very protective of her finances and steadfastly kept all family members out of her affairs for several years past the time when it would have been appropriate for her to let go. She only began to let her sons help when she realized that filling out her income tax forms was too complicated for her to handle, and she only gave up total control when certain of her utilities were turned off for nonpayment of bills. Both instances of relinquishing control over important aspects of her life were accompanied by considerable depression and the deterioration of her condition. Both instances also caused considerable anxiety and stress for her sons.

INTERFACING WITH THE HEALTH CARE SYSTEM

The next major decision point in Mrs. R.'s life came at the time of her discharge after her second hospitalization—when she was 90. At this point, it was clear that if she was going home, she would need considerable assistance on a virtually full-time basis. The discharge planner at the hospital recommended that she arrange for Mrs. R. to go to a nursing home or supportive housing, since her condition would not be covered by Medicare for home care.

Private home care was the alternative chosen by the family. The sons knew that care provided by a formal agency would be expensive and might use up her finances faster than had been planned, or could be tolerated. However, if an appropriate system of care could be constructed without use of a formal agency, it might be more affordable. For the sons, this option meant taking on the responsibility of trying to maintain a continuing system of support for her, with the accompanying problems of recruiting people to work, supervising their work, paying them, and filling in for them when emergencies arose in their own lives and they could not appear. The sons realized that it would have been easier to arrange for their mother to move into some form of sheltered and supervised housing, but they wanted to honor their mother's long-standing wish to remain in her own home ''forever.'' For all of the rhetoric in the health care field about ''helping the frail elderly to remain in their homes,'' the real burden falls on families. Certainly the most difficult and soul-wrenching decision that must be made in all the events in the continuum of care is the decision to place an elderly relative in a nursing home. Ultimately, this decision is made not by discharge planners or social workers or physicians—it is made by spouses and siblings and children. Mrs. R.'s case was no exception.

When it became obvious that the nursing care load was simply too much to continue at home, the sons reluctantly made the decision to seek out a nursing home for their mother. Here again, like most people faced with this problem, they hardly knew where to begin or what to look for or expect. Because Mrs. R. had not been in the hospital recently, they had no help from the hospital staff, and they had no affiliation with any other health or social service agency. The insurance carrier was no help whatsoever. The situation was further complicated by the fact that the sons knew that they were also making the decision to close down and sell their mother's home and that this, too, would involve much work (and emotional strain) on their part.

Indeed, it is frequently not recognized that the decision to enter someone in a nursing home is really much more than the single decision to obtain a certain set of services for the patient. It is also a decision to cause anything resembling independent living to cease for the patient. It is a decision to close up a house or an apartment that the patient may have clung to for many years and to store or sell or otherwise dispose of a lifetime of personal possessions. If there is any chance that the nursing home placement may not work out, the family must balance closing the residence permanently against temporary maintenance and giving the older relative the reassurance that he or she can ''go home'' when there is ''improvement.'' A decision for nursing home placement also forces recognition of the question of inheritance and division of property, thus creating potential for conflict among siblings or the spouses and children of the immediate family members. Finally, if the home is a place in which the elderly patient's children themselves have lived part of their own lives, such a decision may cause a final ending for an important part of family history.

THE IDEAL CONTINUUM

If Mrs. R. and her family were able to construct an ''ideal'' continuum of care, what would it look like and what would be its most important characteristics?

First of all, they would suggest that an ideal continuum of care would provide that care start early, long before there is any crisis. The continuum should help prepare the patient or client and the family in advance for what was ahead. Then, should a crisis arise, the patient and the family would at least be familiar with the possible implications and have a set of guidelines that would assist in enabling them to respond in a manner appropriate to the situation. With the continuum of care to aid them, they could make decisions more calmly and rationally, for they would be familiar with the available options and services and not be operating out of panic, pressure, or, as one son put it, ''the mind-numbing need to do something, but not knowing what to do, where to turn, or who to call.''

Second, Mrs. R. and her family would want some type of continuous and long-term affiliation with a source of advice, counsel, and assistance for the various problems that arise. Mrs. R.'s sons noted that every single event that happened to her seemed to happen in isolation from everything else, and that there was no continuous linkage among events, except for the family physician. ''And he,'' said one of the sons, ''was really hopeless when it came to the practical aspects of handling any nonmedical problems my mother had.''

Actually, much of what Mrs. R. and her sons would want in an ideal continuum of care is now at least partially provided in some of the case management models that are beginning to appear. It should be pointed out, however, that most of these models get involved relatively late in the process of aging (with the attendant increase in disability), and they are only called into play when there is a real need to coordinate some organized professional or semiprofessional set of services. In order to try to head off many of the deteriorating conditions that case management is eventually called upon to handle, Mrs. R. and her family would have liked to have had some kind of assistance and advice much earlier than occurs with the usual case management approach.

Third, Mrs. R. would want to have a much wider assortment of nonhealth personal services available and to have them available earlier in the process of aging. Had Mrs. R. had earlier access to transportation or someone to assist her in shopping, her range of social contacts could have remained much wider, her daily activities more stimulating, and her quality of life higher. Had a continuum of care existed to provide these services, her sons would have been freed from the time-consuming and difficult task of trying to arrange for and maintain such services, as well as from the attendant worries about the quality of the services being provided, allowing them to devote more time to their own families and careers. Assistance with shopping and preparation of meals, transportation, financial management, regular evaluation of her status and reassurance for the patient and the family —all these would be very central to their ideal continuum.

Fourth, an ideal continuum of care would include a wide array of more technical professional services such as hospital care, home nursing care (including home diagnostic services and medical care), and nursing home and related services. Interestingly enough, most of these professional health and social services exist at present, but they exist in a fragmented, uncoordinated, and competitive or adversarial manner. One of Mrs. R.'s sons noted that several of the professional organizations that he had had to deal with over the course of his mother's later years did not really respect or cooperate with the other organizations involved in her care. "The hospital was probably the worst," he said, "because the staff seemed to look down on everyone else and treated them as if they were only important to the degree they helped the hospital accomplish what it wanted to do." Any real sense of reciprocity did not seem to exist when these agencies or organizations needed the cooperation of the hospital.

Finally, if the family of Mrs. R. were designing an ideal continuum of care for elderly relatives, they would want one that would be equipped to help handle the difficult decisions of care, of placement at home or in an institution, of life style in general. Time and again, Mrs. R.'s sons mentioned that the most difficult and perplexing issues involved what to do with and for their mother at certain points in the aging process. Underlying decisions about health care services were often decisions about legal and ethical questions. Unfortunately, the sons had no sense there was professional support to which they could turn or a real source of information about the implications of their decisions for their mother and themselves. They did not have a regular counselor to help them make the appropriate decisions and then live with the consequences of those decisions.

In summary, Mrs. R. and her family would want a continuum of care that

- begins early
- is continuous and allows long-term association
- makes a wide variety of nonhealth, nontechnical supportive services available
- has a wide array of more technical professional services also available
- links all these services together into an integrated, coordinated package
- provides the family with information and psychological support to help them with important decisions

In recent years, many new types of programs and services for the elderly have been developed and the continuous care of the elderly has been expanded considerably both in breadth and depth. If it is to be fully effective, however, the designers and the managers of these new systems of care must continue to look at their services through the eyes of their patients and the patients' families. Only by viewing the health care system from the perspective of those being served and those living through the problems of elderly years will the servers understand what really needs to be done and how best to do it.

Chapter 17

Legal Aspects of Ethical Issues in the Continuum of Care

Jay N. Hartz, Esq.
Patricia Bucalo, Esq.

As health care organizations diversify, expand, and add new services, particularly those that involve an ongoing relationship with the client and family, administrators and clinicians may find that they are dealing with ethical and legal issues of patient care that formerly were not pertinent to their patient operations. For example, hospitals may have established ethics committees, policies for obtaining informed consent, and decision-making processes for withholding life-sustaining treatment. An affiliate organization may have different or contradictory policies or, as is too often the case, no formal policies at all. Staff at both levels may need to be educated; new policies may need to be written or existing ones revised.

In this chapter, we present an overview of some of the basic legal aspects of ethical issues that health care organizations must deal with as they evolve into increasingly more complex health care delivery systems. The issues dealt with are as follows:

1. Informed Consent
2. Medical Information Disclosure and Confidentiality
3. Surrogate Consent
4. Administration of Drugs
5. Patient Restraints
6. Patient Abuse
7. Withholding Treatment
8. Institutional Ethics Committees
9. Liability Implications
10. Management Implications

INFORMED CONSENT

Informed consent requires that a patient be provided with a thorough explanation of his medical condition, the various options for treatment, and the risks of each option. The physician has the duty of obtaining the patient's informed consent. Regulations governing hospitals typically require that prior to surgery, the hospital verify the existence of documentation of the informed consent. The documentation is not itself the informed consent, but is instead evidence that informed consent has been obtained. Additional evidence of informed consent is constituted by the physician's progress notes summarizing the conversation with the patient in which informed consent was obtained. Such progress notes are extremely important evidence of informed consent.

Proceeding with medical treatment without informed consent may expose health care providers to liability if a jury were to find that had a reasonable person been provided with the appropriate information concerning his or her condition, treatment options, and risks, that person would not have agreed to the treatment chosen. Thus, even if the medical procedure is performed without negligence, a basis may exist for liability against the health care practitioner unless informed consent was obtained.

The issue of informed consent, although well established in the law, is problematic for medical practitioners in many cases; it is often especially problematic in the context of the continuum of care. To the extent that the patients are fully competent, the same standards of informed consent apply to patients in all health care settings. Patients must be given adequate information to make an informed choice concerning treatment alternatives and must be advised of the risks of consenting to or refusing such treatment. Such informed consent should be documented in the medical record.

A problem encountered frequently in the long-term care setting is that the patients of nursing homes, hospice, or home health may not be competent, or at least their competence may be in question. Most of these people do not have, and in many cases never will have, a court appointed guardianship or conservatorship established. This leaves health care providers in the difficult position of trying to obtain informed consent for treatment when the patient's ability to give it is in question.

In many states, the laws concerning informed consent are unclear on the issue of whether or not family members are authorized to give or refuse consent on behalf of another adult family member. Indeed, in many states the rule is that family members are not authorized to give consent. Nonetheless, as a practical matter in many such cases where the patient is unable to give informed consent himself or herself, physicians and family members jointly agree to a treatment plan. In essence, the physician obtains informed consent from the family members, whether or not it is formally authorized by the law. It would be preferable either to have a clarification or modification of the law to enable family members to give informed consent in this type of case or to make it easier to obtain the appointment of a guardianship or conservatorship for such cases. However, it is critical that, in dealing with relatives, health care providers remember that the same type of information should be given to them as would be given to the patient, i.e., a full explanation of the risks, benefits, and alternatives of various proposed courses of treatment. Also, the transmission of such information to the relatives should be documented.

MEDICAL INFORMATION DISCLOSURE AND CONFIDENTIALITY

To obtain the informed consent of a competent patient or, as discussed below, of an incompetent patient's surrogate decisionmaker, it is essential to disclose to the patient or the surrogate sufficient information about the medical circumstances. Under relatively few circumstances does prudent medical judgment dictate that a patient not be given such information. Under even fewer circumstances, if any, is medical information appropriately withheld from a surrogate decisionmaker. While state laws and court opinions vary in their approaches to medical information disclosure and patients' rights to it, most recognize such rights in one context or another and are consistent with the federal protections of disclosure and decision making.

The Medicare conditions of participation for general hospitals require, among other things, that acute care facilities comply with their own state and local licensure requirements in order to participate in the Medicare program. Such licensure requirements often include obligations to inform patients of their own medical circumstances. In California, for example, the California Administrative Code provisions governing acute care facility licensure obligate hospitals to adopt a written policy on "patients' rights," including the right to "receive information about the illness, the course of treatment and prospects for recovery in terms that the patient can understand" and the right to "receive as much information about any proposed treatment or procedure as the patient may need in order to give informed consent or to refuse this course of treatment."[1]

From a permissive perspective, although no less important to most hospitals, most Medicare conditions of participation are also deemed to have been met if a hospital is currently accredited by the Joint Commission on Accreditation of Hospitals (JCAH). The 1987 JCAH *Accreditation Manual for Hospitals* includes a statement of patients' rights and responsibilities that JCAH considers to be "reasonably applicable to all hospitals." Among the stated patients' rights is the following:

> The patient has the right to obtain, from the practitioner responsible for coordinating his care, complete and current information concerning his diagnosis (to the degree known), treatment, and any known prognosis. This information should be communicated in terms the patient can reasonably be expected to understand. When it is not medically advisable to give such information to the patient, the information should be made available to a legally authorized individual.[2]

The Medicare program also obligates participating skilled nursing facilities and hospice programs to comply with all state and local licensure laws. Again, support is lent to the states' statutory protection of patients' rights to their own medical information at all stages of their care. California's skilled nursing facilities are also required to establish written patients' rights policies, including the right "to be fully informed by a physician of his or her medical condition, unless medically contraindicated, and to be afforded the opportunity to participate in the planning of medical treatment. . . ."[3]

For hospice provider participation, the Medicare regulations themselves include the obligation to "demonstrate respect for an individual's rights by ensuring that an informed consent form specifying the type of care and service that may be provided as hospice care during the course of the illness has been obtained for every patient, either from the patient or his/her representative."[4] A patient's very participation in a hospice program must undoubtedly be accompanied by the fullest communication of medical information, in the interest of complete cooperation between provider and patient. This hospice model of communication would seem to be appropriate at every stage of illness and treatment.

A legal companion to the patient's right to his or her own medical information is the patient's right to have that information kept confidential. As with the patient's right to disclosure, rights of confidentiality are recognized by JCAH and by federal and state laws governing all levels of the continuum of care. In addition to state licensure laws, statutes like California's Confidentiality of Medical Information Act allow providers, at any level of care, to be privy to a patient's medical information from other providers, at whatever level, in order to properly care for the patient. The transfer of medical record information from an acute care hospital to a home health agency, for example, is likely to be protected under any state's confidentiality laws, as long as the information is used as the statute intends and as long as it is not disseminated to those who are not entitled to it. Local laws should be carefully reviewed for patient consent requirements before disclosing medical information to anyone outside the continuum of providers, even to a patient's family members. In addition, staff on all provider levels should be regularly reminded of these confidentiality constraints; penalties for disclosure without the patient's written consent may be severe.

SURROGATE CONSENT

In cases in which the patient is not capable of giving informed consent, health care providers must look to a surrogate decisionmaker. Some states authorize family members to act as the surrogate decisionmaker for their relatives without formal appointment by the court or other process; other states do not permit this. In the latter states, the traditional method of appointing a surrogate decisionmaker is for the court to appoint a guardian or conservator of the patient. This is done upon a written petition, with notice to relatives and to the patient. This process is typically time consuming and difficult. In many cases, relatives are unwilling, for reasons of time and expense, to go through the court process unless absolutely forced to do so. If a guardianship or conservatorship is created, it is essential that health care providers verify that the documents appointing the guardian or conservator grant that person the authority to make health care decisions for the patient. Not all guardians or conservators are authorized to make such decisions.

A different approach to the issue of surrogate decision making has been enacted in a few states. This involves a document sometimes referred to as a *durable power of attorney for health care*. Such a document enables any person, by signing it, to appoint another person to act as a surrogate decisionmaker at such point in time as the signer is no longer capable of making health care decisions for himself or herself. The benefits of such a document are that, without the necessity of involvement of the courts, it identifies a specific individual to whom health care providers may turn for direction and it may also give such care providers specific information about the desires of the patient. The standard that the substituted decisionmaker is to apply pursuant to a durable power of attorney for health care is that the decisions should be those that the patient would have made (where the patient's desires are known) or those that are in the best interests of the patient (where the patient's desires are not known).

A statutory durable power of attorney for health care is to be distinguished from a *living will*, which is popularly recognized throughout the country but which has no binding authority. A living will is essentially a written statement of a person's desires for the termination of his or her own treatment at some identifiable stage. It is executed either after a person is diagnosed or while a person is healthy and merely planning ahead for a possible catastrophic illness.

The living will provides some indication of a person's wishes under certain medical circumstances. It may be useful when, as discussed in more detail below, a surrogate decisionmaker is obligated to base decisions of treatment withholding or withdrawal upon the expressed desires of the patient.

Some 35 states have adopted statutes, typically known as ''natural death acts,'' that embody the concept of a living will, but give it statutory authority, define its terms, and state the legal impact of such a document. In the absence of such a statute, living wills, although helpful, have no statutory authority.

In all cases of surrogate decision making, irrespective of the mechanism used to appoint or identify the surrogate decisionmaker, sufficient information about the various possible courses of action and the attendant risks and benefits of each should be given to the surrogate decisionmaker to enable that person to make a fully informed decision. Documentation of the provision of this information and of the consent or refusal given by the surrogate decisionmaker is just as important in these cases as it is in dealing with a competent patient.

Occasionally a surrogate decisionmaker takes a position that appears to the health care provider to be unreasonable and detrimental to the patient. In such instances the health care provider should act cautiously and seek further consultation and discussions about the decision to avoid acting in a way that would harm the patient. This could include seeking review by an institutional ethics committee (if one exists), seeking consultation with another physician (if appropriate), or conversing at length with the surrogate decisionmaker to clarify the reason for the decision and to assure that the surrogate decisionmaker understands the potential impact on the patient. Consultation with an ombudsman may also be useful (if one exists).

Most states have statutory procedures that enable a health care provider to seek direction from the courts if it should appear that the surrogate decisionmaker is acting in a way that is not in the best interests of the patient. It may be necessary to seek the replacement of the surrogate decisionmaker by another who *will* act in the best interests of the patient.

Health care providers should not feel compelled to act against what they perceive to be the best interests of the patient in cases where the surrogate decisionmaker acts unreasonably. If a decision of the surrogate decisionmaker is in fact based on the desires of the patient, then those desires should decide the issue, even if the decision is different from that which the health care provider might make. Health care providers need to assure patient autonomy in decision making and at the same time protect the patient against improper decision making by a surrogate decisionmaker who may not be acting in the patient's best interests.

ADMINISTRATION OF PSYCHOTROPIC OR ANTIPSYCHOTIC DRUGS

Psychotropic and antipsychotic drugs are occasionally used to assist in controlling aberrant behavior of patients. Long-term care patients are particularly likely to be given such drugs. Some of these drugs do have beneficial uses and may be appropriately used in certain cases. Long-term care providers, however, have frequently been criticized for overutilizing such drugs and in effect chemically sedating or restraining patients unnecessarily, with a detrimental effect on their health.

Potential risks and liabilities arising from the overuse of such drugs include malpractice claims for damages. Care must be taken to assure that such drugs are used in appropriate quantities, for appropriate duration, and only for patients for whom they are medically appropriate. Periodic review of the use of such drugs should occur.

USE OF PATIENT RESTRAINTS AND POSTURAL SUPPORTS

Postural supports are frequently utilized for frail elderly patients to protect them from falling out of bed or out of a chair. These postural supports are sometimes also referred to as *restraints*. Their use is in some cases appropriate, reasonable, and necessary. However, as with the use of psychotropic or anti-psychotic drugs, a danger exists of overusing such supports or restraints, which will limit the ability of a patient to move freely. Again, a reasonable balance must be struck between protecting the patient and, at the same time, permitting the patient to ambulate safely to the maximum extent of his or her capabilities.

Health care providers are exposed to potential liability in cases where a patient falls and is injured if the patient either has demonstrated a pattern of such falls or is clearly unstable. On the other hand, if, in the past, the patient has been able to ambulate adequately without assistance and has not previously fallen, a fall will not necessarily establish a basis for liability. Potential liabilities could theoretically exist for overutilizing postural supports or restraints to such an extent that the patient loses the ability to ambulate or otherwise use his or her extremities.

In the skilled nursing facility setting, where postural supports are most likely to be used, state licensure laws often specifically recognize and limit such use. In California, for example, the patients' rights policy required by the skilled nursing facility licensure regulations must include the right "to be free from chemical and (except in emergencies) physical restraints except as authorized in writing by a physician or other person lawfully authorized to prescribe care . . . or when necessary to protect the patient from injury to himself or to others.''[5] The burdens of limited staffing in crowded skilled nursing facilities that care for numbers of the frail and elderly are only likely to increase as health care costs are required to decrease. However, in addition to creating potential liability for the physical decline of the patient, excessive reliance on postural supports and restraints can become a form of patient abuse that renders a provider liable on yet other grounds.

PATIENT ABUSE WITHIN FACILITIES OR PROGRAMS

Patient abuse, including abuse of the elderly patient, may take many forms. In California, a recently enacted dependent adult abuse reporting statute defines the "abuse" of a dependent adult as encompassing physical abuse (including unreasonable physical constraint), sexual abuse, neglect, intimidation, cruel punishment, fiduciary abuse, other treatment resulting in physical harm or pain or mental suffering, and the deprivation by a care custodian of goods or services that are necessary to avoid physical harm or mental suffering.[6] This California statute requires all health practitioners to report any known or suspected physical abuse, and it also protects health practitioners from any liability for reporting other forms of abuse that they know have occurred or that they reasonably suspect.

The primary thrust of any state's adult abuse law concerns its reporting obligations. Health care practitioners and others in positions of responsibility for elderly patients or "dependents" are expected to be among the first sources of information about elder abuse, and they may be severely penalized for failing to comply with a statutory reporting requirement. Under the California statute, for example, failure to report in the designated circumstances is a criminal misdemeanor, punishable by up to six months in jail or up to a $1,000 fine, or both. It is essential, then, that health practitioners and custodians of the elderly at all levels of care recognize that their legal obligations to the elderly may go beyond delivering care. State laws should be reviewed for any abuse reporting obligations (not all states impose them), and if such a statute is in effect, its particular abuse definitions, as well as the details concerning time limits for reporting, designated reporting agencies, and other issues, should be carefully read. Skilled nursing facility and home health agency administrators should be especially attuned to the impact of such laws and regularly remind their staff members of any obligations imposed upon them directly.

Prohibitions against patient abuse may also take the form of less explicit, more general obligations to preserve patient dignity. JCAH accreditation standards, for example, expect the accredited facility to preserve the patient's right "to considerate, respectful care at all times and under all circumstances, with recognition of his personal dignity."[7] State facility licensure laws also recognize a patient's right to dignity, as in the California skilled nursing facility regulation protecting the patient's right "to be free from mental and physical abuse . . ." and "to be treated with consideration, respect and full recognition of dignity and individuality, including privacy in treatment and in care of personal needs."[8]

Liability for patient abuse may include loss of JCAH accreditation or Medicare provider status, loss of facility licensure, or civil and criminal penalties for assault, battery, invasion of privacy, and other possible violations. Furthermore, to the extent that the law mirrors the moral and ethical priorities of its society, these legal liabilities reflect a larger social concern for the dignified, respectful care of all patients, whether institutionalized or not.

WITHHOLDING OR WITHDRAWING TREATMENT, INCLUDING LIFE SUPPORT

Historically, health care providers have expressed considerable concern about circumstances in which it is permissible to withhold or withdraw treatment, particularly where such a course of action might hasten the death of the patient. The courts have held that it is not necessary to provide the most aggressive possible treatment under all circumstances.

A general approach to issues concerning the alleged right to withhold or withdraw treatment has been discussed in a number of court cases across the country. The approach that has been followed by most courts in dealing with these cases has involved an analysis based on the premise that a patient has a right to refuse treatment, even if it means that the exercise of the right may shorten his or her life. The courts, however, have held that the right to refuse treatment is not absolute and must be balanced against the interests of society, which have been held to include (1) the prevention of suicide; (2) the protection of health; (3) the protection of the ethical integrity of the medical profession; and (4) the protection of innocent third parties. Usually none of these factors will outweigh the right of a competent patient to refuse treatment in the life support context.

Such considerations will often also fail to outweigh the patient's right to refuse treatment where the patient is not competent and is represented by a surrogate decisionmaker. In such cases, the courts have held that the right to refuse treatment is not lost by virtue of the patient's incompetence but is to be exercised instead by a substitute decisionmaker. The mechanism for identifying or appointing an appropriate substitute decisionmaker may vary from state to state. In many, it is a court appointed guardian or conservator. In some, it may be the immediate members of the patient's family, or a person appointed pursuant to a durable power of attorney for health care. The surrogate decisionmaker, once identified, is to make decisions based upon the expressed desires of the patient if they are known; if they are not known, then the decisions are based upon the best interests of the patient.

Typical treatment issues include the use of "Do Not Resuscitate" orders, which command the suspension of the otherwise automatic provision of cardiopulmonary resuscitation in the event of a cardiac arrest or cessation of breathing. Such orders are typically used when it is determined by the physician that further treatment would be fruitless and possibly inhumane.

It is recommended that facilities develop written policies for the use of such orders so that all personnel within a given facility understand and utilize the standard terminology. It is also recommended that all such orders be required to be entered in writing in the medical record. Nursing staff should not accept an unwritten order not to resuscitate, except to the extent that the facility or agency policy permits telephone communication of such an order. A telephone-communicated order should be promptly entered in the medical record and countersigned by the physician at the first opportunity. Finally, notations in the medical record by the physician should verify the basis for the physician's decision to issue the "Do Not Resuscitate" order and should document communications with the patient (if competent) or with the patient's family or other surrogate decisionmaker (if the patient is incompetent). Such orders should typically not be made if they have not been discussed with a competent patient or with the available family members or other surrogate decisionmakers of an incompetent patient.

As health care organizations form linkages to create a continuum of care, consistency of policies between the various levels in the continuum will become increasingly important. Whereas hospitals often have explicit policies concerning

"Do Not Resuscitate" orders and the like, skilled nursing facilities, home health agencies, and others frequently will not have such policies. Where a patient is transferred from one level of care to another, consistency in pursuing the treatment plan from the one level to the other should be maintained. A review of policies on such matters should be made to assure that consistency can be maintained.

An example follows as to how this issue might affect health care providers. A hospitalized, frail, elderly patient and her physician have agreed that no heroic actions will be taken. When the patient goes home, still feeble and with little hope of recovery, she assumes no resuscitative efforts will be made. The discharge planner arranges for the hospital's affiliated Medicare home health program to assist the patient. The home health nurse identifies a need for a homemaker. The homemaker is present when the patient arrests. She calls the paramedics, who arrive, resuscitate the patient, and return her to the hospital.

In this instance, each person in the continuum of care acted responsibly, but the patient's wishes were not carried out, since there was no mechanism for communicating the patient's expressed wishes. Health care providers should consider how such wishes could be communicated throughout the continuum of care, how provider employees could be educated to know how to react under such circumstances, and how consistent policies at the different levels of care could assist in resolving such issues.

Increasingly, the issue is arising as to whether or not it is permissible to withhold or withdraw feeding tubes from elderly patients who are no longer able to take food by mouth. The acceptability of withholding or withdrawing artificial means of providing nutrition or hydration is not yet fully settled on a national basis. Several approaches to the issue have developed. The California courts, in the case of *Barber v. Superior Court*,[9] have held that the "medical" administration of nutrition and hydration (i.e., through IVs, NG tubes, and the like) is to be analyzed in the same way as any other type of medical treatment; furthermore, the standard to be applied by physicians is that such treatment need not be provided if the burdens of the treatment outweigh its expected benefits. In the case of a permanently comatose acute hospital patient, the court ruled that it was permissible to withdraw the IVs that were providing minimal nutrition and hydration to the patient.

A 1985 decision of the Supreme Court of New Jersey addressed the related issue of the withholding or withdrawing of feeding tubes from noncomatose but incompetent patients in a long-term care setting. In *In Re Conroy*,[10] the New Jersey Supreme Court considered the case of a nursing home patient who was extremely debilitated but not comatose and who could not be said to be "terminally ill" inasmuch as health care providers were unable to say that she would die from any specific malady within a defined period of time. At best, her physicians could only say that they expected her death to occur within the next year and that she was extremely debilitated from a number of factors. She lay in a fetal position in the nursing home and appeared to be basically unaware of her environment. She had no immediate family. Her closest living relative, a nephew, successfully petitioned the court to be appointed her guardian; he then requested permission to refuse further use of the feeding tube on the grounds that his aunt would not have wanted it.

The court held that in some cases it would be appropriate to permit the withdrawal or withholding of a feeding tube from such a patient. The court identified such cases as those in which the patient was expected to die within a year at most and (1) the patient had previously expressed in serious and formal terms a desire not to have heroic treatment provided; (2) the patient had expressed in a more informal fashion desires indicating that he or she did not want heroic treatment, and continued treatment of the patient would appear to be inhumane to the patient; or (3) the patient had made no previous statement concerning his or her desires about the use of life support, but the unavoidable pain associated with the patient's condition indicated that continued treatment would be inhumane.

The court went on to construct a procedure that had to be followed prior to withholding or withdrawal of feeding tubes from a patient in a nursing home within New Jersey. Notification had to be made to the state ombudsman, who then conducted an investigation to determine whether or not patient abuse was involved. The ombudsman was to appoint two independent physicians to review the condition of the patient and the propriety of such an order. Finally, after appointment of a guardian or conservator, a court hearing was to be held to assure that the patient was not capable of participating in any such decision. The court held that if all those procedures were satisfied, and there was unanimous agreement that it was appropriate to withhold or withdraw the feeding tube, then no liability could be imposed on any of the health care providers who participated in the action.

A trial court decision in Massachusetts recently held that even for a comatose patient, it was improper to withdraw a feeding tube; the court in that case concluded that minimum levels of treatment were required for all patients, which included the provision of nutrition and hydration. This decision is currently being appealed and thus is not yet final.

A recent California Court of Appeal decision, *Bouvia v. Superior Court*,[11] suggests that a nonterminal mentally competent patient has the right to refuse the use of a feeding tube, even where the refusal is expected to shorten life.

At present, the issue of nutrition and hydration remains a particularly volatile one, and health care providers are urged to exercise caution in dealing with cases that involve such issues. These issues must be considered even outside the institutional setting. What responsibility does a treating physician, or other health care provider, have in a home care setting where a patient's family elects to terminate care?

Consider the following example. A hospital provides care to a patient during an acute episode. The hospital has an affiliation with a home health agency and a hydration company. The patient is transferred home, and the family decides that it wishes to terminate care. What responsibility does the physician have? The home health nurse? The hydration company? What procedures should be followed if such a situation is encountered? There is little precedent to guide providers under these circumstances, but consideration should be given to these issues since they can be expected to be encountered as health systems expand in size and scope.

The use of institutional ethics committees may provide some assistance in this area, by providing a mechanism to help assure that the withholding or withdrawing of treatment will occur only in appropriate cases and to help achieve a consensus among all parties involved, including the patient's surrogate decisionmaker (if there is one) and all involved health care providers. While the use of such committees does not guarantee protection from liability, it does tend to assure that there is a forum for discussing concerns that hopefully can be resolved within the institution rather than in a courtroom.

The issue of the withholding or withdrawal of treatment, particularly life support, in the context of a continuum of care will take on added significance as the economic limitations affecting the health care system become more pronounced. Health care providers will be increasingly subject to accusations of terminating care for reasons of their own economic benefit rather than for the best interests of the patient, and for this reason, among others, it is particularly important that health care providers develop written policies concerning the withholding or withdrawal of treatment and the procedures to be followed, and that careful thought be given to the use and development of institutional and continuumwide ethics committees as a mechanism by which to review difficult cases and provide appropriate consultation to the responsible health care providers.

INSTITUTIONAL ETHICS COMMITTEES

Institutional ethics committees were first given prominent judicial recognition by the New Jersey Supreme Court in the case of Karen Ann Quinlan.[12] Such committees were subsequently studied and extolled by the President's Commission for the Study of Ethical Problems in Medicine and Biomedical and Behavioral Research.[13] They have become increasingly popular in patient care settings. As discussed above, they are often extremely useful in difficult decision-making circumstances, such as when withholding or withdrawal of life-sustaining treatment is under consideration. But they may also serve important functions such as education, facility policy formation, and multidisciplinary consideration of ethical issues (e.g., the allocation of scarce resources). As organizations increasingly form affiliations with multiple service providers, such committees provide a mechanism for bringing together the representatives of all services involved in the care of an individual patient.

Ethics committees may operate under the aegis of either the administration or the medical staff. Administration committees are likely to enjoy open and free-ranging issue discussion and may include a broader representation of continuum services. On the other hand, medical staff committees may encourage more candor (and therefore be more effective) because, if properly structured, they are likely to be accorded the same confidentiality protections as other medical staff committees. Such protections will be particularly important to the patient's individual physician, who is usually the person most involved in communications with the patient or the surrogate decisionmaker. No state court has yet considered confidentiality protection for ethics committees, but if they are governed by and conducted in accordance with their medical staff bylaws, the confidentiality of their proceedings is very likely to be upheld.

True ethics committees, as distinguished from diagnosis review or prognosis committees, usually include nurses, administrators, social workers, clergy, ethicists, and sometimes legal and community members, as well as physicians. The purpose is to provide a forum for multidisciplinary consideration of difficult health care decisions; it is not to second-guess or dictate a physician's professional judgment regarding the patient. Sharing ideas and perspectives on a problem may assist a physician in reaching a judgment—or assist the hospital or health care organization in the formulation of a policy. Furthermore, such thorough consideration may succeed in keeping providers and patients out of court and in the private arena of mutual decision making.

LIABILITY IMPLICATIONS FOR THE CONTINUUM OF CARE

Potential liability in the situations described in this chapter may be imposed upon only one, or as many as all, of the patient care operations along the continuum, depending upon the legal and factual circumstances involved. For example, a single corporation may own and operate an acute care hospital, an extended care facility, and a home health agency. If while in the extended care facility a patient receives treatment that was not properly consented to, the patient will probably be able to hold the facility's corporate owner liable, which may have a financial impact on its hospital and home health operations as well.

Careful organizational structuring, as the range of offered health services expands, may work to limit liability in an instance like this to the extended care facility operations alone. When the hospital decides to begin providing the extended care services, one important planning consideration should be whether or not to establish a separate subsidiary corporation to own and operate the extended care facility. If the subsidiary's corporate structure is properly maintained and capitalized, any liability to its patients or residents should be confined or limited to the subsidiary itself, without directly affecting the hospital or the home health agency.

Often the acute care hospital is the original operation that finds itself in the position of offering new related services, such as hospice or home health. Another important aspect of such expanded services is the hospital's dissemination and adaptation of its policies and procedures to its new "offspring." Sophisticated acute care facilities are likely to have well-developed risk management procedures, consent and confidentiality policies, withdrawal of life support criteria, and other carefully created legal, ethical, or administrative tools that may be offered to their other health service operations. To help preserve the limited liability of, e.g., a home health corporate subsidiary, the subsidiary may enter into a contract with the hospital to purchase risk management or ethics consulting services from the hospital. But however structured, policy sharing among related continuum providers should be anticipated and encouraged from the beginning of policy formation at any level in order to help maximize patient protection and dignity and minimize legal liability.

Patient referrals from one level of care to another within the same provider network pose additional liability and ethics concerns. A full discussion of legal implications of referrals to related entities is beyond the scope of this chapter. However, federal and state law limitations do exist and should be carefully noted. The ethical implications of these referrals must ultimately center around what care is best for the patient. Administration pressures and financial incentives to refer patients to related providers should never be allowed to overcome the individual provider's best judgment for his or her patient's well-being. Ultimately, the patient has no choice but to rely upon that best judgment.

MANAGEMENT IMPLICATIONS FOR THE CONTINUUM OF CARE

As health care systems grow and develop and linkages are created, management must begin to consider carefully the ability of the system created to adequately service the needs of patients, to act consistently, and to communicate between the various levels of care. It may therefore be appropriate to consider designating a person or persons to think through the functioning of the system from the perspective of the patient in order to assure adequate consideration of such matters. Such an "internal ombudsman" might provide a perspective that differs significantly from typical management perspectives.

Additionally, as patients and the public become more aware of and concerned with various bioethical issues such as refusal of treatment or withholding or withdrawal of care, such matters deserve management's attention prior to the existence of a problem in order to create systems to deal with problems when they do arise. Such issues can benefit from management and advance planning. One approach to managing such issues would include the following strategies:

- Educate physicians and staff about the issues and about the basic legal rules governing them, so that they have a basic awareness of them and an accurate and consistent knowledge base.
- Develop written guidelines or policies for dealing with issues such as "Do Not Resuscitate" orders, the determination of brain death, and the withholding or withdrawing of care, since such policies act as a helpful reference, assure uniformity, and demonstrate to outside observers that such matters are dealt with thoughtfully and carefully.
- Create appropriate ethics committees to provide consultation (but not final decision making), to act as a forum for discussion of difficult cases, and to act as a vehicle for providing continuing education concerning moral issues.
- Establish a relationship with appropriate advisors familiar with such issues, e.g., attorneys specializing in bioethics.

CONCLUSION

Despite the continued shrinking of the health care dollar in the years to come, providers' legal and ethical responsibilities to preserve their patients' safety, comfort and dignity are not likely to change. Nor should they. Instead, it becomes increasingly incumbent upon providers to find new means of supplementing financial resources with ethical ones.

NOTES

1. Cal. Admin. Code, Title 22, Section 70707.
2. Joint Commission on Accreditation of Hospitals (JCAH) Manual, Section title *Rights and Responsibilities of Patients*, 1987, xii.
3. Cal. Admin. Code, Title 22, Section 70707.
4. 42 CFR Section 418.62 (October 1, 1985).
5. *Id.*, Section 72527(a)(8).
6. W & I Code, Section 15600 et seq.
7. JCAH Manual, xi.
8. Cal. Admin. Code, Title 22, Section 72527(a)(8), (10).
9. 147 Cal.App.3d 1006; 195 Cal.Rptr. 484 (1983).
10. 98 N.J. 321 (1985).
11. 179 Cal.App.3d 1127; 225 Cal.Rptr. 297 (1986).
12. *In re Quinlan*, 70 N.J. 10; 355 A.2d 647; *cert. denied*, 429 U.S. 922 (1976).
13. President's Commission for the Study of Ethical Problems in Medicine and Biomedical and Behavioral Research, *Deciding to Forego Life-Sustaining Treatment, A Report on the Ethical, Medical, and Legal Issues in Treatment Decisions* (Washington, D.C.: GPO, 1983).

Chapter 18

The Physician's Role in the Continuum of Care

William R. Hazzard, MD

The continuum of care can enhance or inhibit the role of the physician. It appears that while the opportunities for the former are great, the current direction is toward the latter. This chapter begins by tracing the development of the field of geriatrics and the influence that this specialty has had in the development of the continuum of care model. The second section focuses on the impact that the continuum of care has had on the physician. The chapter concludes by suggesting the individual and collective actions that must be taken by the medical profession, both by academicians and practitioners, to ensure that the role of the physician as the primary manager of a patient's care is enhanced rather than usurped by a complex organization that purportedly provides greater and more efficient service, but in fact may render less flexible, less sensitive care.

The days of the independent physician are fast fading. Many physicians entered the medical profession because they liked the idea of assuming responsibility for the care of a patient and family, including the personal relationship that accompanied such responsibility. Many also liked the idea of one's own practice, where a style consistent with one's own preferences could be created. The past 20 years of government regulation set considerable limits on the range of independence, but physicians have grown accustomed to dealing with the regulations and working around them as much as possible. The past few years have seen an unprecedented change in the medical environment. Not only has technology continued to impress by exceeding its expected limits, but health care delivery system financing and organization have been shaken up, resulting in the evolution of many different and confusing forms. Also, consumer expectations have intensified, and market competition among all sectors, including peers, is a challenge to physicians. One by-product of this maelstrom is the emergence of continuum of care systems. These new arrangements offer some relief in giving a structure and new resources to make it possible for physicians to do more work, yet do it better and more efficiently. They also carry new responsibilities and constraints.

IMPACT OF GERIATRICS ON THE CONTINUUM OF CARE

Older people are the largest single client group of the continuum of care. Their problems tend to be multiple, multifaceted, and chronic, and thus warrant the comprehensive, continuous care offered by the continuum. The exponential growth in the number and proportion of older citizens is one of the primary forces driving health care organizations to create a continuum of care.

The evolution of geriatric medicine (i.e., the medical care of older people) closely parallels—and overlaps—the development of the continuum of care approach to patient care. Growing knowledge in this field and the emergence of geriatric specialists have strongly influenced health care organizations. As practitioners have gained greater understanding of the problems and care of seniors, they have encouraged, prompted, and demanded health care organizations to change their operations in order to create a system of care (i.e., the continuum) to respond more appropriately to their senior clients' needs. Many of the model continuum of care programs that are currently being emulated throughout the nation began with impetus from a geriatrics program. As geriatrics advances, it will continue to have a major impact on the organization and operation of health care systems. Although all areas of medicine affect the continuum, geriatric medicine is the most important to understand and monitor, since it is a bellwether of the changes in health manpower education, training, and practice patterns that in turn will lead to future changes in the continuum.

Historically, the American health care system evolved predominantly to meet the needs of a young population with acute time-limited illnesses. Expanding in a growing and technologically sophisticated economy, the system evolved as though resources were unlimited, and hence intensive and expensive patterns of care predominated. The tertiary care hospital became the apex of the system, and hospital-based, procedure-oriented physicians employing the latest techniques developed by a large scientific medical community were the most highly rewarded, both professionally and economically. Medicine became evermore technical, specialized, and attractive to scientifically-oriented aspiring young students.

A shortage of physicians (specifically of primary care physicians) was perceived, and medical school enrollment burgeoned, supported both directly through government subsidies and indirectly by research grants and liberal reimbursement for the expensive model of hospital-based care that predominated in the tertiary care teaching hospitals. (Ironically and predictably, this spawned more subspecialists, not the desired increase in numbers of primary care physicians.) Passage of Medicaid and Medicare, which funded, respectively, care of the poor and those 65 and older, permitted public expenditures for health care to grow dramatically throughout the 1970s. The role of government in providing a large and stable funding source for institutional care—Medicare for acute hospital facilities and Medicaid for nursing homes—was critical. The number of nursing home beds, for example, increased exponentially throughout the late 1960s and early 1970s because of the availability of guaranteed funding. The contribution of the private sector grew apace, predominantly via employer contributions to employee health insurance. Both public and private insurance mechanisms were passive, reimbursing hospitals and physicians principally on the basis of charges. Hence, the cycle of high technology, high cost, high reimbursement, high-technology development became complete and even self-accelerating.

Unavoidably the aggregate cost of health care rose at a rate consistently above the rate of inflation. This contributed to inflation and governmental deficits, while threatening to bankrupt the Social Security system. Industry began to realize that health care was inordinately expensive.

Enter the demographic imperative and the growing dilemma becomes clear: An aging population and a relative dearth of young persons to care for the health and social needs of the elderly creates a mismatch between resources and needs that will grow dramatically for the next half century. Given the effective cap on total health care expenditures that has arisen because of an unacceptable level of federal deficit, per capita expenditures for the elderly must be reduced simply to keep aggregate costs constant. Thus the need emerges for more efficient health care for older people.

Yet more important, such care must also be more effective. It is becoming increasingly apparent that costly, technologically intensive, procedure-oriented, hospital-based, episodic acute care is to a large extent inappropriate in meeting the needs of older persons. The typical older patient has multiple chronic problems not given to short-term treatment and cure. Multiple health problems beget multiple diagnostic and therapeutic interventions. Multiple medications and iatrogenic illness related to pharmacological misadventures are extremely prevalent among the elderly. Moreover, physiological reserves in the elderly are likely to be limited in multiple systems even in the absence of overt symptoms. This renders the typical older patient vulnerable to other iatrogenic problems: infections, falls, metabolic derangements, mental decompensation, and surgical complications. Hence the hospital environment with its concentration of risk is particularly hazardous to the older patient. And in the absence of special programs to educate physicians about the needs of elderly persons, subspecialized, procedure-oriented, hospital-based physicians may become part of the problem rather than part of the solution.

Meanwhile an alternative health and social care industry has evolved to address the more enduring needs of the chronically disabled elderly dwelling at home or in long-term care institutions. In these alternative systems, nurses, social workers, case managers, rehabilitation therapists, administrators, and volunteers have been the predominant health care professionals. The physician has typically performed a passive and administrative function and even more commonly has had an ephemeral monthly role as an itinerant practitioner. Medical practice in this system has been less glamorous and less lucrative (can you image a TV soap entitled ''General Nursing Home''?), yet in the aggregate, costs for such long-term care are substantial, concentrated in the elderly (and hence funded to a large extent from public sources), and growing rapidly. Furthermore, with the proportion of the very old (85 and older) increasing more rapidly than that of any other age segment of the population, growth in costs will escalate for the next 40 years. With the demand for long-term care increasing, the cost per unit of care is also likely to escalate. The surplus of physicians graduating from overlarge training programs may contribute to this inflation as they discover the long-term care field in the process of searching for a professional niche, tending to introduce into the nursing home and home care arena the expensive, intensive model of care with short-term goals they have learned in the teaching hospital environment. Thus a collision between ''the medical model'' and ''the social model'' in long-term care is evident—unless major course corrections are introduced.

Geriatric Practitioners and the Resolution of the Dilemma

What is the role of geriatric practitioners in the resolution of this dilemma? To get on with the business at hand, the cardinal rule in approaching patient care issues must be ''think of the patient.'' Turf issues, power struggles, battles for space, money, and prestige can all melt away if this rule is followed without exception by all practitioners regardless of discipline. Students and teachers of each participating discipline must identify and focus upon those aspects of geriatric health care specific to their own discipline. Just as important is bridging the relevant disciplines: learning the body of information, the modalities of practice, and the attitudes necessary for effective teamwork.

After years of research, the physiological, psychological, and social aspects of aging, as well as the general needs of elderly patients, are clear. However, these must be taught to and learned by health professionals from all the relative disciplines. The identification of these needs and the means to meet them constitute the specific body of knowledge and practice that is geriatrics. All professionals must know this common body of knowledge, adding to it those aspects peculiar to their specific discipline, e.g., nursing, medicine, social work, psychology, dentistry, pharmacy, public health, podiatry, optometry, nutrition, the ministry, and recreational, occupational, and physical therapy. The list is long indeed. Ignorance among current practitioners, due to limitations of the training curricula, is historic.

The principal barriers to acquiring that body of knowledge and applying it in practice are attitudinal. The negative attitude toward chronic illness prevailing in acute care hospitals, especially tertiary care and teaching hospitals, is inherently ageist. It is the major specific barrier to overcome. Dementia, incontinence, immobility and falls, iatrogenic illness, terminal disease—such is the stuff of geriatrics; little is amenable to complete cure, and the risks of almost any form of intervention are substantial. Unless health professionals accept these realities and operate within these boundaries, they cannot be effective as geriatric practitioners. Moreover, they must learn to gain gratification from helping patients and families cope with these realities and the burdens of irremediable, often progressive disease. Health practitioners must acquire both the requisite skills and attitudes necessary for effective care of the elderly. Otherwise, the system will continue to reinforce the present mismatch between the resources available and the health needs of an aging population.

The Education of Geriatric Physicians

The content of geriatric educational programs is being increasingly accepted.[1] The details are beyond the scope of this text. Fortunately the body of knowledge, both that common to all practitioners and discipline specific, is being steadily refined. Textbooks are growing in quality and quantity,[2] and training programs are proliferating rapidly.[3] The development of geriatric medical education, barely identifiable a decade ago, is accelerating dramatically.

This movement is gaining additional momentum from the support of hospital and public health care administrators who appreciate the gathering storm brought on by the demographic imperative. Medical students and residents looking to their own professional futures are joining the effort.

The estimated need for geriatric medical manpower was quantified in a benchmark study by Kane et al.[4] The actions required by schools of medicine were articulated in a major position paper produced under the auspices of the Institute of Medicine (the "Beeson Report")[5] and publicized nationally through a series of regional institutes on geriatric medical education sponsored by the Association of American Medical Colleges.[6] These reports were based upon the following five assumptions:

1. Physicians will play a key role in meeting the growing health care needs of an aging population.
2. There does exist a specific body of knowledge about the practice of gerontology and geriatric medicine; all students of medicine must acquire and master at least the central elements of that core knowledge.
3. Appropriate attitudes must be adopted by physicians in order for their geriatric practice to be effective and efficient; few role models of the effective geriatrician exist among medical school faculty, and negative, ageist attitudes are extremely prevalent, especially in the tertiary care teaching hospital; overcoming such attitudes represents a major goal of effective geriatric medical education.
4. The settings in which medical student and resident teaching have been concentrated (notably the tertiary care hospital) have limited relevance to appropriate geriatric practice.

5. Given the limited manpower with specific expertise in geriatric medicine, the exponentially increasing need for such geriatricians, the large number of physicians currently in training, and the resources available for support of such training, geriatric medical training programs should focus primarily on future teachers of geriatric medicine. Such leaders must be academically competitive physicians who can teach as well as practice, attract premier students to the field, serve as role models for such students, relate to and re-educate practicing colleagues, and demonstrate effective geriatric practice over time, across the continuum of care, in an appropriately sensitive fashion, and in an interdisciplinary and multidisciplinary manner.

The last task is a tall order, and it would appear most realistic for the academic medical center, with its multiple systems of back-up and division of labor. It becomes particularly problematic outside of that kind of medical center, where the faculty/student/patient ratio, the service requirements, and the reimbursement schemes become inimical to the educational mission.

For this reason the concept of the *teaching nursing home* was introduced by Robert Butler, M.D., during his tenure as the first director of the National Institute on Aging.[7] Teaching nursing homes allow the concentration of faculty and students from medical and the several health professional schools to work in close proximity and collaborate in a learning environment. The role of teaching nursing homes can also be expanded, and they can serve as geographic centers for programs that reach into the community, as well as doing geriatric research. In such an institution, special units or programs may be developed for geriatric assessment, for posthospital convalescent and rehabilitative care ("step-down," "subacute," "transitional," or "progressive care" units), and for the specialized management of common geriatric problems such as dementia, incontinence, and nutritional deficiency. The subacute care units can also serve the episodic, more intensive care needs of patients maintained long-term in units at lower levels of care, preventing unnecessary, costly, dangerous, and dislocating acute hospitalizations, particularly threatening to the maintenance of the continuity of care.

Teaching nursing homes have been developed under the aegis of schools of nursing under grants from both the Robert Wood Johnson Foundation and schools of medicine, with the support of program project grants from the National Institute on Aging. The latter are particularly limited in scope, however, because of legislatively mandated restrictions on National Institutes of Health support to research activities. Acquiring such extra-institutional support, however, is a mechanism whereby institutional commitments can be gained and channeled toward more effective geriatric education. Such grants also provide support for the research activities of faculty based functionally (if not at all times geographically) in such teaching nursing homes. This allows a broader and more traditional academic role for faculty than where salaries are paid entirely from patient care reimbursement sources. Teaching nursing homes (or, more accurately, academic nursing homes) also serve as the natural geographic home for faculty from the participating disciplines, fostering multidisciplinary education, collaborative research, and, increasingly, preparation of future academic geriatricians in formal postresidency fellowship training programs.

The Hospital Initiatives in Long-Term Care is another national demonstration project that has integrated geriatric medical education with redesign of the long-term care system into a continuum of care approach. This program, which is sponsored by the Robert Wood Johnson Foundation, has funded 24 hospitals across the nation to develop comprehensive care programs. This includes providing acute inpatient care, extended (nursing home) care, home health care, case management, mental health care, and medical and health professions education. Of the 24 sites, most have had strong geriatric medicine programs— or developed them as a result of the grant. Like the teaching nursing home, Hospital Initiatives provides an opportunity for geriatric physicians and students to have a learning environment that encompasses a wide spectrum of health, mental health, and social services. More importantly, the program includes involvement of community physicians, and thus is formulating a model for the interaction of geriatric specialists and primary care physicians in institutional and community settings. Finally, the model program demonstrates the feasibility of providing services through an organized continuum of care system, for the research and data required by the program documents the benefits of a continuum.

The Veterans Administration (VA) hospitals have been leaders in developing geriatric training programs. The VA has made a major commitment to the care of the aging veteran population and to the preparation of physicians to administer that care. More university-based programs are emerging. However, it remains unclear whether these will suffice, particularly given the narrow research-only orientation of fellowship training via the National Institutes of Health, the labor-intensive nature of geriatric care (and hence its low level of reimbursement for faculty participation), and the threat to postgraduate education support in general, and fellowships in particular, under the increasingly constrained federal support for postgraduate medical education. The specific curriculum for geriatric medical education from medical student through postdoctoral fellow has been defined in a volume by Robbins et al.[8] The number and capacity of formal fellowship training programs in geriatric medicine have thus far been limited (though growing yearly).[9] Approximately 200 physicians have received formal fellowship training in this country to date. Thus to meet the minimal estimated number of geriatricians that must be trained to provide just for the educational needs of future physicians (i.e., full-time academic geriatric faculty), further expansion will be required.

In the most optimistic projection, such formal fellowship training programs will meet the care needs of only a small fraction of an aging population. Therefore, the efforts of such academic geriatricians must be amplified through physicians, especially primary care physicians, trained in medical schools and residency programs, principally in internal medicine, family medicine, and to a lesser extent, psychiatry, neurology, and rehabilitation medicine. Thus an era is rapidly approaching where gerontology and geriatric medicine will be liberally dispersed throughout the undergraduate and postgraduate curriculum and where all primary care physicians and internists will have had in-depth experience in geriatric medicine prior to becoming eligible for board certification (such programs per-force involve exposure to the entire continuum of care under the direction of geriatric medical faculty).

Also lending momentum to the formal preparation of geriatric medical prac-titioners is the impending certification of physicians for such practice by the American Board of Internal Medicine (ABIM) and the American Board of Family Practice (ABFP). In September 1985, both organizations were approved to grant certificates of "additional competence" in geriatric medicine. This is being translated into descriptions of appropriate residencies and fellowships, i.e., spec-ification of educational content and experience. By 1988, formal testing of candidates and certification of those passing the examination will begin.

Under present planning guidelines, the ABIM will allow internists with sub-stantial experience in the care of the elderly to take the examination under a "grandfather" scheme for a limited period of time (at least four years), following which a formal fellowship in geriatric medicine of at least two years duration will be required for candidates to become eligible to take the examination. The ABFP, on the other hand, plans no such grandfathering scheme but will require only a single year of formal fellowship training (and in addition will require periodic recertification, as in the case for all ABFP certificates).

A rush of applicants for certification is anticipated as the geriatric market place is more appreciated by physicians and available niches for medical prac-titioners vanish because of the surplus of physicians graduating from medical schools and residencies. Thus within a span of less than a decade, geriatric medicine will have evolved dramatically from an underserved, almost vacant area of medical concentration to one potentially crowded with practitioners, a growing proportion of whom will have fellowship training.

The challenge will be to marshal the positive aspects of the momentum to improve geriatric medical care and focus them upon appropriate, efficient, col-laborative, and sensible care. The continuum of care must be a training site for physicians at all levels, from the medical student to the postdoctoral fellow, and developing it as a training site for all the involved professionals is imperative for providing improved, effective, and efficient care of the elderly. Its mainte-nance by appropriate administrative and physical support—and the assurance of its excellence by appropriate leadership and regulation—will be essential to the preparation of physicians to engage in expert geriatric medical practice, just as the contributions of such geriatric experts to the continuum of care are essential to its excellence.

The Consummate Geriatrician

What can the patient, the family, the collaborating nonphysician health care professional, and the administrator expect of a physician trained in geriatric medicine? At a minimum, the following:

- a physician attuned attitudinally to the needs of the elderly patient, the family, and other supporters, one capable of making a real contribution to the patient's care
- specific skills in the management of both common and uncommon problems of the elderly; these will involve not only greater in-depth experience in the care of patients with specific diseases and disorders within the discipline of internal medicine (e.g., myocardial infarction, congestive heart failure, stroke, polymyalgia rheumatica, osteoarthritis, osteoporosis, etc.), but also specific expertise in the management, over time and across levels in the continuum of care, of problems representing final common pathways of decompensation in the elderly—notably the five I's of geriatric medicine (immobility, incontinence, incompetence, impaired homeostasis, and iatrogenic illness)—and of certain crosscutting problem areas confronting the elderly (e.g., maintenance of adequate nutrition, maintenance of spirit and self-care determination, etc.)
- knowledge of the contributions of related health professionals and the ability to collaborate in a multi- and interdisciplinary mode of practice
- knowledge of the array of services and options available to the elderly and to others with complex, chronic conditions
- knowledge of the administrative regulations and mechanisms pertinent to long-term care
- leadership ability and a willingness to facilitate and coordinate complex care of the frail and chronically ill patient
- experience in gerontological research, with a resulting appreciation for the complexities and limitations of present knowledge, as well as for the opportunities and need for rigorous investigation to answer pressing questions
- a generous, forgiving spirit, full of patience, wisdom, and compassion, as well as book learning

IMPACT OF THE CONTINUUM OF CARE ON PHYSICIANS

The continuum of care activities that have occurred to date have forced major changes in the authority, responsibility, and accountability of the practicing physician. Formerly, clinical care was based on a unique relationship between a physician and patient. The hospital was "the doctor's workshop," and extensive physician involvement in home health care, nursing homes, or community service programs was neither expected nor prevalent. The increasing organization of the health care delivery system into mega-organizations, accompanied by continued restraint of public and private funding mechanisms, has made the physician, along with his patient, into pawns in a bureaucratic and externally regulated structure. Simultaneously, the conversion of the health care delivery system from frustrating fragmentation to comprehensiveness and cohesion enables the physician now to gain access for a patient to services that the physician would not have had the awareness of or the time to contact or that perhaps the patient could not have afforded.

The tradeoffs in authority, responsibility, and accountability are difficult to balance, and the future trajectories are uncertain. Roles and relationships with practitioners of other disciplines and with families and patients have changed. Daily tasks, particularly those related to formal health service facilities and programs, have both increased and decreased. Expectations have changed—of other physicians, of other providers, of and by patients and families. The physician's sphere of operation and knowledge in dealing with the elderly and chronically ill has expanded. Most physicians face the demographic imperative within their own practice, and most also face increased competition for patients from other physicians and other organizations. Thus, the physician must adapt to the changes to maximize the control over his own practice that he feels is necessary for providing high-quality, individualized care to his patients.

Case Example: Mrs. J.

Ten years ago Mrs. J., who was 70 at the time, had a stroke. She was in the hospital for two weeks; then Dr. G. transferred her to a local nursing home with an excellent reputation for rehabilitation. She remained there for four months, then went home. Although she seemed to be doing well, Dr. G. ordered home visits by home health nurses and rehabilitation therapists. Dr. G.'s nurse arranged for nurses from the Visiting Nurses Association to see Mrs. J. and asked them in turn to arrange for a homemaker if necessary. Mrs. J. recovered fully, which she largely attributes to the patience and continued rehabilitative assistance she received from the staffs of the nursing home and home health agency, as well as from Dr. G.

Mrs. J. recently had another stroke. This time, the emergency room staff of the hospital delayed admitting her for two hours until they could receive admissions approval from the HMO that Mrs. J. had joined. Dr. G. had to submit an additional form verifying that the admission was warranted and was a nonelective emergency. After Mrs. J. had been in the hospital for a few days, the utilization review staff of the HMO called Dr. G. to inquire how much longer Mrs. J. would need to stay, and they reminded Dr. G. that he and his physician colleagues, whose group had joined the HMO, would exceed their average financial allocation (i.e., lose money) if in many cases such as this the patient remained in the hospital beyond the projected average length of stay and the number of projected hospital physician visits was surpassed.

The discharge planner from the hospital also contacted Dr. G. to inform him that Mrs. J. was nearing the average length of stay for the DRG diagnosis under which she had been admitted. Although the hospital was not at financial risk for Mrs. J., since she was an HMO patient, the hospital was competing with another nearby hospital in contracting with the HMO for all inpatient care, and they wanted to determine as accurate (and low) a contract price as possible. Moreover, the duration of stay would be reflected in the records kept by the hospital on Dr. G.'s inpatient utilization. Too many long-stay patients and he would be called before the Professional Standards Review Committee.

When Dr. G. felt that Mrs. J. was indeed ready to leave the acute inpatient setting, he contacted the family to discuss nursing home transfer. The family expressed preference for a specific nursing home. Dr. G. knew that the hospital had a bed-contract agreement with a different nursing home. He wanted to allay the family's anxiety by sending Mrs. J. to a nursing home they knew, but he also wanted to be supportive of the hospital's budding relationship with the other nursing home, where he felt the care was slightly better due to the accessibility and part-time presence of hospital staff. As it turned out, the discharge planner from the hospital, along with the utilization review staff from the HMO, informed Dr. G. that Mrs. J.'s HMO coverage required her to go to a participating nursing home. Fortunately, a reasonably good facility had a free bed, but the home was across town, making it difficult for Dr. G. to visit as frequently as he would have liked.

After 100 days, Mrs. J. was discharged from the nursing home to home because the 100 days represented the end of her coverage under Medicare; the HMO did not permit an extension because of the degree of her improvement. Dr. G. would have ordered home health care, but since Mrs. J. was not entirely bedbound, the care would not have been authorized by the HMO or Medicare and Mrs. J. would have had to pay for it herself.

The hospital's care manager had maintained weekly contacts with Mrs. J. When he was very busy and had not had time to go to the nursing home, Dr. G. found this helpful; other times he found the constant calls and reports to be somewhat of an intrusion into his relationship with Mrs. J., and he mildly resented the implication that he was not aware of what was going on with his patient. Nonetheless, when Mrs. J. went home, the case manager suggested to her and to Dr. G. that a homemaker stop in two days a week. Mrs. J. could afford the low cost of this service, at least for a short time.

Dr. G. would have preferred to use the homemaker services that had always been arranged through the Visiting Nurses Association; he knew some of the homemakers and the extent of their capabilities. However, the case manager informed him that the hospital had recently entered into a joint venture to provide private home care services, and she felt the hospital's home care agency would be able to send a qualified homemaker to Mrs. J. The case manager arranged for this service, and after the initial call, which was handled by his nurse, and the subsequent weekly reports, Dr. G. agreed that the homemaker seemed to be dependable and competent.

Dr. G. had mixed feelings about the way in which Mrs. J.'s case was handled. On the one hand, he had modified his treatment program to coincide with the regulations of the government as manifested in the hospital's various departments. The constraints imposed by the HMO meant that he had fewer options than ordinarily—however, the HMO financial arrangement saved money for Mrs. J. and guaranteed at least minimum payment to him and his fellow physicians. Neither of them had to hassle with Medicare claim forms. The case manager was, in the end, helpful, but Dr. G. wondered whether she had not contributed more confusion than assistance. He was annoyed that the hospital, too, was infringing upon his service provider options by setting up its own programs—until he remembered a brief presentation and subsequent vote of approval at a medical staff meeting whose primary focus was a much more pressing topic. The extra revenues to be generated from the homemaker and several similar programs were to be contributed directly to the hospital's capital fund to enable the purchase of several new state-of-the-art pieces of equipment. In the end, Mrs. J., though frailer at 80 than at 70, recovered from her second stroke.

New Professional Roles and Interactions

New professionals are emerging, some as a direct result of the emergence of continuum of care systems, others as a result of advances in technology or health manpower education programs. Numbers are growing for the following kinds of clinicians, among others: the geriatrician (as described above), the geriatric nurse practitioner, the geriatric rehabilitation therapist, the geriatric social worker, and the high-technology home therapy nurse. Each of these professional roles has existed for ten or more years. The increasing number of older people and the attempts of health and social service organizations to provide appropriate human resources are reflected in the recent growth in the number of training programs and practitioners. New administrative positions include the case manager, DRG coordinator, formal discharge planner, HMO reviewer, risk management coordinator, ethics committee member, information and referral specialist, and liaison with home health agencies, hospitals, or nursing homes. Each of these positions carries its own responsibilities and has lines of authority, responsibility, and accountability. The physician must adapt his role to adjust to these new personnel. The new personnel can become additional resources for the physician, enabling him to do more for his patients more quickly and more effectively—or, alternatively, they can become handicaps, making the physician work in a slower and more cumbersome manner.

New Responsibilities

As health and social service organizations expand and unite into continuums of care in order to gain a competitive edge and maintain financial viability, the physician's responsibilities become more complex. Previously a physician might have had to deal primarily with the bureaucracies and financing regulations (both private and public) governing hospitals, nursing homes, and home health agencies, and he would have been familiar with the few providers he used often. In the current climate, the physician must deal with the utilization and financing requirements of multiple but distinct entities within the health care system's corporate umbrella, plus a variety of PPOs and HMOs. From the standpoint of time and efficiency, the administrative requirements may be draining—more forms to fill out, the need to keep track of which service entities are part of which organization, etc.

New quirks of patient care also bring new responsibilities: The physician must use services according to the organization's utilization review or financial criteria, and it becomes the physician's duty to know which services are covered by which programs in order to assist patients in making treatment decisions that they can afford. As the continuum is formalized, new administrative structures are added, such as task forces and committees, and the physician is asked to participate in internal structures and those relating to affiliated organizations. New policies must be worked out, written, and approved, and physicians are asked to assume this responsibility directly for medical policies and to act as representatives on task forces developing policies for other disciplines and programs.

More physician involvement is requested in the various other services of the continuum, e.g., the physicians are asked to appoint from among themselves medical directors for senior housing, home health agencies, and nursing homes. The concomitant patient care responsibilities follow: If a patient of one of these services becomes ill, it may be the medical director who ends up with the midnight phone call. Before, such medical directorship positions were often filled by semiretired physicians who enjoyed staying in touch but not having immense amounts of direct patient care. Also, one physician might assume the same position within several organizations. Today, health care systems increasingly are attempting to involve as many physicians as possible, and to involve the most active, not the least active, doctors. Ethics committees, quality assurance, risk management, and a variety of other management control systems are being developed and then expanded to include all of the services linked together in the continuum. As this occurs, the physician is being asked to participate in such committees and to do the associated patient reviews, which adds additional burdens.

New Authorities

The continuum both expands and constrains the physician's authorities. The advent of HMOs, DRGs, PPOs and other capitated systems has given the physician increased authority to control financial returns, as well as patient flow and service use. Group practices of physicians, for example, are contracting with HMOs to assume financial and patient care responsibilities for the provision of primary medical care, specialty care, home health care, home care equipment, and a variety of other services. In contrast, under some new arrangements, the physician may have the ultimate authority, but he must interact with staff who have new positions that also carry responsibilities and authority which may cause conflict. The physician may prescribe home care, but the case manager may have the authority to select and contact a particular home health care agency to arrange for the service. The automatic flags of a computerized information system that identify at-risk patients may give the authority to order the department of social work or discharge planning to meet with a patient and family to discuss posthospital care.

New Accountabilities

Not too long ago, the physician had to answer only to himself or herself and to the patient about what was done and why. Now, it is common for a physician to prepare utilization authorization reports for one or more HMOs; to complete medical record forms that are transmitted to quality assurance, utilization review, discharge planning, the ethics committee, or the malpractice insurance program; and to chart clinical entries that are reviewed by a multidisciplinary team of professionals, as well as by specialty physicians. The physician must account to numerous sources for the clinical, financial, and legal soundness of his actions and decisions.

Conversely, other professionals have secured accountabilities that may or may not conflict with those of the physician. The discharge planner, for example, may be accountable to the director of nursing or director of social services if patients remain beyond the expected length of stay. The case manager may be responsible to the vice-president for patient care for making referrals to a particular set of community affiliates. The single-matrix structure that characterized many health care and social service agencies has become multidimensional, and the physician is likely to find that many clinical and administrative personnel over whom he has little, if any, control are making decisions that affect his practice.

Coordination, Communication, and Cooperation

The emphasis by institutions on continuity of care and the concomitant change in responsibilities of health care professionals, the emergence of geriatrics with its emphasis on multidisciplinary care, and the addition of a whole host of new personnel—from geriatric physician specialists to case managers—all heighten the level of attention that the physician must give to coordinating and communicating with other professionals. Whereas in geriatrics and rehabilitation medicine, team conferencing is built into the daily schedule and roles of each discipline, it is not the common modus operandi for most primary care physicians. Most physicians run very tight schedules and work long hours; they do not have time to hold hour-long case conferences or administrative meetings with six different people during the course of one day. Even phone calls are often returned after 5 P.M., when most employees have left for the day. In contrast, most administrators spend most of the day in meetings, and many clinicians from disciplines other than medicine are likely to spend as much of their day in meetings as with patients. It is difficult for physicians to adjust their schedules, let alone their behavior, to accommodate certain practice patterns potentially warranted by the continuum of care. The very continuity and comprehensiveness promised by the continuum require physicians to coordinate and communicate with other professionals in ways that they do not have the time for and which they thus perceive as detracting from their ability to deliver to patients the quality of care that they aspire to provide.

For all the power that has been eroded, the physician is still the ultimate authority in prescribing patient care. Thus, the organization that wishes to create a continuum must consider how to involve physicians without alienating them. The mechanisms of the continuum must be set up to make efficient use of the time and effort of the physician. Automatic patient referral forms, for example, can be included in the patient's chart, thus enabling the physician to prescribe home care or durable medical equipment without making a call to—or being called by—the discharge planner, the social work department, or the home health agency. The report of a case manager can be sent automatically to the patient's physician through the mail (perhaps with a letterhead and colored stationery that will clearly identify it as patient relevant), thus obviating the need for a call to the physician's office. Team meetings can be held monthly (rather than weekly) and in conjunction with other regular medical staff meetings. An occasional meeting will maintain some degree of personal familiarity, yet not infringe upon the physician's time unnecessarily. In between, phone calls and individual meetings with team members can occur as the physician makes rounds at the hospital, nursing home, or home care program.

Relationships among Physicians

Relationships with other physicians may also change. As the specialty of geriatrics evolves and geriatric consultation is developed at community hospitals, great care must be taken to introduce the service in a positive way. Geriatric assessment units (GAUs, also called geriatric evaluation services, and a variety of other similar terms) were started primarily within the VA. Great Britain was used as a model. The positive benefit of the GAU on patient outcomes has been demonstrated by empirical research. However, the majority of physicians have many older people in their practices, and the suggestion that they do not know how to care for them would be heresy. Thus, the geriatric specialists must build their credibility on the basis that the geriatrics *team* can contribute resources (including perhaps even medical expertise) that will enable physicians to provide a broader range of services for their patients without requiring their office to provide additional staff resources. The geriatric specialists will inspire trust among fellow physicians by orchestrating comprehensive workups on problem cases, then returning the information to the patients' referring physicians. Continuums of care that are built around only one or two geriatricians may be successful as demonstration models and research programs, but in general geriatricians will be consultants and educators (as noted above) and will not assume a primary care role other than that relevant to their educational function.

In the medical community, physicians are reacting variously to the opportunities to expand, diversify, and aggregate. Some physicians are joining HMOs; others are aggressively resisting. This may create changes in referral patterns. Some physicians are starting their own business, which through affiliation, contract, or ownership may become part of a continuum of care. Such entrepreneurial efforts are applauded by some physicians, and shunned by others. Again, referral patterns may change.

Financial pressures, too, are changing the way that physicians relate to one another. If physicians are bound together in a group practice or as one department of a hospital, their personal financial success may become interdependent with the practice patterns of their colleagues. HMO Medicare risk contracts epitomize the strength and the variation of such arrangements. In one current situation, a multidisciplinary group of physicians has contracted on a capitation basis to be at risk for the primary care, specialty care, and home health care of an identified population of enrollees. The hospital used by the group has also contracted with the same HMO to share the risk for hospitalization for the same enrollees, and as an incentive to efficient practice, the hospital has decided to allocate the upcoming year's capital expenditures to the departments that maximize DRG payment.

Suppose a physician from the group has a frail elderly patient who is bedbound and ill, but it is questionable whether hospitalization would measurably benefit her. If the physician orders home health care for the patient for an extended period of time, he may alienate his fellow members in the group. They might argue that he should have admitted the woman and done a workup in the hospital. But if he admits the patient, does an expensive workup, and does not aggressively pursue rapid discharge, he may alienate his colleagues in the department of the hospital, who might argue that he should have kept the woman at home and had the home health service do routine tests and observation. If he admits the woman briefly, then discharges her with home care briefly, he may satisfy both groups of colleagues—but the frail old woman will have had to change locations twice in a short period of time.

As institutional interdependencies increase, they are creating new, multiple, and at times conflicting interdependencies among physicians who previously would have practiced quite independently of one another. The sharing of knowledge and the amount of consultation on individual patients by physicians may suffer, as may the sense of fellowship. Thus the challenges to effective and efficient geriatrics practice are great. The risk of disappointing a particular group of colleagues with a specific, narrow viewpoint must be accepted, and constructive dialogue over points of conflict must be made part of the educational process that is the primary focus of the geriatrician.

Relationships with Patients and Families

Consumers are expecting more of the health care delivery system and more of their doctors. They are also becoming more aware of their ability and need to affect their own health and to participate in decisions about their health care. These trends impinge upon the physician's traditional role as the authoritative diagnostician and healer. In contrast, the former fragmentation of the health and social service systems, which discretely excused the physician from direct responsibility for many aspects of care, is being overcome—with the consequence that the physician is directly confronted with the responsibility of continuing to play a dominant role in the care of the patient regardless of the type or setting of care. Simultaneously, as described in detail above, many other practitioners are intervening at various points in the patient's care. To counter, physicians must spend more of the time with their patients and the patients' families in clarifying their role.

The physician must also be prepared to explain to the patient and family the role of the other actors: the case manager, the utilization review team, the geriatric consultation team, and the home health nurse. Some roles are easy for patients to understand—the picture of the nurse coming to the home is widely accepted. Yet, the majority of patients do not really know what to expect once a nurse enters the home, let alone what a homemaker can and cannot do.

As the use of noninstitutional services increases, physicians will be called upon to prepare their patients for the involvement of other practitioners. They will also be called upon more frequently to hear complaints, to assure quality, and to arbitrate between patients' expectations and practitioners' expectations. This role as an educator is not new, but it will require increased time and attention from physicians and their staffs. In order not to infringe upon patient care time more than necessary, physicians need to build the support resources to enable them to assist patients and families by means of their staff, continuum of care staff, appropriate materials, and referral to experts in particular areas.

Ethical dilemmas have become public domain. Even in the decade of the 1970s, society was not eager to confront ethical issues such as the right of the frail elderly to refuse treatment, the legality of "living wills," or how to allocate scarce resources among generations. Primarily because of public attention to federal and state budget deficits and the pressure placed upon the health field to exercise cost-containment, the public has become keenly aware of decisions made by health and social service agencies to provide or withhold care. Moreover, technological capabilities have been publicly juxtaposed with human frailty, demonstrating the ability of technology to sustain life even when the quality is "lifeless." Thus, through public awareness, both healthy and ill individuals have greater choices about how to deal with physical deterioration.

This places the physician in the position of needing to talk freely with his patients about potential future ethical issues and their resolution. Not that physicians did not always discuss such concerns. But in the past the physician was often able to help an ill person or the family make a decision about treatment based on a long-time relationship and an implicit understanding of the patient's personality, beliefs, and what he or she would elect. The legal system has now codified some of the decision making process, as described by Hartz and Bucalo in Chapter 17. Public law specifies with considerable clarity who can make decisions regarding certain treatments and under what circumstances. The patient and his or her family, not the physician, have been given the legal decision-making responsibilities. Moreover, the physician and the organization may be in jeopardy if they exceed the bounds specified by the law. Thus, the physician must now not only be emotionally prepared and have the requisite legal knowledge, but also be aggressive in discussing legal or medical issues with a patient and the family. The involvement of the latter may itself cause some disruption to the physician's relationship with the patient, as well as require much time to discuss often imponderable and irresolvable issues.

The physician must also be prepared to deal with patients and families concerning ethical dilemmas, life-threatening choices, and issues of personal proclivity. This has always been a responsibility of physicians, and indeed one that strengthens the bond between patient and physician. However, physicians have been able to avoid explicit discussion of many issues with many of their patients. For example, take the case of nursing home patients. Once transferred to a nursing home, a person often becomes the patient of the nursing home's medical director. Although the medical director may get to know the patient, he or she is not likely to have the same length or intensity of contact as the primary care physician. Thus, when physical problems become acute, the patient begins to fail, he may be transported by ambulance to the nearest hospital and die under the care of the physician on call. This example is extreme—yet it occurs all too often. Under the continuum of care concept, the patient cannot be transferred from one setting of care to another with each one failing to claim responsibility. The continuum of care does not promise continuity of care by a single physician, but it does promise continuity of medical care over time by the system. Thus, whether it is the individual physician or a case manager or social worker or nurse, the system will keep the physician informed of where the patient is in the system and what the patient's personal preferences are, and the physician's responsibility will not be abrogated as the patient transfers from one level of care to another.

RECOMMENDATIONS

Perhaps twenty years from now the fragmentation of the health care system will have been overcome and rampant change will have ceased. Perhaps there will indeed be, as futurists project, only 5 or 10 major companies that provide a full range of health and related social support services. Realistically, it is unlikely that the health care environment of the immediate future will become simpler. It is thus incumbent upon physicians—to the extent that they wish to maintain control over their own practices, the availability and accessibility of expensive resources, and the quality of care that they are able to deliver to our patients—to take an active role in creating the continuum of care.

Physician involvement in the continuum of care will be strengthened if physicians in general do the following:

- participate in the committees, task forces, and planning groups of health care institutions in considering the addition of any new services
- serve as medical directors of hospitals, nursing homes, or home care, housing, or community services
- set up mechanisms within the organized medical staff (whether at a hospital, HMO, university, county association, or some other place) to deal directly with the continuum of care as it affects local medical practice
  - —prepare a statement of medical staff involvement delineating the concerns of physicians
  - —gain consensus among physicians (including making concessions if necessary) to be able to present a cohesive position
  - —make sure that the administrators and boards of the relevant health and social service organizations are aware of the physicians' interest in participating in the design of new or integrating service programs
  - —insist on presentation of proposed contracts or affiliations to the medical staff, with voted approval as specified by the medical staff by-laws

- for services arranged through formal or informal contacts, include in the contract negotiations the feedback and control mechanisms that will enable physicians to be kept informed about and direct the care of their patients
- incorporate information about geriatrics, long-term care, and the continuum of care in regularly scheduled continuing education programs, grand rounds, and special educational conferences
- establish quality assurance criteria for any new service, whether owned or operated directly by an organization or accessed through affiliation, management, or contract
- encourage physician participation on internal committees, such as the ethics, quality assurance, and risk management committees
- educate physicians' office staff about the continuum of care
- maximize office staff time and simultaneously facilitate referrals directly to the continuum by informing administrative and nursing staff who often make referrals for patients and families about the services available through the organized continuum of care
- let services not in the continuum of care know about the physician's specialty and the types of patient the physician works with
- gather feedback on the ambiance and success of the continuum by questioning patients during an office visit
- solicit comments, suggestions, and complaints from patients and families who have been involved with the services, staff, financing, or structure of the continuum of care (such feedback should be used to improve the efficiency and effectiveness of the system)

While all of these activities consume precious time and energy, only myopia or nostalgia can explain a failure to participate. The continuum of care is coming, and indeed in some places it is already here. The professional goal of assuring the best care—the most expert, efficient, and compassionate—will demand such participation and leadership by physicians treating an ever-increasing proportion of elderly patients in their practices.

NOTES

1. K. Steel, ed., *Geriatric Education* (Lexington, Mass.: Collamore Press, D.C. Heath, 1981). Bureau of Health Professions, *Issues and Strategies in Geriatric Education: 1985* (Washington, D.C.: Department of Health and Human Services, Health Resources and Services Administration, 1985).

2. W., Reichel, ed., *Clinical Aspects of Aging*, 2nd ed. (Baltimore, Md.: Williams and Wilkens, 1983); R.L. Kane, J.G. Ouslander, and I.B. Abrass, *Essentials of Clinical Geriatrics* (New York: McGraw-Hill, 1984); J.W. Rowe and R.W. Besdine, eds., *Health and Disease in Old Age* (Boston: Little, Brown, & Co., 1982); R.T.D. Cape, R.M. Coe, and I. Rossman, eds., *Fundamentals of Geriatric Medicine* (New York: Raven Press, 1983); C.K. Cassell and J.R. Walsh, eds., *Geriatric*

Medicine (New York: Springer-Verlag, 1984); R. Anadres, E.L. Bierman, and W.R. Hazzard, *Principles of Geriatric Medicine* (New York: McGraw-Hill, 1984).

3. Gretchen Batra, comp., *American Geriatrics Society Directory of Geriatrics Programs for Residencies and Fellowships* (Boston: Boston University Gerontology Center, 1985).

4. R.L. Kane et al., *Geriatrics in the United States: Manpower Projections and Training Considerations* (Santa Monica, Calif.: Rand Corporation, 1980).

5. Institute of Medicine, *Aging and Medical Education* (Washington, D.C.: National Academy of Sciences, 1978); P.E. Dans and J.R. Kerr, "Gerontology and Geriatrics in Medical Education," *New England Journal of Medicine* 300, no. 5 (1979):228–32.

6. Association of American Medical Colleges, *Proceedings of the Regional Institutes on Geriatrics and Medical Education* (Washington, D.C.: Association of American Medical Colleges, 1983). Robbins et al., *Geriatric Medicine*.

7. R. Butler, "The Teaching Nursing Home," *Journal of the American Medical Association* 245 (1981):1435–37.

8. A.S. Robbins et al., *Geriatric Medicine: An Educational Resource Guide* (Cambridge, Mass.: Ballinger, 1981).

9. Anadres, Bierman, and Hazzard, *Principles of Geriatric Medicine*.

REFERENCES

American Medical Association. *Health Care for an Aged Population*. Chicago: American Medical Association, 1983.

Batra, Gretchen R., comp. *American Geriatrics Society Directory of Geriatrics Programs for Residencies and Fellowships*. Boston: Boston University Gerontology Center, 1984.

Beck, John C., and Vivell, Susan. "Development of Geriatrics in the United States." In *Geriatric Medicine* edited by C.K. Cassell and J.R. Walsh. New York: Springer-Verlag, 1984.

Campion, M.D.; Edward, W.; Bang, Axel; May, Maurice, I. "Why Acute-Care Hospitals Must Undertake Long-Term Care." *New England Journal of Medicine* 308 (January 13, 1983):71–75.

Dans, Peter, F.; Kerr, M.; and Marie, R. "Gerontology and Geriatrics in Medical Education." *New England Journal of Medicine* 300, no. 5 (1979):228–32.

Kane, Robert L.; Solomon, David H.; Beck, John C.; Keeler, Emmet B.; and Kane, Rosalie A. *Geriatrics in the United States: Manpower Projections and Training Considerations*. Santa Monica, Calif.: Rand Corporation, 1980.

Rowe, John W. "Health Care of the Elderly." *New England Journal of Medicine* 312, no. 13 (1985):827–35.

Schneider, Edward L.; Wendland, Carroll J.; Zimmer, Anne Wilder; List, Noel; and Ory, Marcia, eds. *The Teaching Nursing Home*. New York: Raven Press, 1985.

Chapter 19

The Role of the Nurse in the Continuum of Care

Marcella J. Griggs, RN, MS

By tradition, nursing has long been involved in the continuum of care. It is the nurse who has consistently cared for the chronically ill, the aged, and the poor through supportive and nurturant activities that fill the gaps in service provision. The current shift in health care financing from a cost reimbursement system to a prospective payment system has forced hospitals to diversify vertically and horizontally into services that provide a wide range of health care options for the consumer and prevent loss of revenue for the institution. Geriatric services have been a major focus of the diversifying process because of the increased proportion of elderly in our population and the historically high rate of consumption of health services by the elderly.

The nurse has emerged as a key player in the changing health care system, and the effectiveness of services in the continuum of care is largely dependent on the diverse skills and expertise of this multitalented professional. This chapter will look closely at the characteristics of nursing, the expanded roles of nursing, and the clinical and administrative skills needed for optimal professional nursing care and collaboration in today's health care environment.

CHARACTERISTICS OF NURSING

The clinical and administrative impact of nursing in acute care hospital settings is well documented and accepted by other health care professionals, the consumer, and the individual members of the nursing profession. However, the expanded roles of nursing beyond acute care settings are not as well defined and in many cases create confusion for the consumer, controversy within the nursing profession, and territorial disputes with other health care disciplines.

The current trend toward shorter length of acute care stay and the development of services outside the traditional hospital setting have created struggles not only between separate health care disciplines, but within the nursing profession itself. For example, the cutback of personnel in acute care hospitals as bed occupancy declines has had both a positive and negative effect on nursing and patients. While registered nurses (R.N.s) have been asked to assume more clinical and administrative roles because of the rise in patient acuity levels requiring more specialized nursing skills and a broader knowledge base, many nurses aides, licensed vocational nurses, and less specialized R.N.s find that they must seek employment elsewhere. A beneficial side effect is that an increasing number of nurses are acquiring expanded skills that enable them to function in long-term care. However, the inequities of pay scale remain for those working in long-term care compared to those working in acute care settings.

Unlike other health care professions, such as medicine or social work, nursing has been plagued by multiple levels of entry into the profession. After many years, the entry level controversy rages on, but recently several state nursing organizations, along with the American Nurses' Association and the National League for Nursing, have advocated that the baccalaureate degree be the basic level of entry for the professional nurse. Many health care institutions have moved to all-R.N. staffing and now require a nurse to have minimally a four-year baccalaureate degree in order to be eligible for promotion to leadership positions as head nurse or supervisor. Presently, graduate schools of nursing are producing clinical nurse specialists, nurse practitioners, and nurse administrators who have not only specialized skills in specific fields but a broad systems approach, which is important for competing in today's marketplace and also for collaborating with other health care professionals. Graduate schools are preparing nurses to assume the integrated roles of expert clinician, researcher, educator, consultant, administrator, and entrepreneur.

To a large extent, the direction of graduate study and nursing specialization is influenced by the economic, political, and social climate. For example, the seeds of gerontological nursing grew for many years in nursing homes and other long-term care institutional settings while society paid little attention to the needs of the chronically ill and the aging. However, with the enactment of the 1965 Medicare and 1972 Medicaid amendments to the Social Security Act, the general lengthening of life span, the emphasis on health promotion and health mainte-nance, and the changing attitudes toward aging, gerontological nursing moved toward specialization and expanded formally into acute care, skilled nursing care, intermediate care, rehabilitative services, outpatient facilities, case man-agement services, and health education. In addition, specialization in nursing has paralleled the specialization of medicine, resulting in numerous specialties.

The gerontological nurse's education, skills, and philosophy are congruent with the development of a cost-effective and efficient health care system that fosters client independence and self-care to the greatest extent possible. The scope of nursing practice is directed toward helping clients maintain or return to the optimal level of functioning consistent with the limitations imposed by the aging process and the presence of acute or chronic conditions. It also focuses on helping clients prevent or control disease and on maintaining life with dignity and comfort until death.[1] The 1980s have seen expansion of gerontological nursing to include responsible care management positions throughout the continuum of care. Similarly, nursing specialties have developed in primary care, rehabilitation, home health, mental health, and numerous other areas. Just as the continuum of care aims to merge diverse services, the continuum offers nursing the opportunity to bring together the expertise of these specialists, many of whom have had to work as lone practitioners in isolated settings.

The aged and chronically ill, as well as those with mental and rehabilitative conditions, enter and exit services and institutions at all possible levels in the continuum of care. They must have access to a full range of coordinated services from acute care, rehabilitation, and extended care to outpatient services focusing on illness prevention, health maintenance, and health promotion. Efforts must be made to strengthen service through less fragmentation, increased collaboration with other health care providers (including nurses of various specialties), involvement of the client and family in health care decisions, use of centralized management information systems, and development of services responsive to identified consumer needs.

EXPANDED ROLES OF NURSING

As organizations adopt the continuum of care approach, new roles emerge for nurses. A widening range of nursing functions means expanded responsibility and increased accountability for the professional nurse. New roles require the nurse to be directly involved in such areas as policy making, program development, marketing, and management, along with clinical practice. These roles require a working knowledge of areas once thought to be out of the domain of nursing. These may include medical and nursing ethics; risk management, utilization review, and quality assurance; health care economics, budgetary concerns, and resource allocation; government regulations, social policy, and political advocacy; reimbursement criteria for third party payers and rules and regulations for Medicare and Medicaid; computer and systems technology; interpersonal and interagency relations; community and professional networks; and marketing strategies for health care programs and professional growth. To be familiar with these areas seems like a tall order when the nurse must also continue to bring to the client her nursing skills, values, and professional strengths for continuity of care.

With the lack of adequate numbers of trained personnel with appropriate knowledge, skills, and attitudes to implement the many nursing components in the continuum of care, the professional nurse having such skills and specialized training must act as a role model and mentor for other nurses and staff. By helping to clarify roles and responsibilities, establishing systematic assessment and approaches to problem solving, and setting priorities for care, the nurse contributes to a smoother flow of clients to services within the continuum of care. With the rapid expansion of health care services, there are often no rules, procedures, or job descriptions to follow, and the nurse must be flexible, creative, and diplomatic as the service roles evolve. As one nurse put it:

> I really had to make my own way, to create my own place in the system. Although I wrote a job description soon after employment, I found that the actual position evolved over the course of the first two years. During that time, other people, both colleagues and clients alike, often asked, "Just what do you do?" I have to admit that I, too, posed that question to myself.[2]

The Nurse as Clinician

The nurse clinician has an extensive knowledge of physical, psychological, and social aspects of human growth and development, along with expertise in specific nursing interventions relative to identified areas of client need. The comprehensive approach of the continuum of care mirrors the traditional orientation and training of nurses. The nurses' holistic view of man does not separate physical, psychological, and social components. Through the use of a comprehensive nursing assessment, the nurse has the ability to recognize early warning signals of biopsychosocial deterioration and of potential client problems prior to explicit changes, as well as the ability to determine courses of nursing action for existing problems. Within both inpatient and outpatient settings, nursing diagnoses and the nursing process of problem solving can be used to establish measurable goals and objectives that are client centered. For the most effective service utilization and care coordination, these goals and objectives should be mutually agreed upon in consultation with the client, family members, physicians, social workers, nurses, and other health care providers, as necessary.

The nurse has emerged as a team leader in the development of a continuum of care coordinating other key providers in the multidisciplinary approach required for proper management of chronic conditions. However, territorial issues continually occur and must be dealt with. The turf issues that exist on many interdisciplinary and intradisciplinary levels can damage a sensible and efficient health care system.

The physician's role in the health care field is changing as large health care conglomerates erode traditional physician authority, but the main focus is still on medical diagnoses and treatment of disease. With the proclaimed market glut of physicians, competition for clients by nurses, physician assistants, and social workers is seen as a threat to the traditional practice of medicine. However, even with the increased numbers of physicians and their interest in moving into areas previously untouched by medical practice, nurses will continually be in demand to do some of the things physicians will not or cannot do.[3] The focus of nurses is on acute and chronic needs and on the responses necessary to improve the client's well-being and health. The nursing role should not be seen as a substitute for the physician's medical care, but rather as a complementary service within the scope of nursing practice in the continuum of care.

Within the economic constraints of the current health care system, power struggles and turf issues between social workers and nurses are perceived to be more of a threat to survival of the two professions than those involving physicians. The emerging positions of case manager and discharge planner further complicate these professional conflicts. For many years, there have been blurred areas of responsibility between nurses and social workers. By tradition, social workers have more expertise in social services, while the competencies of nurses are more in the physical domain. Fuzzy areas of territory and expertise occur in the more nebulous realms of consumer health education, counseling and referral, mental health counseling, and coordination of the informal and formal support systems. With the current emphasis on case management and care coordination that is associated with the flow of clients in and out of services and institutions within the continuum of care, lack of role definitions present more of a problem than ever before. This particular area is perhaps most sensitive to conflict because both the social worker and the nurse bring similar skills to the case management role. As a social worker who collaborates closely with a clinical nurse specialist related:

> We had two major areas of mutual expertise—working with families and coordination of other agencies. I had some concerns how we'd work it out. Perhaps what helped was talking about it right away. We didn't wait for a crisis or blow-up; we decided to keep talking about the process of working together. Almost every time an incident arose in which either one of us could have done the job equally well, we just decided on the basis of current caseloads or interest. I guess you could say that good communication and mutual respect were the key ingredients for successful work together.[4]

Programs such as California's Multipurpose Senior Service Program (MSSP) and Linkages, which are both outpatient case management programs, have found ways to diminish problems by using a team consisting of a social worker and a nurse for evaluation of clients. One or the other assumes the major role in care coordination depending upon specific client needs.

An excellent model of collaborative effort between nurses, physicians, social workers, and other health care providers exists within the Care Account program at Mount Zion Hospital and Medical Center in San Francisco. In this program, a nurse practitioner functions as a central coordinator of care for a group of elderly persons residing in the community. Upon completion of a health status questionnaire by the client, the nurse reviews the data and uses a computerized management information system to help identify areas of potential risk and to facilitate coordination of services. Nursing intervention is targeted to reduce identified risks in the biopsychosocial realms through direct contact with the client and family and through consultation with and referral to appropriate health care providers. Through assessment, care planning, intervention, evaluation, and follow-up, the nurse utilizes the formal and informal care network in providing coordinated care and health education. The nurse is readily available by telephone to advise clients and there is a broad range of educational programs offered to groups. The nurse makes home visits for nursing management and can serve as a physician extender.

The concept of an *advice nurse* is one that has been applied for some time by the Kaiser Permanente Health Maintenance Organizations. In their HMO settings, a nurse skilled in specific clinical areas such as pediatrics, obstetrics, and gynecology as well as in general medical problems is available to answer consumer questions and to triage problem cases by telephone. In other settings, skilled *triage nurses* function in a similar manner by referring clients to appropriate sources for care and thus eliminating overuse of expensive emergency rooms and acute care facilities.

Within the acute care setting, the nurse functions in many diverse clinical roles, ranging from that of a clinical specialist performing direct patient care to that of a unit manager coordinating other members of the health care team. Multidisciplinary teams are often coordinated by the nurse, who acts as team leader and liaison with the client and family. The nurse is frequently a member of such specialty teams as psychogeriatric assessment, cardiac and stroke rehabilitation, pain and stress management, crisis intervention, substance abuse, child and elder abuse, hospice care, and organ transplant programs.

Shorter stays in the acute care hospital involve the nurse in discharge planning with the formal and informal support systems soon after admission of the patient. Many gaps currently exist in discharge planning processes, and early discharge complicates the picture. Increased collaboration with the family, physician, social worker, and with community services can provide the linkage of skills and resources necessary for well-coordinated posthospital care. Nurses can also coordinate more with their colleagues in other settings, forming a team of nurses who span the service settings that a patient traverses during the course of an illness. As organizations add services through formal arrangements, frequent contact with the same service providers will occur. Nurses must assume responsibility for establishing mechanisms to foster interpersonal collaboration and team-building activities for the nurses from various parts of the community.

It has been suggested that the concept of *transition nursing* or *staff sharing* might help to provide an optimal flow in the continuum of care. In transition nursing, a specially trained primary nurse tracks and guides a client through the maze of services along the continuum of care over an extended period of time. This could be especially beneficial for the client with a chronic illness that requires a carefully managed program of care. However, numerous complexities make it difficult to use the concept, including variations in areas of individual interest, skill and task variations, scheduling and pay differentials between acute and chronic care services, limited financial resources for rehabilitation and preventive care, ineffective communication systems for information sharing, and territorial overlaps of function that naturally result when the boundaries of health care professionals intersect. Through careful planning it is possible to overcome the major obstacles to this concept, and the role of transition nursing needs to be explored more fully in pilot programs.

The nurse is positioned along all key points in the continuum of care to maximize the benefits of clinical nursing expertise for clients. The expansion of outpatient services and home health care requires the nurse to assume greater autonomy and decision-making authority for designing and implementing appropriate courses of action in a setting removed from acute care. Furthermore, community satellite clinics and adult day health centers are primarily overseen by nurse practitioners or other clinical specialists. It is also well known that nurses are the primary care coordinators for clients residing in nursing homes, skilled and intermediate care facilities, life care and retirement communities, and senior housing complexes. In many settings, a nurse can offer quality at a cost below that of a physician and may function as an independent service contractor. The complexities of care demanded by each setting vary greatly and require the professional nurse to be prepared to function both as a team player and as an independent practitioner.

The Nurse as Educator

Education encompasses two major areas: staff education and consumer education. Specialized continuing education courses and lectures are available for professional staff in work settings, institutions of higher learning, and private businesses that have developed a wide range of programs. It is frequently the nurse skilled in a specific field of nursing who coordinates and presents education programs. For example, specialized continuing education courses offer health teaching techniques and technical skills for nursing personnel faced with greater complexities of patient care in the home health setting. For many years, nursing has provided in-service education for hospital employees when health-related topics are presented. More recently, the scope of education has broadened to include topics beyond the traditional nursing care lectures and demonstrations. Nurses now offer programs that range from training in highly specialized technical skills to presenting topics such as nursing ethics, management techniques, personal health promotion, and stress reduction on the job.

Patient teaching, both in the hospital and in the community, has long been a concern of nursing and has become even more important in the current health care environment of finite resources. Furthermore, chronicity and disability have become increasingly visible problems, and health maintenance education for those with chronic conditions can no longer be neglected. Health care organizations are changing traditional medical models of care and instead are emphasizing that the consumer should take more responsibility for his or her own health. However, the provision of consumer information and the increase in choices have received little attention to date in this era of health care reform.[5] To accomplish this shift in responsibility, the health care consumer must receive extensive health education focusing on illness prevention, health maintenance, and health promotion, along with being given access to a full range of coordinated services from acute care to home health care.

Little attention has been paid to health promotion and preventive health services. The lack of available health promotion services exists primarily because of current reimbursement policies, which cover only illness care. The consumer can be forced into a sick role by the traditional medical models and reimbursement mechanisms. The goal must be to promote full and active participation in health care, for when professionals exclude the client and family from decision making, dependency is reinforced.

An example of a health promotion series in a semirural area of Virginia demonstrates what can be done. Adult groups have collaborated with health departments, hospitals, and colleges of nursing to provide a series of seminars for the elderly population who live in the community and in local retirement homes. The seminar topics have included safety in the home, use of over-the-counter medication, care of teeth and dentures, examples of positive health care behaviors and self-care techniques that promote good health, and how to be assertive with health care providers in mutual decision making. Coordinated by a nurse, the seminars make use of a wide variety of professionals who speak on topics of interest. The health care providers and student nurses often comment afterwards on how much they learned from interaction with the participants and find promise in the emphasis on mutual decision making with the client, family, and health care team.

The practice of nursing is consistent with nursing theories that recognize the right and responsibility of client participation in self-care. Dorothea Orem's Self-Care Deficit Theory of Nursing is based on the belief that individuals should be self-sufficient to the greatest extent possible.[6] The basic notion is to minimize the deficit between the action capabilities of individuals and their therapeutic self-care demands and to help clients compensate for any health impairments by reinforcing their capabilities and decision-making opportunities.

The capacity for self-care among the chronically ill and elderly has been a focus of concern for some health care professionals, since self-care implies a high level of mental and physical functioning. However, as Lantz suggests, for those clients who do not exhibit the desire or ability to carry out self-care activities to maintain maximum levels of health, the nurse can develop learning activities and teaching strategies to enhance and build upon the abilities that do exist.[7]

The nurse acknowledges the client's rights and ability to make conscious and independent decisions about his or her own health to the fullest extent possible. Retention of choice is empowerment for survival.

Nursing practice should be structured in such a way as to encourage the interdependence of the client and family on the one hand and the health care system on the other, allowing maximum participation in health care to promote a sense of control. This supports positive health behaviors by focusing on maintaining strengths rather than highlighting problems. "Contracting," in either written or verbal form, has been advocated (and used) to enable the client and the formal caregiver to share in decision making. Mutual goals are decided upon and a plan of action is discussed. Responsibilities of the nurse and the client are agreed upon, and progress is evaluated frequently as the client and nurse move toward attainment of specific and time-limited objectives for care.

The use of contracting and shared decision making fosters appropriate dependence, interdependence, and independence in the formal health care system, as the following case illustrates. Elizabeth, a 68-year-old divorced woman, left the psychiatric hospital after a prolonged stay punctuated by several suicide attempts. Except for one daughter, her family was estranged by her behavior and refused to be involved in any postcare activities. The nurse, in collaboration with the daughter and the client, developed a contract for expected behaviors for all three participants. Elizabeth agreed to attend a day hospital program three days a week and would see the nurse for 30 minutes on each of those days. The daughter would provide transportation. The nurse would explore with a local group the possibility of volunteer activity. Elizabeth, however, would need to obtain and complete the application forms. The contract in this case provided a structure to ensure consistency, dependability, and responsibility for nurse, client, and daughter. The manageable pragmatic nature of the contract agreement provided the means for a successful re-entry into community life for a woman who had been labeled as "unmotivated" and "hospital-dependent."

Fries and Crapo maintain that clinical manifestations of most chronic diseases can be postponed effectively through health promotion and lifestyle changes. They suggest that this would in turn compress morbidity and allow for a decline in the function of vital organ systems, resulting in a natural biological death rather than a premature death or extended disability.[8] In practice, this means that the oldest old, through earlier efforts toward improving health and preventing illness, could suffer less disability and disease but would ultimately live no longer. To the extent that disabilities and serious chronic illnesses can be prevented or postponed, there is a potential for reducing overall health care costs.

Foreseeing a need to focus on wellness and self-care, national guidelines have been provided to aid in moving toward the 1990 goals for health promotion and disease prevention. Examples of goals set for people 65 and over include control of hypertension, prevention of injuries and falls, increased diet education, improved nutrition, decreased nosocomial infections, decreased alcohol and drug misuse, increased exercise, and better monitoring of infectious disease trends.[9]

The trend toward health promotion requires the integration in educational systems of the related disciplines of medicine, nursing, and social service. A better understanding of the aging process and the attendant physical, psychological, and social problems will help eliminate negative attitudes and stereotypes and will provide incentives in clinical practice to focus on disease prevention and health promotion. In addition, interdisciplinary training programs provide a reasonable and realistic perspective on turf issues among health care providers.

A model program developed by the University of California San Francisco provides opportunities for groups of students in the health sciences of nursing, medicine, dentistry, pharmacy, and medical social work to collaborate in a number of health care settings around the city. It is found that a team effort for program development and problem solving offers maximum benefit to the client, facility, and providers.

Counseling and education for adaptation to disability and management of chronic conditions begin in the acute care setting. But with shortened hospital stays, this service must continue long after discharge. The nurse is in a position to offer these services, since clients continue to be seen by nurses in clinics, outpatient settings, homes, senior centers, and long-term care facilities. It is the nurse who provides the continuity of care with the client and family and can place the necessary emphasis on health promotion and illness prevention services. Physical fitness and exercise programs, medication instruction, diet and nutrition consultation, counseling for improved quality of life through behavioral changes, social interaction and recreational activities, and general health education for maximizing health and self-care efforts are among the services provided by nurses.

The Nurse as Administrator

Nurses have traditionally functioned as middle managers. They have found themselves responsible to two distinct constituents: the executive administrators and the service staff. In such a challenging position, perhaps the chief requirement for success is the ability to be a team player. Managerial skills cover a wide range of expertise, but the required basic skills include the ability to coordinate with others, to have a sound knowledge of the organization and its goals, and to have a working knowledge of health care economics, including allocation of manpower and financial resources. These basic skills are necessary for most middle management positions, ranging from head nurse on a unit to clinic supervisor, program director, director of nursing service, and on up the ladder to director of professional services or vice-president for health affairs.

The nurse administrator must have a knowledge of local, state, and national health care policies, trends, and statistics, and must be active in professional nursing organizations. The nurse administrator is frequently asked to speak to community groups, professional organizations, and special interest groups, and therefore must be knowledgeable and articulate in order to adequately represent the institution and the nursing profession.

Within the hospital setting, the nurse administrator may be requested to do a feasibility study concerning development of a new service, to evaluate existing services, or to define or redefine policies and procedures. In addition, nursing intensity measures are now being studied in many acute care settings in an effort to determine the costs and benefits of separate nursing services and procedures relative to Diagnostic Related Groups (DRGs). Cost-benefit analysis is of increasing concern to management, and the nurse administrators are becoming more involved in developing tools and criteria for measuring the contributions of nursing care relative to client outcomes.

In both acute and long-term care settings, the nurse administrator is directly involved in risk management, utilization review, and quality assurance. Risk management generally involves a multidisciplinary committee charged with the task of analyzing areas of potential or existing risk and establishing policy and procedures that reduce the risk.

Utilization review considers issues such as allocation of resources, patterns of over or under utilization of services, efficiencies or inefficiencies of scheduling, appropriateness and necessity of admissions, length of stay, and conditions of discharge or of termination of services.

Quality assurance looks at the quality and appropriateness of care in order to determine systematically whether the care was right and the task well done. Standards of care are selected and defined. Quantifiable indicators, such as the number of falls or the number of program participant dropouts, are selected as criteria to be monitored over time. Monitoring activities are developed (such as patient recordkeeping in a timely manner) that can be regularly spot-checked on a continuing basis. Existing or potential problems are identified and categorized, then action plans are developed for the identified problem areas. Evaluation measures (such as questionnaires on patient education or patient satisfaction) are decided on and used as specific quality indicators.

There are numerous factors that influence quality and appropriateness of care; for example, the credentials, job description, and activities of the clinical nurse specialist, the continuing education requirements for nursing staff, the mechanism for formal case review with peer groups or multidisciplinary teams, and the collection and analysis of monthly summary reports. Nurses are directly involved in and continue to spearhead efforts to maintain and improve patient care.

The areas of risk management, utilization review, and quality assurance become even more important under capitated funding programs, such as HMOs. In these settings, careful tracking of service utilization and appropriateness of care become critical factors for budgetary management and fiscal responsibility, and the nurse must often account for program dollars spent.

Nursing management involves extra time for team conferences to develop procedures and policies for newly developed services and programs. Emerging ethical issues such as the right to life, client and family rights, and allocation of finite resources also require extra time for discussion and the development of group consensus. Nurse managers find that extra time is also required for providing emotional support and counseling to staff who work in high stress areas such as intensive care or hospice programs. Finally, senior nurse managers must educate other nurses at management and clinical levels about new developments in administration and policy that affect their specific duties.

As health care organizations expand and diversify, the administrative duties of the nurse become more complex and each of the above tasks more extensive and time-consuming.

The Nurse as Consultant

With advanced education and the development of specialized areas of nursing practice, nurses are prepared to assume the role of consultant to the informal and formal care systems within the continuum of care. In complex health care systems, the nurse acts as consultant to the client and family for effective and efficient utilization of the system. The nurse must often consult with other members of the health care team when representing the client. The nursing role may include advocacy in behalf of the family and client, e.g., with respect to rights (such as the right of informed consent) or in appealing against early discharge from an acute care hospital concerned with DRG regulations and length of stay.

Long-term facilities use the geriatric nurse consultant to assist in problem solving and program development for specific areas of need. Examples include control of incontinence, risk management to prevent falls, prevention of staff burnout, and helping to deal with feelings associated with death and dying. Both institutional and community settings find the psychiatric nurse consultant helpful in outlining nursing care plans for staff and family members who work with clients having mental health problems.

The public health nurse consultant is active with business and community groups in developing health promotion programs. These programs include a wide variety of topics, such as control of high blood pressure, diet and exercise, communication techniques, and stress reduction techniques. People in the community who have similar interests or problems appeal to nurses for consultation and assistance in formation of peer support and self-help groups. Caregivers for clients with Alzheimer's disease, parents of children with chronic diseases, and people with sleep disorders are examples of groups organized and led by nurses.

Local and state regulatory agencies employ nurse consultants to assess the compliance of licensed agencies (e.g., nursing homes or group homes for the developmentally disabled) and to recommend corrective measures for getting the established requirements met. Nurses may also be engaged as independent consultants or as team members of consulting firms that assist organizations in the development of health care systems.

The scope of nursing consultation is expanding, and it varies widely within the continuum of care, depending upon individual nursing expertise and need. The range of types of consultation requested extends from presentations at health seminars for large groups of people to a one-to-one discussion with a peer about a specific issue of concern. Nurses place an emphasis on a holistic view of client and family and use of systems approach to consultation in health care. This combination, along with expert clinical skills, provides a rich resource to be tapped by providers and consumers alike.

The Nurse as Researcher

Nursing research has moved beyond the ivory towers of academia and is currently being done by many nurse clinicians in clinical settings. Nursing faculty in graduate schools are working collaboratively with clinicians in work settings to advance nursing science. Use of controlled research studies and methods, which carefully characterize and quantify client outcomes based on specific nursing interventions, provide data for sophisticated multivariate analysis as well as opportunities for improving the quality of patient care.

Professional nursing journals publish reports of research studies, and nursing research conferences provide an arena for discussion, including the implications of research findings. The benefits to the consumer, as nurses strive to improve their clinical practice through the application of research findings, are substantial.

Nurses are also involved in clinical research undertaken by multidisciplinary teams, and they are often participants in research studies of other health care providers. In any type of clinical research, the nurse has a responsibility to protect confidentiality and anonymity of the person from whom information was obtained. This can be of particular importance when working with elderly clients, who may be vulnerable due to physical, emotional, and social conditions. Thus, the nurse must be a strong advocate with respect to the protection of personal rights. Clinical research also places the nurse in a position of power that must not be abused, since the nurse may have the role of both researcher and clinician.

Rising national health care costs and efforts toward cost-containment have increased the need for nurses to measure the product of nursing services in terms of quality of care and result for the client. This type of nursing research must document services and outcome, and findings must be shared, which can affect institutional decisions and resource allocations. Effective management of nursing resources requires a link between the costs of services and the clients who receive them.[10]

Direct linkage between nursing functions and client outcome is difficult to document, especially in an outpatient setting, because of the many extraneous factors interfering with a clearcut analysis. But benefits to the client and to the health care system can accrue both in the short-term and the long-term. A time and function study, using a time-interval sampling technique, can track nursing functions and client outcome, monitor referral patterns and service utilization, and pinpoint service needs that are not being met.

Determination of cost-benefit is not a simple task, and there are many elusive questions that need answers.[11] Questions that require continuing nursing research include the following:

- How do the various nursing activities affect the use of services within the continuum of care?

- How can the nurse promote increased access to services through care co-ordination without increasing health care costs or merely shifting costs from acute care to expanded outpatient services?

- Can the emphasis on health promotion, health maintenance, and illness prevention help to reduce morbidity and improve well-being for the elderly and those with chronic illnesses?

By tradition, nurses have been reluctant to gather measurable, quantifiable data to prove their worth. However, in this critical period of cost-containment and competition in the market place, nurses must be willing and able to justify their specific role functions. The continuum of care provides excellent opportunities for nurses to demonstrate the value of the nursing function in individual and multiple settings. The efforts of nursing researchers in both clinical settings and administrative roles benefit the entire health care system.

IMPLICATIONS OF THE CONTINUUM

The health care professionals emerging as leaders in the continuum of care exhibit finely honed skills in biomedical technology, health care systems design, business management, and sociopolitical maneuvering, as well as expertise in their particular field. To be a key player in this rapidly changing scene, the nurse must reach out to establish links with other health care disciplines and be more actively involved in positions of influence where social and political policy decisions are made that crucially affect the health care environment.

Mounting paperwork and tighter regulations required by institutional bureau-cracies can be infringements on a nurse's time and a drain on energies, or they can be a challenge to the professional nurse in a new leadership role. A greater knowledge of business management systems, health care economics, social trends, and political forces, combined with up-to-date technical and people skills, will prepare the nurse to have a more direct influence on health care decision making.

At the present time, health care costs continue to rise faster than inflation, and health care expenditures make up a significant percentage of the gross national product. Weaknesses in the cost control system, expensive technical equipment, and rising malpractice insurance are often cited as major contributing factors. However, some economists claim that the problem is exacerbated by physicians and hospitals finding ways to circumvent the cost control system. The nurse must continue to advocate appropriate services to the health care consumer while guarding the purse of finite health care resources and resisting efforts to subvert cost control. Simultaneously, the contribution of nursing and the benefits of the continuum of care must be examined and documented.

The multiple roles of nurse clinician, educator, administrator, consultant, and researcher all require a broad, current knowledge base acquired and maintained through ongoing academic and clinical experiences. Opportunities for continuing education abound in many forms and should be utilized. Professional nursing journals such as *Nursing Economics, Journal of Nursing Administration*, and the *American Journal of Nursing*, along with various nursing research and clinical specialty journals, provide up-to-date information. Video tapes are available through numerous professional organizations and businesses. Many institutions subscribe to the satellite television networks that present a broad range of current health care topics. Membership in professional organizations and attendance at professional conferences and seminars allow exchange of ideas with others in the health care network.

It is important for employers to encourage continuing education and to provide financial support to the nurse—an essential member of the health care team. A sophisticated and comprehensive education allows the professional nurse to be a competent collaborator, a spokesperson for the nursing profession, and an advocate for the consumer.

SUMMARY

The continuum of care can be seen from many different perspectives. Federal and state governments may view it as a means to control allocation of health care resources. Health care institutions may view it as the answer to marketing competition and a way of keeping clients under the organization's umbrella of services. Health care professionals may view it as the most efficient and effective way to eliminate fragmentation and to guide and track the client through a complex array of services. However, the client and family may perceive it as a cause of the lessening of their control over their own lives as they are caught up in struggles within the health care system.

Efforts to streamline the continuum of care through tighter controls on service utilization give rise to the ethical issue of who shall and who shall not have access to services, including life support systems, scarce medical technology, and long-term care. The nurse, along with others in positions of influence and power, must guard against stripping consumers of their right to make the choices they determine are necessary or important to their health and well-being. Rather, the nurse must ensure that the continuum increases clients' access to services and options.

Dealing adequately with the uncertainties of the future of health care depends on the ability of health care providers to work as a team in the continuum of care and to discipline themselves to make the best use of available health care resources. The ultimate goal must be to make the most effective and efficient use of limited health care resources, while providing quality care for people to live happier and healthier lives—lives of richness and meaning.

NOTES

1. American Nurses' Association, Division on Gerontological Nursing Practice, *Gerontological Nursing: The Positive Difference in Health Care for Older Adults* (Kansas City, Mo.: American Nurses' Association, 1980).

2. K.S. Castleberry, R.N., C.S., Ph.D, personal communication, August 23, 1986.

3. C.E. Lewis, "Nurse Practitioners and the Physician Surplus," in *Nursing in the 1980's: Crises, Opportunities, Challenges*, L.H. Aiken, ed. (Philadelphia: J.B. Lippincott, 1982), 249–266.

4. M.K. Erikson, M.S.W., personal communication, April 18, 1986.

5. C.K. Davis, "Health Care Reforms: What Can We Expect?" *Nursing Economics* 4, no. 1 (1982): 3rd ed. 10–11, 49.

6. D.E. Orem, *Nursing: Concepts of Practice*, 3rd ed. (New York: McGraw-Hill, 1985).

7. J.M. Lantz, "In Search of Agents for Self-Care," *Journal of Gerontological Nursing* 11, no. 7 (1985):10–14.

8. J.F. Fries and L.M. Crapo, *Vitality and Aging* (San Francisco, Calif.: W.H. Freeman, 1981).

9. National Center for Health Statistics, *Health, United States, 1983*, DHHS Publ. No. (PHS) 84-1232, Public Health Service (Washington, D.C.: GPO, 1983).

10. M.S. Thompson, *Benefit-Cost Analysis for Program Evaluation* (Beverly Hills, Calif.: Sage Publications, 1980).

11. J.E. Veney and A.D. Kaluzny, *Evaluation and Decision Making for Health Services Programs* (Englewood Cliffs, N.J.: Prentice-Hall, 1984).

Chapter 20

The Social Worker's Contribution to the Continuum of Care

W. June Simmons, MSW, LCSW

These are times of rapid, massive, and unceasing change in the health care system. Health care providers are grappling with major shifts in types and amounts of funding, dramatic changes in technological capability, and new insights regarding optimum human services systems. The intense and growing complexities related to the health care arena demand special skills as new systems are developed in response to the pressures for change. The social work professional is placed particularly well to make a major contribution to the evolving continuum of care approach to client care.

The unique qualities of the social work clinician and administrator in health settings will have increasing value in the emerging continuum of care systems. The knowledge base of social work, and its skills, perspectives, and strong linkages with other disciplines are valuable assets in the adaptation of a health care organization to the changing environment. The growing contribution of social work is making an impact on hospital, nursing home, home care, and community care systems. While the process of change is demanding, it can result in far greater opportunities than liabilities.

CHARACTERISTICS OF SOCIAL WORK

The profession of social work and its practice in health care settings has a number of unique characteristics. While the impact of clinical and administrative social work practice is considerable, it is not well understood in many health care settings. The social worker is distinguished by being one of the few health care workers who is trained to a Master's level or beyond. The result of this advanced training is a "soft product," which is manifested largely as conversation and the exchange of information. The technical tools of the trade in health care are largely physical; the technical tools of the professional social worker are largely mental. This makes it more difficult for the observer to grasp the concrete nature of the social work contribution. It was only in 1982, for example, that the American Hospital Association formally acknowledged the professional social worker as an essential member of the health care team and critical to the successful and effective operation of hospitals.

There are three major areas that serve as the basis for the increasingly natural fit between the professional social work perspective and the needs of health care institutions. For example, the social worker has in-depth training in mental health services (ranging from assessment to crisis services) and expertise in facilitating communications. This training allows a social worker to assist physicians and nurses in the management of patients with special emotional needs or psychiatric problems. Such problems often accompany medical conditions, either as a separate, pre-existing condition or as a side effect of the health care experience itself (particularly in patients with complex, multifaceted, and chronic conditions).

Recognized as one of the leading mental health disciplines, social work has a strong tradition of concern with the design of human services in the total community. Social workers have been responsible for developing most of the primary nonprofit human services systems throughout the country, including family service agencies, child welfare systems, community-based parole and probation, adoption, and welfare agencies, as well as a host of youth and adult service agencies, such as shelters and senior centers.

The many community systems that refer patients to, and receive patients from, the health care system are enhanced and strengthened by having close working relationships with social work staff. Interventions by social workers are guided by their clinical skills, but also by their knowledge of the structure of the social service delivery systems, their leadership abilities, and the kinship of common disciplinary training. This facilitates the provision of quality social work in the areas of information and referral, discharge planning coordination, financial counseling, assurance of adequate payment for health care needs, and access to appropriate support systems.

Professional social work training is unique in its focus on an individual as a total person, including that individual's relationship to the larger context. This broad systems approach makes an important contribution to the highly specialized health care team and is an asset to any organization that has a continuum of care orientation. It provides a special capacity to view patients in terms of their psychological and social needs, their financial needs, their roles in a host of settings, and in terms of the impact of illness on those roles and on the patient's interface with other caregiving systems. This capacity is the basis for one of the social worker's contributions: the interpreting of the patient to the rest of the team to enhance their understanding of the patient's and the family's experience.

This broad and holistic viewpoint also serves as an important perspective for conceptualizing the redesign of the health care system in the face of declining resources and changing incentives. Viewing the total person in that person's many contexts is important to moving patients and their families as swiftly as possible from acute health care services to less expensive or less acute settings in a safe and acceptable manner. The holistic perspective allows the professional social worker to deal with an organization and its staff as just one context of many with which patients and their families interact. This has led to the natural and growing role of social work in employee assistance programs in health care and other industries.

Another characteristic of professional social workers is the special perspective that emerges from the nature of their clinical role in health care settings. For example, there are a number of kinds of interventions that social workers do not engage in, and this makes them different from other hospital professionals. Social workers engage in no physical interventions—they bring no pain medications, provide no food, and do not assist with toileting. Social workers wear no uniforms, thereby reducing the aura of medical authority. Patients do not depend on the social worker for cure or physical safety as they do on others in the hospital. In addition, the social worker's job is structured so that there is time to sit down at the bedside, ask how things are going, and listen to a full reply. Many other disciplines do not provide the clinical training for such in-depth interactions, or there are role conflicts that interfere.

The characteristics of the social worker's role make it more likely that patients will give the social worker clearer and more accurate data about their experiences than they will give others on whom they are dependent, and thus more eager to please. Also, social workers work throughout the entire health care system and have the opportunity to observe among the staff differing approaches to patient care and differing capacities for guest relations and quality interface with patients and families. This is valuable administrative information.

The social worker's mental health skills are critical in facilitating an appropriate decision-making process for the major changes in a patient's life style and for the complex, comprehensive, coordinated care plans that ensure continuity as the patient's needs change over time. With increased stress on all health care personnel, these skills also help to maintain the health of those working in the host setting itself. In a time of widespread litigation, the counseling skills of social work are even more valuable in assisting patients and families to resolve fears and angers about a health care experience through communication rather than legal action. This is a cost contribution of social work to the risk management sector. Social worker's mental health skills also assist other staff in successfully managing job-related stress, including stress from assisting in the personal dilemmas that accompany caring for aging or disabled relatives. Thoughtful and humane intervention can result in fewer workers' compensation claims and lower absentee rates when change contributes to an escalation in stress.

The social worker is frequently the coordinator of discharge planning, carrying responsibility for interdisciplinary planning for complex cases. Routine discharge planning may be conducted by a nurse or a physician without social work involvement, but where complex, long-term care needs require high-quality team collaboration and the mobilization of a wide range of community-based resources and payment mechanisms, social workers usually take the lead. The social work role in discharge planning becomes even more essential with the increased concern to reduce length of stay in hospitals and home health settings and to avoid denial on insurance coverage.

With more emphasis on providing assistance with complex discharge planning cases, there is a growing need for social workers to take the lead, together with nursing, in developing sophisticated organizationwide systems to assure appropriate discharge planning for all patients. This is particularly true for hospitals, but it is also applicable to HMOs, home health agencies, and nursing homes. Discharge planning takes more time than in the past because of the reduction of available community resources resulting from withdrawal of government support of services in some settings, increasingly complex referral networks created by HMOs and PPOs, and the growing number of clients. In addition, the high-technology resources now available for community-based care and the increasing reliance on home health services in the face of shrinking Medicare reimbursement for this needed support complicates the discharge planning function. The social worker is constantly balancing need for services with limited accessibility and availability of resources.

Involvement with the most at-risk patients of the health care organization in regard to their ongoing needs for care places social workers in a prime position to identify the gaps in the community system of care. This provides important data on resources, payment mechanisms, and barriers to accessing community systems. A powerful and essential base for collaborative health planning, such data assure a community safety net of supportive services so that early discharge from formal health care is safe discharge. In addition, the links social workers commonly maintain with a wide range of community agencies enable them to involve those systems in shared planning to build a proper substructure of human supports for those who need ongoing care of various types.

THEORETICAL FRAMEWORKS

A theoretical framework will provide a further basis for understanding the impact of the clinical and administrative practice of social workers in a continuum of care organization. The most helpful framework is the ecological approach developed by Germain[1] and well articulated by Coulton.[2] Social work interventions focus not only on individuals, but also on the interface between the individuals and the systems with which they interact. Such interventions optimize the interface between the patient or client and the environment. The concept of social work practice can be depicted as a series of concentric circles with the patient and family represented in the center (see Figure 20-1). Putting them in the center illustrates the directness of the clinical interventions the social worker makes with patients and their families, including

Figure 20-1 Patient Care and Treating the Context of Patient Care

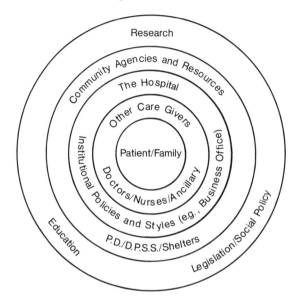

Source: Reprinted with permission from *The Transition from Social Work to Hospital Manager: An Exploratory Study* by Gary Rosenberg and Sylvia S. Clarke (Editors), Haworth Press, in press.

- assessment of psychological and social needs
- crisis intervention
- family treatment
- development of support groups for patients who share common problem areas
- provision of information and referrals
- coordination of complex multifaceted discharge planning to assure appropriate attention to a range of human needs

The needs or problems (of patients and families) that the social worker attends to include

- basic physical needs, such as housing, food, and personal needs
- social needs—to assure avoidance of extreme isolation and resulting development of emotional problems
- identified mental health and substance abuse problems that require treatment or other intervention

- the need for placement in specialty facilities such as foster homes, skilled nursing facilities, board and care and retirement homes, psychiatric facilities and other inpatient specialty programs (including for substance abuse, eating disorders, and acute psychiatric disturbances), and physical rehabilitation programs
- the need for special treatment interventions (for high risk populations, such as victims of child abuse, child sexual assault, elder abuse and neglect, and other specialized populations)

To plan for these support systems requires identifying the patient's needs, selecting appropriate resources, and assuring their proper utilization through counseling interventions, as well as assuring available funding mechanisms. Such planning has always been a collaborative process involving the patients themselves, family members, neighbors, other professionals in the health services community and relevant community systems (e.g., a church), and, at times, legal advisors. Here the boundary agent aspects of the social work role become clear—the professional deals not only with a single unit of the health care organization but with the full range of community systems that impact the patient's supports for independent living or institutional care. As will be discussed later, this has become far more complex under the changing health care system and the emerging continuum of care than previously.

Identifying breakdowns in health care systems and fixing them is another important social work role. This includes education for clinical professionals and other members of the health care organization who interface with patients (e.g., admissions and business office staff and receptionists). In the long run, it is a more effective use of the professional social worker's time to improve the health care system itself than to handle patients and their families upset due to system problems. As previously noted, the social worker frequently has occasion to identify problem areas in other agency systems as well. Thus, collaborative service delivery system problem solving and planning is needed to assure sufficient availability of quality community resources to meet the needs of patients over time. Indeed, the social worker can be helpful in constructing the continuum of care by identifying and negotiating with other community agencies that might become involved in the continuum as formal or informal affiliates.

Gaps and breakdowns in social policy and unanticipated side effects of well-intentioned legislation and regulations are also problem areas where social work can be helpful to administration and internal policy development. The social worker sees a large number of people who experience the impact of public policy and public systems. The social worker can thus provide anecdotal information, as well as trends in clinical observations, to the public decision-making sector. Utilizing appropriate health care and social work professional advocacy organizations, the broader system that affects all patients and their families can be amended.

In the past, the multifaceted aspects of health care social work practice tended to focus on the inpatient hospital experience. Patients stayed longer and were available for counseling interventions of greater depth. The reduction of length of stay has made some kinds of hospital clinical social work practical for only a proportion of inpatients. Because of the high degree of acuity of the health problems treated in hospitals at this time, patients are frequently too ill to participate in crisis intervention and posthospital care planning activities. Moreover, in developing a continuum of care approach, inpatient care is being linked more closely with home health, nursing home care, and other services. Thus, the social work focus has shifted to providing some direct services in the outpatient and home settings and collaborating more extensively with the family and other key decisionmakers involved in providing ongoing care for the patient.

SYSTEM CONSTRAINTS

A long-standing social work concern has been to complete, coordinate, and complement the continuum of care. Shrinking resources and increasing complexity (due to multiple finance sources) make this a more difficult task than ever before. The many players and decisionmakers compound the task. While patients, families, physicians, and nurses remain involved in the long-term care planning or discharge planning process, insurance companies, the Medicaid system, professional review organizations (PROs), utilization reviews, community-based case managers, and increasingly active health care organizations (e.g., home health agencies and outreach programs) complicate the work. Burgeoning contracts for care and coverage have resulted in additional bureaucratic requirements, including the often frustrating need for planners to make multiple calls to receive approval for payment from the third party payers for both hospital and community-based care. For example, 40 states now have pre-admission screening programs, many of which require approval prior to discharge of a patient from a hospital to a skilled nursing facility. Also, HMOs and other insurers are often eager to plan care, creating liability and ethical dilemmas for social workers and others who plan care in provider settings.

These growing bureaucratic and technical requirements, as well as the many legal and ethical conflicts of interest, reflect the need to optimize the expenditure of increasingly limited health care dollars. For instance, the California Medicaid system requires hospital discharge planners to make fully documented calls to 15 convalescent facilities each day to establish a lack of bed availability for a Medi-Cal patient. California's new pre-admission screening program is designed to assure that Medicaid patients avoid convalescent placement and remain at home whenever possible. The case manager and the discharge planner must deal with an outside reviewer who duplicates their assessment and care planning efforts in order to obtain authorization to place a Medicaid patient in a skilled nursing facility when that is deemed necessary. Further, each insurance company that contracts with the hospital or other provider has different requirements for authorizing community care benefit coverage.

Learning the rules, keeping current on changes, and interfacing with these additional systems can mean that the skilled negotiator is able to obtain "bending of benefits" to assure optimum coverage. But, in general, the case manager's and discharge planner's day is filled with frustrating clerical tasks required to achieve clinical outcomes instead of being largely devoted, as previously, to appropriate decision making, patient compliance, and family support. The significant losses in effectiveness of such professionals' work could be offset by adding clerical assistance to optimize use of professional time. In the face of declining or uncertain census and an uncertain economic future, however, most health care organizations are unwilling to augment staffing resources in this way, despite its reasonableness.

Interdisciplinary turf struggles further complicate collaborative practice and appropriate systems design. Discharge planning is one focal point of the struggle where the roles of the physician, nurse, social worker, and case manager (if appropriate) need to be clarified. Clearly, discharge planning is an interdisciplinary task, yet members of one discipline often attempt to assume the territory of members of another. It is important to assure the integrity of each discipline, since no one discipline can operate without the others—because of the complexity of the task. Building collaborative skills to assure optimum utilization of the contribution of each discipline is critical to the redesign of all care systems.

Other pressures are shared among the hospital, the home health setting, and the skilled nursing facility. Sharing is a reaction to the emerging federal strategy of denying coverage through redefining the regulations regarding government-sponsored health care benefits. Tightening coverage of skilled nursing placement for long-term care, a dramatic escalation in retroactive denials of home health services, and terrible pressures to reduce the length of stay in the inpatient setting threaten the quality of health care and require diligence and advocacy on the part of all major disciplines. Given the shrinking resources and threats to job security, health care providers are in a dilemma. Professionals often feel that their performance evaluations rest on avoiding benefit denials, reducing length of stay, and complying with financial guidelines. Home health nurses, for instance, may tend to reduce the number of nursing visits per patient in order to avert denial of visits actually needed. The number of referrals for ancillary services appears to be decreasing for the same reasons. It is difficult to retain appropriate levels of clinical coverage in the face of the fears these professionals experience.

A shocking reduction in home health benefits has been implemented since January 1986, when fiscal intermediaries were asked to change the rules. In addition to creating extreme pressures on the performance of all the disciplines involved, these economic regulatory changes could damage the very fabric of the health care system. Delays in timely payment to hospitals and home health agencies, unreasonable retroactive reviews and denials (with extreme scrutiny of the details of accountability), and dramatic increases in costs due to expanded bureaucratic reporting requirements could break the economic back of the nonprofit sector of the health system. Coupled with the drop in patient volume in most individual agency settings resulting from the increasing numbers of for-profit systems in home health and acute hospital care, these regulatory burdens pose a threat to the American health care system.

Competition was introduced to drive down costs in the acute care setting. Yet, the introduction of proprietary systems into this traditionally nonprofit sector has posed basic threats to indigent care and has artificially forced a breakdown in the competitive model. In the competitive marketplace, better systems should be able to assure higher quality based on consumer preference. The reality is that as small nonprofit hospitals, and even large ones, reach an economic crisis because of their inability to meet daily costs through current financing mechanisms, proprietary systems purchase these failing systems, partially in the name of creating a "continuum of care." However, such purchases have resulted in creating—though possibly unintentionally—a glut of hospital beds in a market of shrinking acute inpatient care demand. The maintenance of these beds through acquisition of at-risk systems poses a threat to the entire nonprofit system. All across the country, hospitals and home health agencies are operating at less than optimum volume because there are too many facilities. Health care should not be an arena for profit.

Infusion of this business mentality, however, has also brought many benefits to the nonprofit sector. A greater utilization of business principles and a deeper understanding of the "business of health care" has been helpful. But the continued support of an oversupply of services through private capital hurts both proprietaries and the nonprofit facilities in the health care system. It continues to drive up costs for all purchasers and to create terrible pressures on administrators and clinicians alike. The previously mentioned bureaucratic solutions to drive down the escalating costs entangle a good practitioner in a bureaucratic web of multiple players and documentation demands.

These heavy pressures place learning demands on staff and increase the need for outside training. Unfortunately, the current constraints on resources have resulted in a reduction in training and travel budgets. Reliance on technological training methods, such as audio and video tapes, is growing, although these reduce the vital networking and interaction between professionals in group education settings. Use of national teleconferences is one solution, which can be coupled with less sophisticated methods such as telephone conferences and use of regional radio programs.

Some groups are beginning to experiment with other approaches. For instance, the nationwide Society for Hospital Social Work Directors (SHSWD) is deeply concerned about the fact that many of its members are unable to get needed training to adjust their skills and knowledge base to the changing health care environment. Staying current is particularly a problem for those who are sole practitioners or who practice in small organizations. The SHSWD is responding by expanding the use of audio tapes and testing the development of low-cost video training tapes that can be utilized by individuals and small groups of practitioners in isolated areas with little or no educational budgets.

BROADENING THE SERVICE BASE

The issues discussed above reflect some of the negatives of the current efforts to redesign health care into a continuum of care. There are many positive developments occurring in the same environment. Some of the constraints have led to the creation of new approaches that result in valuable and appropriate utilization of professional skills and are economically more viable than the older approaches.

For example, we see greater involvement of social work professionals in the outpatient sector of the community and some other settings. Social work consultation and staffing in skilled nursing facilities is an emerging phenomenon that is intended to improve a specialty health care industry area designed many years ago for a much smaller and more impaired elderly population. The intensification of social work services in home health agencies is critical, especially with the reduced length of home health treatment and the greater acuity of patient needs. As more and more at-risk patients are cared for in the home, careful oversight of compliance, together with assurance of methods to acquire and pay for all needed services, is important. HMOs and insurance companies, along with direct providers, are experimenting with case management. The case management role is easily filled by social workers.

For instance, medically related psychotherapy is an important service that has been rarely provided in the hospital. Similarly, traditional community psychiatric personnel are unfamiliar with the impact of chronic pain, low energy, or loss of physical function. Medical social work specialists are much more effective in managing these crises, as well as counseling for related issues, such as sexually related fears of cardiac patients or patients with special disabilities and physical changes. Thus, many general hospital social work departments are moving their clinical counseling into outpatient settings and developing specialty mental health services to bridge the existing gap. This enables both the acute hospital and the psychiatric hospital or mental health center to expand the range of care they offer.

Developing medically based services to treat mental health and stress management needs for patients who are unwilling to go to traditional psychiatric centers is important for maintaining the mental health fabric of human services. In the hospital, the patients are able to access important mental health services that will enable them to mobilize and cope optimally with the threats to social and personal functioning that significant health care problems can pose. Incidents of illness and injury can leave permanent psychic damage if not appropriately addressed. Posttrauma counseling is one solution and an important element in the newly emerging hospital-based mental health intervention programs.

In addition, stress is a major factor in many medical problems and exacerbates pain and makes its management more difficult, as well as contributing to cardiac problems and such conditions as multiple sclerosis. Social workers are developing programs (e.g., biofeedback and group stress management education) and new treatment interventions to deal with stress.

Another new approach is to lend professional social work staff from a health care organization to help in the formation and maintenance of community self-help groups. This has been done in the areas of oncology and neonatology, among others. These self-help groups are easily based in a group practice, ambulatory care center, or the outpatient clinic of the hospital. They can expand the health care organization's ability to follow patients and deliver a complete range of clinical services without overloading the inpatient setting. Some clients will use counseling in a medical setting that they wouldn't feel comfortable using in more traditional settings.

Health education is another critical emerging arena. Not all patients and their families require actual mental health intervention. While some need the development of support systems, others can mobilize themselves if they receive sufficient information. Optimum utilization of inpatient and outpatient services with a reduction in litigation and an increase in the ease of patient management can be achieved through proper orientation and educational programs. These can include programs to prepare pediatrics patients before hospital admission to assure a calmer, quieter, and more medically beneficial stay. Preparation for adults can have the same benefit, especially for major procedures such as open heart surgery. Preparation of elderly patients and pediatrics patients for day surgery can be beneficially done when the patients are in for lab tests and other procedures prior to the surgery. Services can be provided on a modest fee-for-service basis and become financially self-sustaining. In addition, educating patients for their complex posthospital and community-based care needs is vital.

The area of prevention is essential for the reduction of health care costs that occurs through treating risk factors to lower the incidence of physical breakdown. Thus, the provision of health education that targets risk factors is important. Smoking cessation classes, assistance in proper dietary management, stress management, access to appropriate social support systems, and utilization of adequate exercise regimens are important interventions conducted under social work leadership, often in conjunction with other key disciplines.

Another new mode of practice now gaining popularity is known as coordinated care. Building on the valuable concepts that underpin utilization review and case management, coordinated care programs address the needs of at-risk and chronically impaired children, adults, and the frail elderly by providing comprehensive, ongoing care in the community. Coordinated care includes assessing and managing medical care needs, as well as managing social, physical, financial, and sometimes legal problems. With coordination methods and technologies in place, health care provider organizations are able to follow the patient in the community and monitor the quality of the set of services required in the home.

Previously, the discharge planner in a hospital made intensive and comprehensive postcare plans, and then hoped for the best. Sometimes limited follow-up was possible. Under a coordinated care system, the discharge planner has collegial partners to assist the physician and the patient in successfully implementing the posthospital care plan. Due to the prevalence of generally earlier discharges, posthospital care needs have changed considerably. A coordinated care system assures there is a professional to monitor the patient and to tailor the care plan to the changing needs.

Coordinated care also allows oversight of the care rendered by providers. It is not uncommon to arrange for personal care in the home only to find that a caregiver failed to show up. With an extremely frail elderly patient, this can cause a serious problem and must not be tolerated. In addition, the coordinated care program accesses new clients by working with patients who have never been in the hospital in order to prevent or delay institutionalization.

These programs draw on the same kinds of capabilities described as necessary for coordination of complex discharge planning. While best directed by a professional social work administrator having in-depth experience with the specialty population served, coordinated care requires a close partnership between social work and nursing. The nursing perspective is critical to the success of the program. A close relationship with the physician is essential to assure that orders are carried out and that the doctor is completely apprised of the care received by the patient in the home. Familiarity and frequent contact with payer organizations adds the remaining dimension requisite to assuring the financial accessibility of care.

PROFESSIONAL SOCIAL WORK ASSOCIATIONS

The new roles of social workers reflect significant changes and point to a greater need for their active involvement in professional organizations. The new roles account for the current burgeoning of specialty practice associations across the country. The National Association of Social Workers is a long-standing organization that provides support and advocacy for professional social work. Specialty needs are often met by membership in additional organizations. For instance, the Society for Hospital Social Work Directors (SHSWD) of the American Hospital Association has a membership of 2,500 social work administrators faced with the complexities of health care systems in their local communities.

Great benefit is garnered by each through participating in shared education and networking experiences, as well as by solving common problems through task forces and committees. While travel for national committee work may require more time and financial resources than are available in today's compressed and economically constrained environment, the innovative utilization of telephone conference calls facilitates devising national solutions to common problems.

Membership in these organizations becomes more important as the need to cope with increasingly complex professional environments intensifies. Written materials, training events, and training materials are critical tools for these organizations. It is essential that advocacy in the social health policy area is done through groups. Clinical groups, such as groups of oncology social workers, are forming rapidly, both locally and nationally. Groups of neonatal intensive care unit and perinatal social workers have also formed. There is now a national pediatric social work organization. Social work assistance for trauma victims is another important area undergoing special organizational effort. Social workers are also involved in problem-specific groups such as the Association for the Care of Children in Health. Other groups focus on developing policies in the area of disaster management, care of the elderly, and a host of other key issues, such as domestic violence. While there is not yet a special group focused primarily on the broad-ranging issues of the continuum of care, SHSWD focuses intensively on these issues among others.

NEW CLINICAL SKILLS NEEDED

The changing context requires a set of clinical skills that need to be developed and maintained. Tolerance in dealing with ambiguities, changing rules, complexities, and unexpected patient volume cycles is needed. Maintenance of equanimity in the face of turf struggles with colleagues from other disciplines is key to building the kind of trusting relationships basic to successful mobilization of the health care community in these challenging times. Stress and time management skills are of increased importance for the professional social worker, as are collaborative skills, the ability to facilitate planning and coordination, and the ability to guide decision making within a small group.

The social worker must also master the giving of brief, comprehensive assessments to assure that wherever the patient is seen in the continuum—the hospital or a home health or other coordinated care setting—a holistic perspective on the total person is part of the care planning process. In the inpatient setting, the capacity to make brief, yet highly focused, interventions appropriate to the time available is crucial, as is the ability to assure effective referral connections. Financial planning competencies have always been central, but they take on a new dimension in the rapidly changing fiscal environment surrounding care.

Creative problem solving must be used to help the patient in the health care setting address continuity of care issues. Recently, hospitals have been experimenting with methods for assisting the patient to overcome artificial barriers to transfer. For example, hospitals can now provide a deposit to a skilled nursing facility for a Medicaid-pending patient until Medicaid is actually approved. This not only reduces the risk for the skilled nursing facility, but allows the patient to leave the hospital on a timely basis, and frees the hospital from providing an inappropriate level of care. Most important, the predictability offered by such arrangements enables special workers to assist families in planning transfers rather than awaiting transfers to an unknown location at an uncertain time. Negotiating benefit flexibility with insurance providers is another area requiring creative problem solving.

Documentation skills must be highly refined. Careful and accurate descriptions of the patient within the bounds of confidentiality and relevance to the medical chart are important in all settings. Providing complete details helps to assure that patients are judged eligible for services to which they are entitled. Proper documentation can be the key to entering or remaining at the appropriate level of care. Accurate charting might be the difference between denial and paid care. Accurate verbal descriptions of patient conditions are essential for the kind of advocacy that assures the least restrictive level of care which a patient is entitled to and physically qualified for.

Social workers must be able to identify key incidents and trends in the clinical arena and report these skillfully to the appropriate decisionmakers. This vital aspect of clinical work safeguards the basic standards of hospital and community agency practice. Patient safety is at risk in these changing times, and reporting incidents will assist the system in adjusting to new formats of care. Incidents can also point to the need for new policies, procedures, or programs. Such an incident in California led to a new law that permits division of community properties for spouses when one spouse is faced with convalescent placement. This protective legislation, which serves to benefit both society as a whole and the individuals involved, resulted from repeated documentation of needless bankruptcy of spouses. Clinicians who do not report the travesties that occur as the unintended side effects of social policy fail to adequately and completely serve their clients or the community.

NEW LEADERSHIP ROLES ARE EMERGING

Owing to the impact of these various trends on the practice of social work in the health care setting, a variety of new leadership roles have emerged. Throughout the country many social work administrators in health settings have been promoted to higher administrative positions with greater responsibilities for giving direction to new program development and design. Social work's long-standing concern with continuity of care, combined with its expertise in collaborative planning and community service delivery systems, makes this a natural step.

After many turf struggles, it has generally been concluded that care management and discharge planning are interdisciplinary processes to be shared between nursing, physicians, and social workers. The natural expansion of the concept of care management is the move toward coordinated care, i.e., community-based care of at-risk individuals to avoid institutional placement. Comprehensive assessment by a physician, nurse, and social worker and conjoint care planning are vital. Social work's long history as a leader in the care of most at-risk populations makes it a fitting discipline to develop these new programs, regardless of whether they are privately funded or are government alternatives to expensive institutionalization.

These and other emerging services—such as adult day care programs, health promotion programs, hospital outreach in health education, and outpatient-vendored services in mental health, stress, and financial management—represent new developments in social work administrative practice. Employee assistance programs are growing in importance and are also frequently directed by social workers. Coordinating social work services for home health agencies and providing support groups and membership programs for the elderly are also natural tasks for social workers.

NEED FOR SYSTEMS TRANSFORMATION

With the advent of prospective pricing, capitation, contracting, and the new formats of health care emphasizing cost containment, a significant need for system transformations has occurred. Thus, the continuum of care approach has emerged. The new systems are highly compatible with social work values and capabilities. In fact, the social work perspective greatly enhances the planning of these systems. A major contribution is the marketing data that come from sitting at the bedside in a nonphysical care delivery role and helping patients to plan for successful adaptation to community living. The insights gained by collecting the data accumulated from patient interviews and from solving many patient problems fuel the transformational fire.

The natural leadership opportunities provided by the changing health care delivery system mandate the development of new and better administrative skills as part of social work practice. Social workers must develop the capacity to successfully identify problems, develop an appropriate range of potential program solutions in collaboration with others, and propose needed changes to key decisionmakers and funders in an effective way. Building consensus for new solutions to emerging problems is vital. An essential condition for success in this regard is the ability to build a solid business plan and accurately forecast and plan for the financial self-sufficiency, or even profitability, of programs. Social work administrators are becoming increasingly creative in funding programs from outside sources. They are developing a skilled ability to pursue grants from government, foundations, and individual donors, as well as from the United Way and other resources such as the local AAA (Area Agency on Aging). They also are developing the skills to acquire seed capital for testing ideas for new model programs.

Social workers must demonstrate strong program implementation skills, as well as administrative and clinical expertise. The ability to recruit, select, and train effective and well-qualified staff and to build a harmonious and high-quality caregiving team may be new to some who have previously concentrated in clinical one-on-one patient care. Like other health care professionals, social workers must learn how to develop business, records, and referral systems. They must also learn the ability to manage change and the conflict that results internally and in the community when a health care organization moves into new types of service and in new program directions. The importance of these skills cannot be overstated.

Marketing skills are particularly well suited to the social work administrator's capabilities. The building of a referral base for a new program—whether a coordinated care service, a health promotion program, or a membership program to build volume—is supported through the natural alliances that the social work director has with other human services leaders.

There is some mistrust and distance between the health care community and the social services system in the community. Social work directors quite naturally bridge this gap, being members of both professional communities. They are accustomed to working closely with other agency staff and their directors in facilitating referrals. They also have the trust of those communities, which can help to mitigate some of the fears and the reluctance to cooperate that a medical person might initially encounter upon entering the social services system. A health care organization tends to be perceived in the community as a large and powerful organization, with greater business skills and a more profound funding base than many social service and grassroots organizations. Therefore, it is viewed as a threat when it begins to diversify and move into services traditionally provided by others. Much trust and communication is needed to build collaborative and nonduplicative services that assure the health and independence of the individuals cared for within continuum of care systems. The communication and teaching skills natural to the trained social worker are valuable in conceptualizing and articulating the benefits of proposed new programs.

As noted before, strong advocacy is needed to avert the complete dismantling of the best elements of the health system in this country. Here, again, the role of professional associations (e.g., the American Hospital Association) and specialty social work groups (e.g., the Society for Hospital Social Work Directors) is to assure that access to quality health care services is available and that basic patient health and safety issues are attended to appropriately.

COMMUNITY LINKAGES

Community organization is a traditional area of specialization in social work practice. There is a full body of literature about it, and a range of resources are available, as is community organization training in most professional schools of social work. A community organizational background and perspective is crucial both for a health care organization's practice (given the frequency of referrals to a variety of community-based services for additional care) and for the successful building of new community-based continuums of care. In the discharge planning arena, the social work director and staff are frequently involved not only in accessing community-based services, but in serving on boards, committees, and networks for solving common client problems. These affiliations facilitate meeting the special requests of patients in unusual circumstances. They also serve as the groundwork for collaborative planning for change and system enhancement for both the health care system and the wider human services system.

Such relationships are now extending into new constituencies and new collaborative structures. The new structures are perhaps most evident in coordinated care programs and at-risk financing arrangements, where the health care organization may actually become a contract agent on behalf of the patient. This changes the nature of the relationship between organization and patient and is best done only where there is a long history of cooperation and collegiality. Better clinical services and better pricing are often obtained based on a long-standing affiliation. New partners are also required to help in the transformation of a fragmented, overly specialized health care system into a more cohesive continuum of care. Diversification requires tying program products into a cohesive whole that works as a system. Health systems, personal care systems, emergency response systems, social and mental health support, home repair, meals and transportation, the range of residential long-term care systems—these must all be drawn together into a single system through which the patient can move with ease and comfort.

As an inpatient in the hospital or in dealing with a discrete problem in a doctor's office, a patient operates somewhat in isolation from his or her normal life. When engaged in ongoing community-based care, a wide group of persons are potentially involved. The landlord, the neighbor, the church and its membership, the attorney, the bank, and sometimes the bank's trust department all may become members of the collaborative planning team. Their decisions may have broad and enduring consequences. They are also referral sources and partners in care. These liaisons can be extremely beneficial to the health care organization in many ways, including by serving an outreach function and helping to build a base for new types of services.

CONCLUSION

The role of the social work professional in the health care setting is changing dramatically. It is unlikely that there will ever be a return to the old status quo. Despite the pressures, complexities, and aggravations of the change process, the incentives and program directions of the new continuum of care health systems are very much in accord with social work values and will benefit from social work leadership. While requiring new skills and needing the energy and instinct to adapt in this tremendously volatile period of change, the social work clinician and administrator are essential contributors to the productive redesign of the health care system. Their perspectives and their natural links make them valuable team partners of those in other key disciplines, especially health care administrators, in optimizing the utilization of health, mental health, and social services and in facilitating the creation of community-based continuums of care. Building new management systems for these sorts of emerging organizational structures is made substantially easier by the development skills of the social work administrator and staff.

NOTES

1. Carol B. Germain, "An Ecological Perspective on Social Work in Health Care," *Social Work in Health Care* 3, no. 1 (1977):67–77.

2. C.J. Coulton, et al., "Discharge Planning and Decision Making," *Health and Social Work* 7 (November 1982):253–261.

Chapter 21

Organizational Leadership, Culture, and Excellence

Dean M. Crowder

A continuum of care makes remarkably good sense for all concerned—health care institutions and systems, payers and buyers of care, and, most importantly, customers. For those patients who have complex health problems requiring comprehensive care over an extended period of time, a continuum clearly assists in attaining optimal health recovery. For hospitals and health systems that must find new ways to offer services in a changing health care market place with prospective and capitated payment systems, it offers an efficient, cost-effective, and rational approach to providing quality care to customers. And for those organizations committed to excellence, it offers the superior customer service that is their ultimate good.

Providing a continuum of care is clearly within the grasp of those health care organizations where visionary leadership and committed staff strive together to provide superior care. A collective commitment to offer an integrated, customer-oriented system of care will increase an organization's ability to respond and adapt to the population's changing care needs. Each organization, whether a hospital, clinic, home health agency, or an integrated health care system, large or small, possesses the capability of offering a continuum of care to those patients who will benefit from systematic integration and continuity of services. However, creating a continuum of care is not easy to do. The evidence: continuums of care are rare.

Leadership, which includes the ability to mobilize the commitment, enthusiasm, drive, and action of all involved, is the single most critical element determining success in achieving a continuum of care. This chapter focuses on three aspects of leadership: (1) inspiring change through vision, (2) establishing appropriate organization and structure, and (3) creating a supportive corporate culture. The legal, financial, and other mechanics of creating a continuum of care are described elsewhere in this book. This chapter emphasizes the significance of the human element and describes techniques used to persuade administrators, clinicians, support staff, and organizational allies to change their attitudes and operations in order to function as part of an integrated continuum of care system.

The issues and suggestions described here are drawn partially from my experience as a chief executive officer (CEO) of a health care organization. Within a span of four years, we moved from being a tertiary general hospital on one site to a horizontally and vertically integrated health care system with 22 locations. The added services and programs included

- a second acute care general hospital with programs in stroke rehabilitation, senior outreach, vision care, and drug and alcohol rehabilitation
- a joint venture for high-technology home therapy
- a Medicare-certified home health agency
- a medical group practice with 120 physicians and eight sites
- a skilled nursing facility
- two free-standing senior care centers
- a free-standing preventive medicine center
- six urgent care centers.

It was evident throughout this growth in size, scope, and complexity that management leadership was important—indeed, crucial—in moving the organization and its people toward a continuum of care.

VISIONARY LEADERSHIP

Organizational leadership—and that means management leadership—is essential to success in today's changing health care marketplace. Organizational leadership is the driving force that is decisive in achieving long-range performance. The ability of hospitals and health delivery systems to thrive hinges entirely upon well-informed and visionary leadership. It is the innovative, creative, risk-taking, and inspirational leadership of the CEO that will foster organizational growth and success in a market-oriented system by effectively defining and strategically directing the health care business. Leadership must have the vision, knowledge, skills, and latitude to position the organization for confronting and responding effectively to change.

The powerful social, economic, and political forces that are reshaping and increasing the management requirements and the complexities of current health care delivery systems promote the need for organizations that are market-driven. Health care is moving toward an economic, competition-based delivery model on the thesis that the clinical and social needs of customers and the financial and market realities of the environment mandate that health care organizations offer a comprehensive array of integrated health care services in a systematic way. In addition, hospitals and health care delivery systems are evolving from predetermined, fixed-price retrospective payment systems to prospective, capitated payment systems, which create greater customer and/or buyer satisfaction, greater price sensitivity, but also have more stringent physician payment constraints. It will be essential for top management to understand and to respond to these forces and other overarching trends that are reshaping health care delivery today.

These trends indicate the direction the country is moving. Trends, like horses, are easier to ride in the direction they are already headed. If a decisive action is compatible with an overarching trend, the trend aids the action. The organization may decide to ignore or buck the trend, but it is at least helpful to know it is there. It is essential that management leadership fully understands where the trends are headed and what their implications are in order to manage the enterprise to gain a competitive advantage over time. Leaders can then prepare their organizations to move in new directions and to confront, anticipate, and respond effectively to change.

How does a CEO instill vision in an organization? A first step is answering the question "What business are we in?". Health care has changed so rapidly in recent years that many organizations have acted in response to external forces rather than deciding first where they wanted to go. Long gone are the days when doctors and hospitals saw their responsibilities limited to "providing care to the ill." The business of caring has an acknowledged market orientation and a recognized need to pay attention to the financial aspects of operations. Preparing a long-range strategic plan is one concrete way of articulating the vision of where the organization is going so that all can understand.

Defining goals and measurable objectives is critical. Done as part of the strategic plan or as part of the annual plan of each department, specifying goals, objectives, and specific actions should involve staff of all management levels of the organization. As the CEO and senior managers work with midlevel managers and staff to articulate and refine work plans, the vision of the leadership is translated into concrete activities that staff can accept as their contribution to implementing the vision. By being involved in shaping the day-to-day operationalization of the vision, staff members adopt it as their own and become committed to it. They will also have a greater understanding and acceptance of changes that senior management might make, changes that would otherwise seem threatening or inappropriate.

Creating a continuum of care inevitably involves change. And, just as inevitably, most people resist change. Change is easier to achieve if the organization has a focus. Focus facilitates change by identifying niches. No organization can be all things to all people. In spite of that, many health care organizations amazingly try to do everything. This is a particular risk in setting up a continuum of care, given how large and complex continuums tend to be. Thus, it is especially important that an organization define its focus and publicize its niche in a way that the staff and the community can understand and accept. Focus enables leaders then to invest valuable resources toward implementing successful and lasting change.

The effort needed in moving from the mindset of acute care and from a state of competition between operating entities within the organization to an integrated system of health care services requires an enormous commitment to excellence. The leaders of the organization must induce change in attitudes and orientation, then facilitate the translation of these into actions and new patterns. As already noted, health care is changing from a provider-controlled to a market-driven, consumer-oriented, cost-conscious field. Yet many staff members, particularly clinicians, do not fully appreciate the extent of the change.

Ongoing internal marketing will convey and continue to reinforce the leadership's vision. Internal publications, such as a physician newsletter or an employee bulletin, can be valuable in first explaining the vision of where the organization is headed, then continuing to reinforce the vision by reporting progress. Continuing education programs directed systematically toward various staff and colleague groups, about environmental trends can educate those directly and indirectly involved in the continuum. The greater the understanding of the vision among all staff related to the organization, the greater the ease in gaining cooperation and enthusiasm to make it become reality. Moreover, the initial vision of the leaders may be enhanced and its details filled in by employees and colleagues at all levels who can relate to the overall goal and make specific contributions based on their own day-to-day activities.

ORGANIZATION

Vision must be accompanied by appropriate mechanisms to enable action, i.e., structures to support and facilitate tasks.

With ten subsidiary operating entities, I quickly discovered that my most challenging tasks were (1) to provide a special brand of visionary and inspirational leadership to edge key management people, with their individual operating responsibilities and accountabilities, toward a systematic integration of the array of services available and (2) to operate the collective enterprise as one organization. Getting a comprehensive range of services under one organizational umbrella is obviously a major achievement, but to operate on a day-to-day basis as a continuum requires the additional steps of formulating and installing the essential structure and integrating mechanisms.

To design and manage the continuum of care requires a sophisticated and refined planning effort that requires all members of top management to work together. Strategic planning, penetrating to all levels of the organization and coordinated to achieve corporate goals, is essential. Such planning is much more complex than simply hiring an external consulting firm to examine the environment and prepare a strategic plan for the corporate executives. To achieve the excellence of performance and collective commitment sought by the organization, managers at all levels, and their staffs, must be involved in the planning process. More time must be allowed for the planing process; goals, objectives, and performance criteria must be set by top management to guide the process. However, careful attention to the participation of staff of all levels in the preparation of the strategic plan contributes in the end to the desired result: organizational excellence over time in providing superior customer service.

Informed and committed governance is also essential. The board and the medical staff must be apprised and accepting of change. These two groups must be convinced that service integration and a continuum of care are beneficial for patients, physicians, and the organization. Their recognition of this and their support are crucial.

Governing board and physician support is achieved through a joint planning and evaluation process with senior management participation. In many organizations, the board's strategic planning committee, with members representing the board, medical staff, and management, is the central mechanism not only for developing the strategic plan but, in the process, for addressing change and new directions.

Input to the strategic planning process from other board committees, top management, hospital-based physician directors, and medical staff executive committees results in identification of actual and perceived issues that must be considered. The organizational planning director staffs this function. Under the direction of the CEO and with the support of the committee chairman, the planning director assures that the agenda deals with issues that concern where the organization is headed. The committee must stay on course and not wander aimlessly into counterproductive areas. Otherwise, the strategic planning process can become politicized and end up serving special interests to the detriment of the organization's programs and progress.

Responsibility and accountability for program development rest squarely on the shoulders of the CEO and senior management. As in the development of goals, objectives, and business and marketing plans, the inauguration of a continuum of care program is the responsibility of top management—with the collaborative participation of those administrative and departmental representatives necessary to achieve an effective service continuum.

The chairman or leader of the organizational task force in charge of planning and developing the continuum must be an executive individual placed strategically high in the organization. Ideally, this person should be the same executive who has the responsibility for planning and implementing the business plan, but at least must be someone who reports directly to the CEO. If the task force leader does not have the organizational power and influence to get task force recommendations approved, the program's development will flounder.

The continuum of care effort must be viewed as a top priority. It must be structured so that recommendations are properly channeled into the top management planning and decision making process.

Continuing education is a key element in keeping management abreast of trends and future directions. The organization's human resources program should include management development courses to assist managers in acquiring the knowledge and developing the skills to inspire their staffs to work together toward the achievement of organizational objectives. There are management educational programs sponsored externally by a host of hospital and professional associations. Many of them are excellent for keeping management people current on health care issues.

The American College of Healthcare Executives regularly conducts seminars on timely topics. These highly targeted programs offer a productive way to increase management awareness and understanding of current health care trends and of new techniques for effective response to such trends. In addition to sponsoring the annual Congress on Administration, the Fellows Conference, and the Western Conference, the college conducts seminars led by knowledgeable individuals on such topics as business planning, joint ventures, financial strategies, market place competition, corporate restructuring, institutional leadership, and executive skills. The annual college conferences feature a wide variety of current subjects. These educational programs also enable each participant to learn from the experiences of the other participants, who are from organizations all over the country. In addition, the college conducts programs on the lessons to be learned from other industries—valuable information that is applicable to health care settings.

In the progressive "front runner" health care organization, there is an ongoing and close collaboration among the CEO, other top management executives, the governing board, and the physicians. There must be a trusting partnership in which the members not only recognize the efficacy of working together, but also understand the need for decisive, tough-minded, but sensitive management guidance.

It is especially critical that hospitals and physicians be united. Physicians must be encouraged and enabled to participate actively in the decisions and the policy development process and, at the same time, be held accountable for implementing policies such as those governing patient care. Most assuredly, hospitals and physicians must begin to act like a team. The CEO, by means of management skills and delegated authority, must direct this necessarily unified structure and collaborative effort.

Collaboration on policy development and decision making must become part of the organizational fabric. Physician and top management participation in governance is now common, with physician membership on governing boards recognized as essential for achieving effective organizational decision making. Physicians now often sit on board committees such as executive, finance, strategic planning, and audit. Management support and participation in medical staff committee functions promote continuity, effective communication, and appropriate recommendations for governing board action.

Beyond board and medical staff committee participation, there are a number of mechanisms used to facilitate collaboration. Ongoing discourse among top management, medical staff leadership, and hospital-based physician directors is essential to assure that the departmental clinical or administrative directors are included in the communications and decision-making process. Regular meetings, preferably weekly, between the board chairman, the CEO, and the medical staff chief provide ongoing communication and an opportunity for identification of critical problems, together with workable methods for their resolution. This then sets the stage for organizationwide cooperative effort.

Including physicians on boards of subsidiary corporations formed for business development activities and joint ventures is another frequently employed mechanism. Today, an important focus of collaboration is the development of alternative systems such as HMOs and PPOs, as well as joint venture programs such as surgical and urgent care centers. Some hospitals and health systems employ a skilled executive whose sole responsibility is to work with physicians individually and in groups outside the medical staff structure in the development of alternative systems and joint ventures between the hospital organization and physician groups.

Effective relationships with local business and industry are becoming increasingly important. With competition and the evolution of alternative delivery systems, communication with business leaders in the development of insurance packages, wellness programs, and preventive medicine services for their employees becomes important in maintaining a competitive edge. It is better for the health care organization to take the initiative to develop a collaborative relationship with business and industry than to allow business to develop health care programs by itself.

Increasing the level of understanding by business leaders about health care issues is critical in today's health care marketplace. One mechanism to achieve this is a business advisory council created by the health care organization. Conversely, management may participate in advisory groups sponsored by the local business school, in community management roundtables, and in the chamber of commerce. All such participation can be useful in promoting better relationships with local business.

Collaborative relationships with other health-related organizations are now focused on common interests. Information sharing and political advocacy continue to be the major roles of hospital councils and associations. Individual institutions are getting together to enhance their respective economic and competitive positions. Mergers, acquisitions, and joint ventures are on the rise. The result is the continued development of health care systems, whether horizontally or vertically integrated, regional, statewide, or national, for-profit or nonprofit, or some creative combination of these.

Hospitals and health care systems today must be strategically managed. They simply cannot react to crises on a daily basis. Management leadership in a time of increasing competition requires that the CEO serve as the organization change agent. The days of the ''administrative staffer'' are over. Being passive or being a follower just won't work. More and more, health care executives must make things happen or they will fail. The CEO and senior management must take the initiative.

Responsibility for advocacy is another new facet of the CEO's role. A CEO must be outspoken on behalf of the organization and of the programs he or she supports, as well as politically astute and skilled in the art of communicating. In promoting a continuum, for example, the CEO must have the ability to articulate points effectively. Conveying a clear vision makes a tremendous difference in achieving planned results. Advocacy is becoming more important. This is true both internally and externally.

Achieving and sustaining excellence requires a commitment to superior performance. This entails measuring and rewarding performance. Excelling presupposes the pursuit of all endeavors with the conviction that they can be accomplished in a superior fashion. Excellence is clearly the outcome of superior customer service, constant innovation, and committed people. Leadership allows and encourages humanism to pervade the organization. In addition, leadership promotes excellence by establishing measurable performance objectives and by installing an employee evaluation system that conscientiously measures performance and a rewards system that acknowledges effort and outcome.

Teamwork, if lacking, will also need to be fostered. Under effective leadership, teamwork achieves results while allowing participants to derive satisfaction from their efforts. Productivity is accomplished through people, and coordination and integration are essential. The basics of understanding and respecting the roles of various disciplines is a necessary first step.

All of these changes now require reassessment and modification of the personnel system. Many hospitals and most integrated health systems have moved to a human resources approach, with an experienced professional director orchestrating the organizationwide human resources functions. This is critical when the organization grows in size, scope, and complexity and when new operating entities are assimilated into the growing system. Installation of new approaches like product line management, where staff employees are organized according to product lines rather than by traditional departments, may also require modifications in how the organization is structured and how it functions.

People within the separate operating entities must perceive that they belong to one integrated organization; this is achieved partly through consistent and rational personnel policies and practices. When such policies exist and when the organizational culture is supportive, personnel are more willing to work collaboratively toward instituting mutually beneficial programs, which is critical when moving toward service integration and continuity of care.

The creation of a continuum of care occurs when people representing different entities, departments, product lines, and disciplines work together. An organizationwide human resources program directed by a professional at the top management level is also important for promoting the necessary kind of productive effort.

CORPORATE CULTURE

To promote and enhance organizational performance and long-range success, the CEO must be an organizational visionary bringing a compelling thematic vision to the enterprise. The CEO's leadership abilities must include the capability to get others committed to this vision. The leadership must be the kind that creates and sustains a strong corporate culture embodying the CEO's views, attitudes, and values—and allows those values to pervade the entire enterprise. Such a supportive culture is a potent means for bringing people together. It serves as a dynamic vehicle for responding to change.

Corporate culture is a pattern of beliefs and expectations shared by the organization's members. These beliefs and expectations are based on common values; they produce norms that shape the behavior of individuals and groups within the organization. Culture is usually well ingrained and thus difficult to change. An organization's culture is the shared sense of the "way we do things around here." It is a factor in guiding day-to-day behavior and shaping future courses of action.

While excellent organizations are driven by value systems, all of them are marked by the personality of a leader who laid down the value set. Engraining the set of values is not done by charisma alone, but even more by overt, sincere, sustained personal commitment to the values, coupled with extraordinary persistence in reinforcing them. The leader's visibility in advocating the values and consistent, positive reinforcement of employees' actions are vital to excellence in organizational performance. Frequent appearance by the CEO at medical staff and employee meetings; frequent appearance around the facilities to visit, listen, and respond to questions; regular reports on the status of the organization; an open-door policy for dealing with complaints; a regular statement in the newsletter; all of these serve to keep the leadership visible and approachable. They also keep the senior management in touch with the realities of their organization and thus ensure the vision is realistic.

Culture building in today's health care systems is based on strategic thinking and an orientation toward satisfying customer needs, gaining a sustainable advantage over competitors, and capitalizing on organizational strengths. Actions aimed at culture building should instill a collective commitment to a common purpose, foster excellence among employees, and establish consistency; doing these things also helps attract and develop leaders at all levels of the organization.

Corporate culture is a means of bringing people together to make a vision a reality. Together with strategic thinking, corporate culture building requires that leaders not only cultivate broad vision but master the skills to implement that vision. Such leaders create a future equally responsive to the bottom line and to the organization's personnel.

As a complex, multiservice organization, we attempted to develop a corporate culture based on a humanistic approach imbued with the values of creativity, integrity, respect, competence, and recognition of each individual's worth and contribution. When an organization acknowledges and rewards an individual's creativity, it encourages innovation, enthusiasm, perserverance, and dedication. Treating people with respect in turn gains their respect for the organization and fosters loyalty and commitment. In a service organization dealing with traumatic and intimate aspects of people's lives, honesty, warmth, and a high moral standard are central to successful performance. We envisioned this humanistic approach as the basis for achieving excellence in the delivery of client-oriented health care.

Building a strong corporate culture will be one of the fundamental leadership tasks of the next decade. Health care organizations, particularly those which choose the continuum of care approach, are human institutions, oriented toward creating long-term relationships among committed staff and patients. Thus, for the benefit of staff and clients, they must engender the expressive aspects of living: soul, spirit, magic, heart, ethos, vision, commitment, and excellence. The future holds promise for those organizations with a vital corporate culture and with an ability to respond and to adapt to changing conditions.

EXCELLENCE

Excellence is the ultimate goal. It depends on a belief in the value of superior service and quality. It involves commitment, passion, energy, care, respect, and enthusiasm—in abundance. As the CEO of an integrated health care system where excellence is crucial, I long held that my top concern was to achieve and sustain excellence throughout the entire organization.

Excellence is the outcome of superior customer service, constant innovation, and committed people. These things do not result from brilliance in the executive suite, slight-of-hand techniques, or mystical strategic moves on a game board. Instead, they result from having an organizational ethic that includes such values as listening, trust, respect for people and their creative potential, appreciation of quality, and attention to detail. In turn, such an ethic would not exist without one important element: leadership that allows and encourages humanism to pervade the organization. Excellence is an all-hands operation, but it starts at the top.

In health care systems, excellence is clearly a matter of committed and caring people. Caring about patients and about each other is built on an organizational culture of respect for others. People readily embrace the value of respect for human dignity and recognize its impact on excellence in the care given to those who are sick, injured, diseased, and distressed. A special caring humanitarianism becomes the spirit of the organization, and the strong value system sets the tone of the whole enterprise—for the people who work in it and who encounter it. Caring is the essence of health care service, for a health care organization's business, after all, is the business of caring.

SUMMARY

Organizational leadership is the one element that connects all the others in achieving successful performance. The ability of hospital and health care systems to thrive and to be managed for competitive advantage today and in the future hinges on visionary, creative, humanistic, and competent leadership; on a culture based on strategic thinking that instills a collective commitment throughout the enterprise to deliver superior performance; and on an organizational structure that facilitates and fosters such commitment and performance. Creating and sustaining excellence requires a strong value culture where committed people focus on quality and move continuously toward perfection. Achieving a continuum of care is within the grasp of those health care organizations where inspirational leadership and committed people come together to provide superior care.

REFERENCES

Bice, Michael O. "Corporate Cultures and Business Strategy." *Hospital and Health Services Administration*, July-August 1984.

Bolman, Lee G., and Deal, Terrence E. *Modern Approaches To Understanding and Managing Organizations*. San Francisco: Jossey-Bass, 1984.

Haller, Terry. *Secrets of the Master Business Strategists*. Englewood Cliffs, N.J.: Prentice-Hall, 1983.

Hartley, Robert F. *Management Mistakes*. Columbus, Ohio: Grid Publishing, 1984.

Hickman, Craig R., and Silva, Michael A. *Creating Excellence*. New York. New American Library, 1984.

Levering, Robert; Moskowitz, Milton; and Katz, Michael. *The One Hundred Best Companies To Work for in America*. New York: Addison-Wesley, 1984.

Luther, John W. "Generating New Business Innovations: How C.E.O.'s Can Improve The Odds for Market Success." *Management Review*, July 1984, 18–24.

Naisbitt, John. *Megatrends*. New York: Warner Books, 1982.

von Oech, Roger. *A Whack on the Side of the Head*. Menlo Park, Calif.: Creative Think, 1983.

Williams, William J. "Leadership in Hospitals and Health Care Systems." *World Hospitals*, November 1985.

Part V

Preparing for the Future Continuum of Care

Chapter 22

The Remaining Questions

Connie J. Evashwick, ScD
Lawrence J. Weiss, PhD

The futurists predict that by the year 2000, five to ten megacompanies will dominate the U.S. health care scene. Will this happen? The data showing the growth of multi-institutional health care systems and the increase in diversification and expansion cannot be ignored. Will the systems all be organized as continuums of care? The increase in such integrating mechanisms as care coordination, Medicare HMOs, preferred provider organizations (PPOs), computer management information systems, comprehensive senior service programs, and vertically integrated organizations cannot be denied.

The ideal concept of the continuum of care has not been realized or even made feasible yet. Given the imprecise definitions and the differing motivations and goals among health care entities, the ideal continuum of care may not be attainable. The concept may never have a precise definition because any continuum is local and unique to each community, built upon the resources, environment, and corporate culture of each organization. However, Part II was written to provide some practical direction to those who want to continue pursuing the ideal. The search for excellence is fraught with complex or divergent goals and objectives, differing organizations and structures, new interpretations of regulatory and financial issues, and human resource issues. Hopefully, the search for excellence will not disregard the human component.

Are continuums cost-effective and efficient? Existing evidence is mixed. Most of the rigorous research to date has been very favorable, but it has mostly been done on demonstration projects in community-based organizations, not health care organizations. Additional evaluation is necessary to determine the areas and the conditions in which cost savings occur. The efficiency must be examined from both a management operation perspective and a clinical perspective.

Do patients, clients, and families prefer a managed system of care? With limited current experience and limited research to date, the answer is difficult to provide. However, we do know that enrollment in Medicare HMOs and PPOs has increased rapidly (more than a 100 percent in the last two years), which indicates at least an initial interest. Consumers and families who experience care coordination through one of the existing programs generally rave about its benefits and the help it has provided. Of course, whether we are consumers, providers, or patients, we all prefer attention, support, trust, understanding, and at least some control over our own environment. As future generations of adults, with years of experience as consumers in managed care systems, reach age 65, their expectations for themselves and their parents may portend greater, not lesser, demand for well-organized, comprehensive care that focuses on prevention as well as early intervention. Simultaneously, consumer responsibility and choice will continue to grow; the new continuum of care system must accommodate both.

As future generations of seniors experience the dwindling of government support and a concomitant increased need to manage their own finances more astutely, choices for comprehensive and cost-effective care are likely to grow. Choice will keep provider and insurer organizations competitive. Increased consumer knowledge and greater availability of long-term health care delivery systems mean a greater consumer-provider partnership. Consumers will take a more active role in coordinating their own health care, thereby enhancing the effectiveness of the organized continuum.

Does the continuum of care approach really enhance quality? Does coordination among services and continuity over time make any difference? These questions involve the issue of subjectivity and are very difficult to answer. From a researcher's point of view, studies of quality are fraught with methodological problems and, hence, unclear empirical results. Qualitative research, however, provides some evidence that comprehensive, continuous, and coordinated care does make a difference. From the manager's perspective, the results of the research are not as important or respected an indicator as the census and number of patients who return or leave. From the clinician's perspective, the answer is in the satisfaction of being involved with a patient and family long-term, of meeting their needs appropriately, and of receiving a smile of familiarity and appreciation.

Is the continuum of care possible? Continuums of care do exist. They are not refined or complete. They also have not solved all problems, since they are breaking new ground on a daily basis. But the field seems covered with seedlings about to blossom. It just isn't clear how long it will take or what will be the genera, species, and varieties of the flowers.

Is the continuum of care practical from a business perspective? The lawyers, accountants, financiers, actuaries, and managers are refining what they know about how to do it and how and when not to. Ten years ago, Ernst and Whinney would not have devoted an entire publication to joint ventures—because they are all different. Now there is enough experience with joint ventures to describe at least common themes and basic principles. Moreover, Ernst and Whinney would not have been able to find 200 chief executive officers with enough experience to be part of a national survey on the topic. Finally, the publication would not have been produced because few would have been interested in reading it.

Each organization must assess each step of the continuum of care as a distinct business decision. Each step should make good business sense. Not all actions, services, programs, or arrangements will make good sense for all organizations— and some should not be implemented. The practical realities forcing a no should not be outweighed by the lure of conceptual novelty that prompts a yes.

Is the continuum of care practical from a clinical perspective? If clinical practicality means easier access to services that enhance prevention (or at least early intervention) and that achieve maximum levels of independent functioning, then the answer is yes. Model programs have demonstrated the practical value of managed care systems from both a financial and clinical perspective. However, much like the organization and structure of the continuum of care, the direct clinical services are developing as well.

Is the continuum of care successful? The goals and objectives of the continuum of care are complex. It would be excellent to accomplish them all, but many compete with or contradict one another. Developing a continuum of care is a costly and challenging, even a radical, endeavor. It is not to be taken lightly. Thus, careful attention and precise delineation of purpose are essential. Monitoring and evaluation of the continuum from business and medical perspectives, among others, must be incorporated into the ongoing operation. Detailed and continuing assessment is critical for refining and guiding the evolution so that it parallels developments in the environment.

At the beginning of the book, the conceptual complexity and newness of the continuum of care was noted. The implementation of a complete continuum is still off in the distance. The concept of a continuum is still blurred because of the many distinct organizational parts and clinical juxtapositions that need to be woven together. As the economic pressures continue to impose change, the advances in high tech increase the treatment sophistication, and the consumer becomes more participatory, the result will be greater collaboration in developing and refining the continuums of care. The important questions are presently beginning to become clear. The future will provide a sharper focus that will have a more highly developed internal infrastructure and brilliant external colors.

Index